CHASING VERMEER

CHASING VERMEER

BLUE BALLIETT

ILLUSTRATED BY
Brett Helquist

Thorndike Press • Waterville, Maine

Recommended for Middle Readers.

Chasing Vermeer is a work of fiction. While some of the settings in Hyde Park are actual, others have been altered or invented.

Published in 2004 by arrangement with Scholastic.

Thorndike Press® Large Print The Literacy Bridge.

The tree indicium is a trademark of Thorndike Press.

The text of this Large Print edition is unabridged.
Other aspects of the book may vary from the original edition.

Set in 16 pt. Plantin by Ramona Watson.

Printed in the United States on permanent paper.

Library of Congress Cataloging-in-Publication Data

Balliett, Blue, 1955–
    Chasing Vermeer / by Blue Balliett ; illustrated by Brett Helquist.
    p. cm.
    Summary: When seemingly unrelated and strange events start to happen and a precious Vermeer painting disappears, eleven-year-olds Petra and Calder combine their talents to solve an international art scandal.
    ISBN 0-7862-7007-1 (lg. print : hc : alk. paper)
    1. Large type books. [1. Art — Fiction.   2. Vermeer, Johannes, 1632–1675 — Fiction.   3. Mystery and detective stories.   4. Large type books.]   I. Helquist, Brett, ill.   II. Title.
PZ7.B2128Ch 2004
[Fic]—dc22   2004042304

For Jessie, Althea, and Dan,
my three questioners
— B.B.

For my mother, Collen
— B.H.

Acknowledgments:

Many thanks to the hundreds of kids at the University of Chicago Laboratory Schools with whom I was lucky enough to work, and who taught me so much about thinking and seeing. I am indebted to Lucinda Lee Katz, Beverly Biggs, and my colleagues at Lab for making it possible for me to teach and write. The Mary Williams Award was a great surprise and a big help. Special thanks go to my mentor and friend Bob Strang, who introduced me to the world of pentominoes and the marvels of constructivist teaching.

There are various opinions on Vermeer, his work, and the actual number of paintings he created. I based the facts in this book on the research of Arthur K. Wheelock, Jr., Curator of Northern Baroque Paintings at the National Gallery of Art in Washington, D.C., and author of several fascinating books on Vermeer. I am extremely grateful to Dr. Wheelock for answering my many questions.

I want to thank him, also, for his advice on the muscle power of eleven-year-olds.

Will Balliett, Betsy Platt, Lucy Bixby, Anne Troutman, and Barbara Engel all took the time to look at early drafts and talk about ideas, and Nancy and Whitney Balliett have been helpful throughout — thank you all so much. My agent, Amanda Lewis, steered me with the greatest skill through a number of adventures. Three cheers to my editor, Tracy Mack, whose wisdom, imagination, and belief got me where I needed to go. Thanks to Leslie Budnick, associate editor, for also putting many thoughtful hours into the manuscript, and for being available and helpful at all times.

I want to thank my amazing husband, Bill Klein, who has helped me in a thousand ways. This book wouldn't exist without him.

Contents

One can't learn much and
also be comfortable.
One can't learn much and
let anybody else be comfortable.

— CHARLES FORT, *Wild Talents*

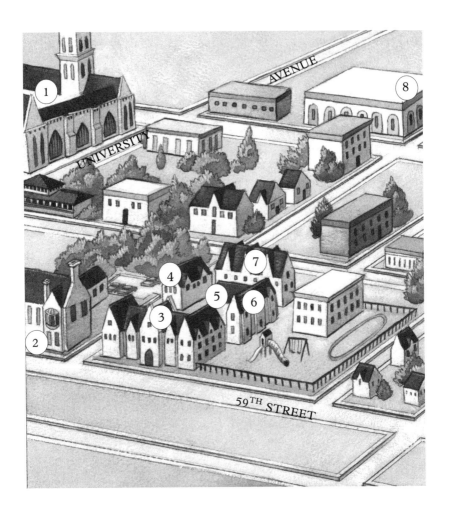

CHASING VERMEER MAP KEY

1 FARGO HALL

2 DELIA DELL HALL

3 GRACIE HALL

4 KING HALL

5 HIGH SCHOOL

6 MIDDLESCHOOL

7 POPPYFIELD HALL   10 CALDER'S HOUSE

8 POST OFFICE   11 PETRA'S HOUSE

9 MRS. SHARPE'S HOUSE   12 POWELL'S USED BOOKS

ABOUT PENTOMINOES
AND ABOUT THIS STORY

A set of pentominoes is a mathematical tool consisting of twelve pieces. Each piece is made up of five squares that share at least one side. Pentominoes are used by mathematicians around the world to explore ideas about geometry and numbers. The set looks like this:

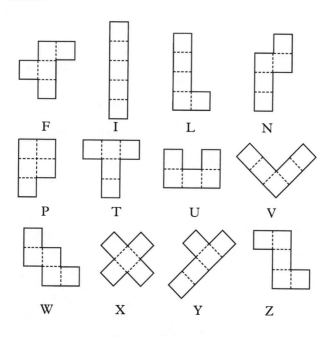

Pentominoes are named after letters in the alphabet, although they don't all look exactly like their names. With a little practice, they can be used as puzzle pieces and put together into thousands of different rectangles of many sizes and shapes.

This book begins, like a set of pentominoes, with separate pieces. Eventually they will all come together. Don't be fooled by ideas that seem, at first, to fit easily. Don't be fooled by ideas that don't seem to fit at all. Pentominoes, like people, can surprise you.

ABOUT THE ARTWORK:
A CHALLENGE TO THE READER

If you look carefully at Brett Helquist's chapter illustrations, you will find a hidden message. It is related to the pentomino code in the book, but not presented in exactly the same form. A certain living creature plays a part in deciphering this code, and pieces of the message appear in the artwork at regular intervals that create a pattern within the book.

Here is a hint: This pattern is even but odd. It has as many pieces as a set of pentominoes.

To check your answers go to:
www.scholastic.com/chasingvermeer

Chapter One

THREE DELIVERIES

On a warm October night in Chicago, three deliveries were made in the same neighborhood. A plump tangerine moon had just risen over Lake Michigan. The doorbell had been rung at each place, and an envelope left propped outside.

Each front door was opened on to an empty street. Each of the three people who lived in those homes lived alone, and each had a hard time falling asleep that night.

The same letter went out to all three:

Dear Friend:
I would like your help in identifying a crime that is now centuries old. This crime has wronged one of the world's greatest painters. As those in positions of authority are not brave enough to correct this error, I have taken it upon myself to reveal the truth. I have chosen you because of your discriminating eye, your intelligence, and your ability to think outside of convention.

19

If you wish to help me, you will be amply rewarded for any risks you take.

You may not show this letter to anyone. Two other people in the world have received this document tonight. Although you may never meet, the three of you will work together in ways none of us can predict.

If you show this to the authorities, you will most certainly be placing your life in danger.

You will know how to respond. I congratulate you on your pursuit of justice.

The letter was not signed, and it had no return address.

The man had sat down to a late dinner. He liked to read when he ate, and he was on page four of a new novel. Book in hand, he answered the door.

His spaghetti and meatballs were cold by the time he remembered them. He sat at the table for a long time, looking first at the letter and then out at the moon.

Was this a joke? Who would go to the trouble of writing and sending such a letter? It was printed on expensive stationery, the kind you buy if you want to be impressive. Or pretentious.

Should he feel flattered? Suspicious?

20

What did this person want from him? What kind of reward were they talking about?

And who was it who knew him well enough to know he'd say yes?

A woman tossed and turned in bed, her long hair trapping moonlight against the pillow. She was going over lists of names in her mind.

The more she thought, the more agitated she became. She was not amused. Could this be a coincidence, or was it a clever warning? What exactly did this person know about her past?

She finally got up. A cup of hot milk would calm her nerves. She moved carefully in the dark, using the watery rectangles of light that fell across the floor. She wasn't about to turn on the kitchen light.

The names scrolled in tidy columns through her mind, each group belonging to a different chapter in her life. There was Milan, there was New York, there was Istanbul. . . .

But this was an invitation, not a threat. If things got strange or frightening, she could always change her mind.

Or could she?

★ ★ ★

Another woman lay awake under the moon, listening to the wind and the occasional whine of a police siren.

This was one of the weirdest coincidences ever.

Was this letter insane, or inspired? And was she just being gullible, thinking this person was really writing to *her?* Maybe hundreds of these letters had gone out. Had her name been picked out of a phone book?

Fake or not, the letter was intriguing. . . . A centuries-old crime. What could this person be planning?

And what about the spooky part? *If you show this to the authorities, you will most certainly be placing your life in danger.*

Maybe this was a maniac, one of those serial killers. She pictured the police going through her apartment and finding the letter, standing over her body and saying, "Jeesh, she shoulda called us first thing. She coulda been alive today. . . ."

A lone cat yowled in the alley below her bedroom, and she jumped, her heart pounding. Sitting up in bed, she shut the window and locked it.

How could she not say yes? This was a letter that could alter history.

Chapter Two

THE LETTER IS DEAD

The letter is dead.

It was a strange thing for a teacher to say.

By the sixth week of sixth grade, Ms. Hussey still wasn't a disappointment. She had announced on the first day of school that she had no idea what they were going to work on that year, or how. "It all depends on what we get interested in — or what gets interested in us," she had added, as if this was obvious. Calder Pillay was all ears. He had never heard a teacher admit that she didn't know what she was doing. Even better, she was excited about it.

Ms. Hussey's classroom was in the middle school building at the University School, in the neighborhood known as Hyde Park. The school sat on the edge of the University of Chicago campus. John Dewey, an unusual professor, had started it a century earlier as an experiment. Dewey believed in doing, in working on relevant projects in order to learn how to think. Calder had always liked the man's appropriate name. Not all teachers at the U., as it was called, still agreed with Dewey's ideas, but Ms. Hussey obviously did.

They began the year by arguing about whether writing was the most accurate way to communicate. Petra Andalee, who loved to write, said it was. Kids like Calder, who hated it, said it wasn't. What about numbers? What about pictures? What about plain old talking?

Ms. Hussey had told them to investigate. They took piles of books out of the library. They found out about cave art in France, about papyrus scrolls in Egypt, about Mayan petroglyphs in Mexico, and about stone tablets from the Middle East. They tried things. They made stamps out of raw potatoes and covered the walls with symbols. They invented a sign language for hands and feet. They communicated for one whole day using nothing but drawings. Now it was almost mid-October. Would they ever study regular subjects, like the other classes did? Calder didn't care. What they were doing was real exploration, real thinking — not just finding out about what a bunch of dead, famous grown-ups believed. Ms. Hussey was cool.

D-E-A-D. She had written it on the board.

They were talking about letters that morning because Calder had groaned about having to write a thank-you note, and said that it was always a waste of time. No one cared what you put in a letter.

Then Ms. Hussey asked if anyone in the class had ever received a truly extraordinary letter. No one had. Ms. Hussey looked very interested. They had ended up with a strange assignment.

"Let's see what we can find," Ms. Hussey began. "Ask an adult to tell you about a letter they will never forget. I'm talking about a piece of mail that changed their *life*. How old were they when they got it? Where were they when they opened it? Do they still have it?"

Petra, like Calder, was fascinated by their new teacher. She loved Ms. Hussey's questions and her long ponytail and the three rings in each ear. One earring had a small pearl dangling from a moon, another a high-heeled shoe the size of a grain of rice, another a tiny key. Petra loved how Ms. Hussey listened carefully to the kids' ideas and didn't care about right and wrong answers. She was honest and unpredictable. She was close to perfect.

Ms. Hussey suddenly clapped her hands,

making Petra jump and setting the little pearl earring into orbit. "I know! Once you find a letter that changed a life, sit down and write *me* a letter. Write me a letter *I won't be able to forget.*"

Petra's mind was already racing.

Calder pulled a pentomino piece out of his pocket. It was an L. He grinned. L for letter — *this* letter was definitely not dead. L was one of the simplest pentomino shapes to use. Most letters, the kind you mailed, were rectangles, he realized, just like an accurately put-together pentomino solution. L was also the twelfth letter in the alphabet and one of the twelve pentominoes. Today was the twelfth day of October. Calder's grandmother had once told him that he breathed patterns the way other people breathed air.

Calder sighed. If only thoughts didn't have to be broken down into words. Too much talk was hard to listen to, and writing, for him, was a brutal process. So much got left behind.

Ms. Hussey ended the class by saying, "Got it? First find, then do. Who knows where this will take us?"

Calder and Petra lived on Harper Avenue, a narrow street next to the train line.

Their houses were three blocks away from the U. School, and three houses away from each other. They often passed on the street, but they had never been friends.

Families came from all over to study or teach at the University of Chicago, and many of them lived in this part of Hyde Park. Since most parents worked, young kids traveled on their own around the campus and to and from school.

On the afternoon of October 12, Petra walked home from school with Calder half a block ahead of her. She watched him fish around for his key and open his front door. She knew his pockets were full of puzzle pieces. He sometimes muttered things and always looked like he had just woken up. He was kind of weird.

Scuffing through the first fall leaves, Petra drifted into the game she often played with herself: Ask a question that doesn't have an answer. Why was yellow cheerful, she wondered, and why was it always a surprise — even when it came in an ordinary shape, like a lemon or an egg yolk? Picking up a yellow leaf, she held it in front of her face.

Maybe she would write to Ms. Hussey about this. She'd ask her if she agreed that humans needed questions more than answers.

Calder, at that moment, looked out his front window to see Petra walking by holding a leaf several inches from her nose. He knew he was kind of weird, but she was *exceptionally* weird. She was always by herself at school, and didn't seem to care. She was quiet when other kids were loud. Plus, she had a fierce triangle of hair that made her look like one of those Egyptian queens.

Calder wondered if he was becoming just as much of an oddball. No one had asked him what he was doing after class that day. No one had told him to wait. He'd taken his buddy Tommy's presence for granted. Not now.

Tommy Segovia had lived across the street from Calder until this past August. They had been great friends since second grade, when Tommy poured his chocolate milk on Calder's bare legs and asked him how it felt. A teacher rushed over, and Calder had explained that it was an experiment and that it felt just perfect. That was the first of many collaborations.

He and Tommy had decided back in July that they weren't going to be mediocre kids. They swore that they were going to do something important with their lives — solve a great mystery, or rescue somebody, or be so smart in school that they'd skip

grades. That was the same day Calder had received his first set of pentominoes. A cousin in London had sent them as a twelfth birthday present, even though Calder's birthday wasn't until the end of the year.

The pentominoes were yellow plastic and clacked against the kitchen table in a satisfying, decisive way. Determined, Calder moved the shapes into one combination after another, flipping and turning them. The biggest rectangle he had put together so far was six pieces. A breeze was coming in the back door, and some mourning doves that had nested on the back porch were cooing, making that slippery, burbling sound that Calder always associated with summer in his neighborhood. Every detail of that morning with Tommy was strangely clear.

At once Calder had known what to do — the Y had to slide into the U, which had to fit next to the P. He even remembered the sequence of letters: YUP. He had gotten his first twelve-piecer, and gotten it fast. When he looked up afterward, he saw the pentomino shapes echoed in the kitchen. The hinges on the cabinets were Ls, the water faucets were Xs, the burners on the stove stood up on neat N legs. Maybe the entire world could be communicated in some kind of pentomino code, kind of like a Morse code. He knew, at that moment, that he would be a great problem-solver. Or so he told Tommy, who punched him in the arm and told him he had a swelled head. "Yup," he'd said with a grin.

Calder's head didn't feel too swelled these days. He looked at the clock. He was already late. When Tommy moved away, Calder had taken over his job at Powell's Used Books. Calder helped out one afternoon a week now, delivering books in the neighborhood or unloading boxes. With Tommy gone, it was something to do.

Calder gulped a glass of chocolate milk, stuffed a cookie in each cheek, and set off at a run.

Powell's was one of Petra's favorite places; it was peaceful, and you never knew what you might find. It looked more like a warehouse than a store — books were piled everywhere, and the rooms were jumbled together in a mismatched way. Although Petra had been inside many times, it always felt like a labyrinth: One dimly lit area led to the next, and suddenly you were back where you started without knowing how you got there. No one asked if you needed help. No one frowned if you read but didn't buy.

Petra's mom had sent her to get milk and bread at the grocery store around the corner. Powell's was on the way.

Petra had just settled herself on a footstool with a copy of *Kidnapped* when she saw a long ponytail whip by.

Ms. Hussey?

Petra stood up carefully. She peeked around the corner, ready to pretend to look surprised. There was no one in sight. Petra looked across rows of cookbooks. She tiptoed carefully through the next room, past English, History, Psychology, and Pets. She only wanted to see what Ms. Hussey was reading.

Darn — the next person she saw was Calder. He was bending over a box of books, a piece of paper in his hand. Don't turn around, don't you dare turn around, Petra thought. She didn't want anyone from the class to see her spying.

She tiptoed around the next corner. Ms. Hussey was crouched by the art books. Petra couldn't see what she was looking at, but she noticed several paperbacks next to her on the floor. Agatha Christie, Raymond Chandler — Ms. Hussey moved suddenly, and Petra jumped backward.

To her surprise, Calder was right behind her. He had obviously seen what she was doing. Petra cupped her hand quickly as if to cover his mouth, but stopped before she touched him. They looked equally shocked. Calder, recovering first, peered around the corner. He ducked back in a flash.

"She's coming!"

It felt too late to do anything but hide, so they hurried out of History and into Fiction. Ms. Hussey was at the front desk now. She plopped down her books and began talking to Mr. Watch, the man with red suspenders who was usually at the cash register. They were laughing. Did they know each other?

"Can you see what she has?" Petra whispered. Calder walked quickly behind their teacher, his eyes on the counter. Ms. Hussey never turned her head.

"Murder and a big art book — *Never* something," he muttered to Petra when he returned.

Ms. Hussey left the store with her purchases. A moment later, Petra ducked outside empty-handed, her cheeks burning.

She was furious with herself.

Powell's had always been her private

hideaway, her refuge. Now she'd spoken to Calder there. She'd practically attacked him. And he'd seen her spying on Ms. Hussey.

What had she started?

Chapter Three

LOST IN THE ART

Twenty minutes later, Petra opened her notebook on the desk in her bedroom. Letters. Think about letters.

The 5:38 southbound train went by Petra's window exactly three seconds before it passed Calder's. In between, it shot by the Castiglione's and then the Bixbys' — Petra had once calculated that it passed a house per second on Harper Avenue. She liked the trains. Looking out, she saw the bright shout of a red hat, a child in a purple jacket pressed against the window, a bald head just rising over a stiff rectangle of newspaper. She'd noticed that colors sometimes left their shapes when things flashed by so fast.

She wrote:

October 12
Yellow leaf: surprise.
Loud hat, square coat, bald head like moon:
red, lavender, salmon.

Question: What does Ms. Hussey really want us to see?

"Petraaaa! Can you get me some TOY-let PAY-per?"

"CAA-ming!" Petra sighed heavily and got up to help her younger sister.

Petra's household was a tornado where life swirled in noisy circles. Sneakers, books, and backpacks traveled through the rooms on unseen currents, and there was always food underfoot and an old frying pan or two on the steps outside the back door. The cats and dog drank from the toilets, having despaired of getting their water bowls filled every morning, and everyone in the family talked to one another at the top of their lungs.

Petra wished that things were different. She wished that her parents would sit quietly at dinner and ask her how her day was, and that her four younger brothers and sisters would carry tissues with them instead of wiping off rivers of goo on their shirtsleeves in public. She wished she wasn't shy, that she wasn't shaped like a lima bean, and that her left ear didn't stick out farther than her right. She wished she was a famous writer already, and didn't have to go through the unfamous stage. She wished her mother wouldn't ever put baba ghanoush in her lunch box. When Denise Dodge had towered over her at lunchtime, saying, *"Eeeeeuuuw!* What's *that?"* Petra had wanted to murder her on the spot, but only came out with a pathetic "Don't you wish you knew!" As Denise moved away, Petra heard her saying loudly to her friend, "Blech! Aren't you glad *you* don't have to eat baby gush for lunch?"

The family socks basket was another thing Petra didn't like — she always ended up with one sock either too big or too small. Since no one wanted to sort all the clean socks that went on to fourteen feet every morning, the socks went straight from the dryer into a gigantic, handwoven basket, and it was every person for themselves. Each fall Petra's mom bought the same color socks for all seven of them so that, in theory, there was always a size that fit. But reality in the Andalee family was never that tidy.

Like many kids in Hyde Park, Petra was a club sandwich of cultures. Her father, Frank Andalee, had relatives from North Africa and northern Europe, and her mother, Norma Andalee, was from the Middle East. Petra didn't think much about what racial category she belonged to

— her family had let go of that way of looking at things a long time ago.

She did know that for many generations on her mother's side, every first child who was a girl had been named Petra. She also knew that Petra was the name of an ancient stone city in Jordan, a sophisticated and graceful city that had risen out of the desert more than two thousand years ago. Three-quarters of its ruins were still covered with shifting sand; she liked the thought that she was named after a mysterious place of buried secrets.

The last "first daughter" had been her grandmother, who lived in Istanbul now. When she had visited Chicago a couple of years ago, she had told Petra that all of her namesakes had grown up to be very beautiful and very lucky. The younger Petra had looked doubtfully at her grand-mother, who just looked whiskery and wispy, and who seemed to spend all day losing everything she needed, like her slippers or her black eyeliner or even the bathroom.

Glamour might have been easier in the past. Petra was sure that every Petra before her hadn't had to put up with thick glasses with blue-and-purple-speckled frames. And every Petra before her probably hadn't had to worry about what she was going to step on first thing in the morning — dried cranberry juice or a plastic dragon or something coughed up by the dog.

On her way to get toilet paper, Petra stepped heavily on a headless soldier. Served her right for being so nosy about Ms. Hussey.

Then Petra heard her parents arguing downstairs.

"But everyone has something to hide!" her dad was saying angrily. He was a physicist at the university, and Petra knew he'd been worried about his job. She heard her mom say something in an impatient tone, and then the words "letter" and "forgotten" and the quick, harsh sounds of tearing paper. What could this be about? Her parents hardly ever disagreed.

A forgotten letter! She wouldn't bring a family secret to school, but she had to look. When she crept downstairs later, however, the garbage was empty.

Calder was in a bad mood. The letter assignment felt too hard. How could he ever write Ms. Hussey an unforgettable letter? And where was he going to find a stupendous letter now that Grandma Ranjana was gone? Good letters were no longer written. He was sure of it.

Calder's dad, Walter Pillay, was slicing eggplant in the kitchen. As he stacked the pale slices neatly next to the frying pan, he looked over at his son. Calder was sketching a fierce column of five-piece pentomino squares down the margin of his notebook.

"Anything wrong?" asked his dad.

Calder opened his mouth when the 5:38 train went by, rattling the windows, making the floorboards bounce, and filling the kitchen with the *whoosh-whoosh* of passing steel. As Calder mouthed, "Nope," his dad grinned at him and mouthed back, "Good."

Calder, like Petra, was a hybrid kid. His dad was from India, and he had a calm way of speaking that made everything sound important. His job had to do with planning gardens for cities. Every year he brought home a new batch of plants to try out in the yard; by August, the front walk had vanished beneath a tangle of green. This year a trumpet vine leaned eagerly against a cool lily, pointy leaves fought to see who could take over the steps, purples and blood reds argued loudly with each other. It was a good yard for hiding things.

Calder's mom, Yvette Pillay, had short hair the color of an apricot and a jingly laugh that made other people laugh even when they didn't know why. She was Canadian and taught math at the university.

Calder had never seen either one of them look amazed when they opened the mail. He was suddenly tired of the whole idea. He didn't think he wanted to hear about letters. If he asked his mom and dad, they'd probably tell him too much. That was the problem with being an only child: Your parents were always paying attention to you. He envied kids whose families forgot about them once in a while.

Walking down the block the next morning, Calder stirred the pentominoes in his pocket. He pulled out the P.

Funny, Petra was walking ahead of him. He was beginning to think he had been kind of lame yesterday, following her and then ruining her adventure.

He ducked into a driveway and crept through a number of backyards. Under a lilac bush, around an old boat, then over two fences. The only way out was a raspberry patch. He dove in, yelped with pain, and burst out on the sidewalk just ahead of Petra.

"*Sheesh,* you scared me!"

"Sorry!" he said, pretending to be surprised. "You scared me, too."

Petra did not look pleased. "What were you doing?"

"Oh, Tommy and I always used to go to school this way. . . ." Feeling a stinging on his cheek, Calder wiped off some blood. Right. This conversation wasn't going the way he'd planned. They walked in silence for several minutes.

"Heard anything from Tommy?" Petra asked finally, though she'd hardly said a word to Tommy Segovia in her life.

"Not much." Calder groped madly for something to say, but everything he thought of sounded stupid. He was going to tell Petra that all the kids in Tommy's new neighborhood had crew cuts, but that was pretty nothing. His pentominoes were making a loud clacking sound.

"Hey, what do you think about Ms. Hussey? She's let us do cool stuff so far, don't you think? I mean — cool for school." Petra, embarrassed by her accidental rhyme, looked sideways at Calder to see if he had noticed. A raspberry twig was standing upright over one of his ears. He looked like a lopsided bee. She was saying dumb stuff, but she hoped Calder would get the message: What happened yesterday in Powell's didn't need to be mentioned.

Calder was wondering if Petra had any interest in pentominoes or puzzles. Did she know what was in his pocket? Forget it — he'd sound like he was showing off if he asked her. He noticed that she had a couple of Rice Krispies stuck in her hair but decided not to say anything about that, either.

By the time they got to school, both were worn out by trying to think of something to say, and trying *not* to say what they were really thinking.

The cold cereal and the twig were still in place as they headed in opposite directions to their lockers.

Ms. Hussey had looked strangely pleased when the assignment failed.

After two days of hunting, no one in the class had come up with anything worth sharing. There were several letters about distant relatives dying, school and job acceptance letters, invitations to weddings.

Ms. Hussey suggested that they go back a few hundred years.

"Like find old books of letters and stuff?" Petra asked, thinking of Powell's.

There was a wave of grumbling.

"How about paintings? All you have to do is look." Ms. Hussey said she'd noticed that art often showed what was important to people in any given time. It revealed things. Besides, she'd said with a smile, she was tired of being in school all day. It was time for a field trip.

Everyone sat up.

"Something else," she went on. "*Getting* an unforgettable letter happens once or twice in a lifetime. *Writing* an unforgettable letter is a pretty tough thing to do unless you have something very real to say. It shouldn't be artificial. Perhaps I made a mistake."

She always said the same thing after she had an idea, and always with an undercurrent of *we're-in-this-together-and-it-might-be-dangerous:* "Do you agree? Should we bag the assignment for now?"

There were whistles and cheers. Calder caught Petra's eye, and she shrugged and almost smiled. Everyone looked relieved. This year was beginning to feel either like something was very right or very wrong — it was hard to tell which.

On the following Monday they took the train to the Art Institute and walked several blocks in the October sunshine. It was difficult to keep up with Ms. Hussey's bouncy stride. Calder noticed with approval that she never even looked back to see if everyone was with her; she was one trusting teacher.

After they ate bag lunches next to the bronze lions on the steps of the museum, they fanned out in the European wing.

Petra took off on her own. She passed the Degas dancers, the big painting made completely of dots, the Monet haystacks and bridges, and headed into the older works.

When she was in third grade, she'd had a baby-sitter who took her to the Art Institute once a month. The baby-sitter would sit in front of a painting, sigh a great deal, and sometimes write things down. She'd tell Petra to stay in one area, but not to bother her.

Petra would walk around looking. Soon she began to wonder which paintings would be fun to go into, or which ones she might like to take home to her room. She thought about which of the children in the paintings she'd like to play with. Her baby-sitter gave her a pad and pencil, and Petra made lists. She once counted all the paintings with red clothing in them. Another time she secretly counted all the bare

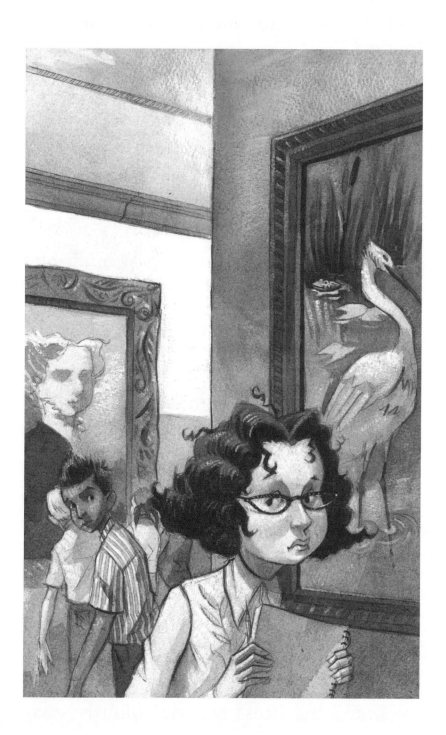

bottoms. She also counted all the hats and found 123.

Now she walked slowly from room to room, hugging her clipboard. She was sure there was a letter somewhere near an angel . . . or was it rolled up in someone's hand? They had one hour to look, and she knew she'd find something.

When Calder saw Petra disappear, he decided to follow her.

He stayed a gallery-length behind, and was so busy trying not to be seen that he barely noticed what was on the walls. Then, quite suddenly, Petra was gone.

Calder walked slowly through the next two galleries. It was getting late. He'd better start hunting on his own.

Turning a corner, he spotted something promising. It lay on a bedside table inside a French painting by an artist named Auguste Bernard. The date was 1780. Calder looked around — he was alone. He leaned against the wall opposite the painting and began in a businesslike way to take notes.

The letter was folded up, but had a red wax seal that had been broken. He knew this meant it had been opened. The woman next to the letter was rolling her eyes, and her dress was ridiculously small for the top part of her body. Calder concentrated on the table, which also had a necklace of beads and a book with French words on it. He was copying the words down — *L'Art D'Aime* — when the wall behind him moved.

"What the —" Calder staggered backward into a dark doorway and stumbled over someone's feet.

The person gave him a sharp push. Then the two of them shot back into the brightness of the gallery. A guard strode over and grabbed Calder by the elbow.

"*Restricted.* Can't you read?" Too stunned to answer, Calder twisted around to see who had shoved him.

"What were *you* doing in there?" Petra hissed.

"How about *you?*" he snapped back.

The guard, a pink-and-gray sausage of a man, crossed his arms. "Storage room. No public allowed. Where's your school group, anyways?"

Calder and Petra walked in silence, on either side of the sausage, to where Ms. Hussey was talking with a group of their classmates.

"Here's where she turns into a regular teacher," Calder whispered behind the guard's back.

Petra glanced his way with a twinkle and a quick flash of "We'll see, won't we?"

"You in charge? Found these two in a storage room."

Ms. Hussey looked surprised, but not shocked. The kids standing around her tittered. Petra and Calder looked grim.

"Thank you," Ms. Hussey said to the sausage, making it clear that the conversation was over.

When the guard was out of earshot, Ms. Hussey smiled warmly at Calder and Petra, looking first at one and then the other. "Good thinking. Find anything?"

When Denise changed seats on the train, a scrap of paper floated into Petra's lap:

**Calder and Petra lost in the art.
First a KISS and then a FART!**

Petra brushed it onto the floor, hoping Calder hadn't seen it. Why did kids have to be so stupid sometimes?

By the time everyone got off at Fifty-seventh Street, it was too late to go back to school. Ms. Hussey waved good-bye, and Calder and Petra started awkwardly down Harper Avenue.

"See you," Petra muttered over her

shoulder as she hurried ahead and zoomed up her porch steps.

"Petra?"

"What?" Petra turned around.

"What were you doing in there?"

"Just looking. Most museums have too much stuff to have all of it hanging. So if it's not hanging, it's got to be stuck in a closet."

"Yeah, I guess Ms. Hussey would've thought that was cool, finding a letter that was off-limits," Calder said.

"That's not very nice. You don't like her?"

Calder began stirring his pentominoes around in his pocket. "I do."

Petra looked curiously at him. "You're jealous of me."

"I am *not!*"

"Admit it." Petra grinned.

"Well, just about your storeroom idea."

Petra's face closed. "Of course." Then she was gone.

What had just happened? Calder pulled out one of his pentominoes and tossed it up in the air. "I for idea," he said aloud.

Or was it I for idiot?

Chapter Four

PICASSO'S LIE

Ms. Hussey had an extra gleam the next morning.

She agreed that the trip to the museum hadn't exactly worked. They'd found three religious scrolls and the letter with the red seal, but that was it. Ms. Hussey said she'd enjoyed the search. She didn't seem upset at all.

"You know, one of my favorite painters was interested in letters and made them important in a bunch of his paintings. Maybe that's why I thought we'd see more of them. Funny how you can project things."

She changed the subject, her voice suddenly businesslike. "So, what now? Have we reached any conclusions about communication?"

Petra raised her hand. "Maybe that it's hard to study. How about we work on something else to do with art?" She liked exploring the Art Institute. She was sure they could come up with another worth-while subject to investigate.

Denise said, "I thought some of the art was pretty gross. I mean, a lot of it was gory and violent, or fat and naked, or plain old boring — just people dressed up. I mean, you couldn't *make* me live with some of those pictures."

There was a murmur of agreement. Denise sniffed happily.

"I doubt you'll need to, Denise," Ms. Hussey said evenly, crossing her arms. Then she stood still and looked at the ceiling. When she didn't move, the room grew quiet.

"You know," Ms. Hussey said finally, "Picasso said that art is a lie, but a lie that tells the truth." She was pacing now. "Lies and art . . . it's an ancient problem. So if we work with art," she said slowly, "we'll have to figure out something else first: What makes an object a piece of art?"

Denise rolled her eyes but stayed quiet.

"Here's what I want you to do: Start by choosing one item at home that feels like a work of art to you. It can be anything. Don't ask anyone for advice — this has to be your own thinking. Describe this object for us without saying what it is. And this time, I won't let you off the hook." She

grinned. "We'll read some of your ideas aloud."

Calder wondered what Picasso had meant. Was it that art wasn't exactly the real world, but it said something real?

He began thinking up other combinations of art, a lie, and the truth that made sense. It worked almost like the logical arrangements of five squares that made up each piece of his set of pentominoes. How about: Art is the truth that tells a lie? Maybe all of life was about rearranging a few simple ideas. Calder, smiling at the chalkboard, now squirmed in his chair with excitement at the thought. If he could just get to those simple ideas, with a little practice, he'd be a cross between Einstein and the mathematician Ramanujan — or maybe Ben Franklin —

"Calder?"

He was twisted sideways in his chair, his arm resting on his head. His pentominoes had somehow gotten onto his desk. He scooped them hurriedly into his pocket, but one fell to the floor.

"Calder, did you want to say something? It looked like your hand was up," Ms. Hussey said.

"I was just thinking. You know, about what Picasso said. But I'm still thinking," he finished. There was a ripple of unfriendly laughter from the class around him, and Calder could feel the back of his neck getting hot. If only Tommy had been there, he would've elbowed Calder earlier and gotten him back on target.

The bell rang. Denise stepped on Calder's pentomino piece just as he reached down to get it. Her knee hit him on the ear.

"*Ooooops!* Sor-ree I stepped on your toy!" She laughed and gave the plastic piece under her foot an extra scuff. It shot under Ms. Hussey's desk.

"Sor-ree your feet are so big," Calder heard Petra muttering behind him. Not sure he'd heard right, he turned to look for Petra, but she was gone.

Calder groped around for his pentomino as his teacher erased the board. He wanted to tell Ms. Hussey that he'd been thinking about important stuff, but he didn't know how to say it.

Ms. Hussey turned toward him and smiled. "I know, Calder. I get caught up in my own ideas, too. Maybe one day I'll try having us all write down daydreams for a week and see what we come up with. Maybe we'll decide they're a lot more important than what I thought we were supposed to be working on."

Calder nodded gratefully. Ms. Hussey was the best.

As he wiped off his pentomino piece, he looked at the T shape. T for what? Trouble . . . but why trouble?

There was nothing at home that felt like a piece of art.

Petra considered an embroidered pillow, but it had a big tear in it; she found a silk caterpillar kite, but it had lost one eye; she thought of the stick her mom used to make a bun for her hair, the one with amber on it, but it had been missing for days.

What *was* art, anyway? The more she thought about it, the stranger it seemed. What made an invented object special? Why were some manmade things pleasing and others not? Why wasn't a regular mixing bowl or a spoon or a lightbulb a piece of art? What made certain objects land in museums and others in the trash?

She guessed that most people who went to museums didn't ask that question. They just believed that they were looking at something valuable or beautiful or interesting. They didn't do any hard thinking about it.

She wasn't going to be that kind of a person — *ever*.

She thought about pictures at the Art Institute that made her feel as if she could leave everything predictable behind. She always felt that way when she stood in front of Caillebotte's *Rainy Day* painting — the wet cobblestones underfoot, the people going places in their long skirts and top hats, the inviting turn of the street. This was art that was an adventure. It let her into another world. It made familiar stuff seem mysterious. It sent her back to her life feeling a little different, at least for a few minutes.

She was still thinking about Caillebotte's Paris street on her way to the grocery store. If he had painted Harper Avenue, would it have looked just as intriguing? As she approached the corner, she noticed the man with suspenders, the one who had talked to Ms. Hussey, step out the front door of Powell's, look around, and drop a book into the giveaway box outside. She sped up.

The book had a cloth cover with several dark stains, and the paper was thick and creamy, soft at the edges. The title jumped out at her: *Lo!* The illustrations were done in black and white — distorted, rubbery figures clutched each other or screamed.

She read a few paragraphs:

Terrified horses, up on their hind legs, hoofing a storm of frogs.

Frenzied springboks, capering their exasperations against frogs that were tickling them.

Storekeepers, in London, gaping at frogs that were tapping on their window panes.

We shall pick up an existence by its frogs.

Wise men have tried other ways. They have tried to understand our state of being, by grasping at its stars, or its arts, or its economics. But, if there is an underlying oneness of all things, it does not matter where we begin, whether with stars, or laws of supply and demand, or frogs, or Napoleon Bonaparte. One measures a circle, beginning any-where.

I have collected 294 records of showers of living things.

What? Petra flipped back to the front and saw that the book had been written in 1931 by a man named Charles Fort.

She tucked it under her arm.

Chapter Five

WORMS, SNAKES, AND PERIWINKLES

That night, flipping around in *Lo!*, Petra was more and more amazed. She had never seen a book like this. It was, first of all, peppered with quotes from journals and newspapers around the world — there was the *London Times*, the *Quebec Daily Mercury*, the *New Zealand Times*, the *Woodbury Daily Times*, the *New York American*, *The Gentleman's Magazine*, the *Ceylon Observer* . . . the list went on and on.

There were hundreds of stories of bizarre happenings, many of them similar. Venomous snakes dropped into backyards in Oxfordshire, England; red and brown worms fell with snowflakes in Sweden; bushels of periwinkles fell from the sky on Cromer Gardens Road, outside Worcester, England; luminous, floating lights traveled slowly over open land in North Carolina and in Norfolk, England. Wild animals turned up where they shouldn't have. People disappeared and then were found far away, disoriented and confused. There were crashes and explosions that no one could explain.

Fort had apparently spent twenty-seven years going through old newspapers in libraries. He had copied out thousands of articles about unexplained goings-on.

It is the profound conviction of most of us that there never has been a shower of living things. But some of us have . . . been educated by surprises out of much that we were 'absolutely sure' of. . . .

Petra read this twice and turned a few pages.

I have never heard of any standard, in any religion, philosophy, science, or complication of household affairs that could not be made to fit any requirement. We fit standards to judgments, or break any law that it pleases us to break. . . . We have conclusions, which are the products of senility or incompetence or credulity, and then argue from them to premises. We forget this process, and then argue from the premises, thinking we began there.

Petra struggled with this language and had to look up the words "credulity" and "premises." Rereading each sentence in pieces, she began to get a grip on what Fort was saying: Depending on how you looked at things, your world could change completely. His thought was that most people bent over backward to fit everything that happened to them into something they could understand. In other words, people sometimes twisted what was actually in front of them to fit what they thought should be there, never even realizing they were doing it. People liked to see what they were supposed to see, and find what they were supposed to find. It was quite an idea.

And then:

See London newspapers, August 18th and 19th, 1921 — innumerable little frogs that appeared, during a thunderstorm, upon the 17th, in the streets of the northern part of London.

Farther down:

There have been repetitions of these arrivals. . . . There is an account, in the London <u>Daily News</u>, Sept. 5,

1922, of little toads, which for two days had been dropping from the sky, at Chalons-sur-Saône, France.

Could this be true?

Why wasn't more time in school spent studying things that were unknown or not understood instead of things that had already been discovered and explained? Ms. Hussey always asked for their ideas. Wouldn't it be great to go digging for weird facts like Charles Fort did? To try to piece together a meaning behind events that didn't seem to fit?

And why wasn't this book a piece of art? She grabbed her notebook and began to write:

This object is hard on the outside and bendable on the inside. It is the color of an unripe raspberry, and it weighs about as much as a pair of blue jeans. It smells like a closet in an old house, and it is an ancient shape. It holds things that are hard to believe. There are living creatures falling like rain and objects that float by themselves. People vanish and reappear.

It is made of substances that once grew, that once bent in the wind and felt the night air. It is older than trips to the moon or computers or stereo systems or television. Our grandparents might have seen it new when they were young.

There was a woman's name in faded brown ink inside the cover. Petra wondered who else had loved this book and why it had ended up outside Powell's. Why had it been thrown away?

She would never lose it. Not ever.

Before closing the book, she looked again for that one terrific sentence: WE SHALL PICK UP AN EXISTENCE BY ITS FROGS.

Hours later, under a sliver of moon, Petra was almost asleep. As she rolled over, squashing her pillow into position on top of her arm, a strange thing happened: Although her eyes were closed, she seemed to be looking at a young woman.

This person was old-fashioned. She was dressed in a yellow jacket that had dappled fur on the edges, and her hair was pulled back tightly with shiny ribbons. Dangly earrings, perhaps pearls, caught the light. She had been sitting at a table and writing; something had interrupted her. Quill pen in hand, she had paused to look up.

The woman was gazing directly into Petra's eyes. Her expression was knowing,

filled with kindness and interest, and she had the look of someone who understood without being told.

Petra found herself soaking up every detail of the image. Although the room was dark, light touched the metal fastenings on a wooden box, a fold of blue cloth on the table, the curve of the woman's forehead, the creamy lemon of her jacket. This was a calm, deliberate world, a world where dreams were real and each syllable held the light like a pearl. It was a writer's world — and Petra was inside it.

And then, as suddenly as she had appeared, the woman began to fade from Petra's mind. As this happened, Petra felt recognized, as if this person knew who she, Petra Andalee, was. It was a shocking feeling — exhilarating, shivery, true. And somehow inevitable, as if things had always been this way.

Wide awake now, Petra thought of Charles Fort. Was he responsible for the woman's visit? Had he brought them together? *Educated by surprises . . .* Fort understood what Petra had often felt: There is much more to be uncovered about the world than most people think.

If she'd had any idea *how* much more, Petra wouldn't have slept at all that night.

Chapter Six

THE GEOGRAPHER'S BOX

On the day Ms. Hussey had given the art assignment, Calder went straight up to his room after school.

He sat down at his desk and pulled out his pentominoes. The W fit with the Y and the U, and the I slid in agreeably next to the L . . . the X was difficult to work into the rectangle, but it might fit here between the P and the U. . . . Pentominoes always helped him think.

He wrote down the word ART. He followed it quickly with: RTA
RAT
ATR
TRA

It wasn't what he'd meant to put on his list, but his pencil kind of took charge. He read what he'd written aloud. It was a tongue twister, he noticed with delight, aside from being every combination of A, R, and T.

Calder shook himself back toward the

assignment. Was his weird list a piece of art? How about the old-fashioned kind of art, the kind in museums that turned up on postcards and posters in people's kitchens, the kind that they'd been talking about in school today? Ms. Hussey was always saying, "Listen to your own thinking." Well, what if *he*, and not those museum people, was the one to decide what was wonderful to look at? What would he choose? The same stuff that was now famous? Probably not the French lady with the too-small dress.

Art, for him, was — something puzzling. Yes. Something that gave his mind a new idea to spin around. Something that gave him a fresh way of seeing things each time he looked at it. What was he remembering?

He crawled under his bed and dragged out a dusty crate filled with green army men. He dug down into the corner and pulled out a small box.

Calder held the box carefully in both hands. It was made of a dark wood, and the corners were covered with inlaid silver vines. The painting on the top showed a man with ponytail-length hair leaning over a table. He was dressed in a fancy bathrobe, and his face was turned thoughtfully toward a window. A tool that resembled a compass was held lightly in his right hand. A large roll of paper lay under his right arm. There was a wrinkled Oriental rug bunched up on the corner of the table in front of him, and his left hand rested on what appeared to be a book. A globe sat high on the cupboard behind him. His expression looked as though he'd been thinking important thoughts, and something had, just in that moment, interrupted him. Calder felt a sense of understanding, of sympathy for this man. This was what he felt like when he suddenly had to pay attention in school.

Calder had always loved this picture. Reaching for his magnifying glass, he held it over the top of the box. He saw light sparkle from the old glass in the window, and the rug came alive with blues and warm golden tones. On the tall cupboard was written the word "Meer." Meer, Meer . . . he rolled the word around in his mind. He wished Grandma Ranjana had told him more.

He tried to remember exactly when she had given him the box. He had been small enough to sit on her lap and play with her reading glasses — he might have been four or five. He could remember her blue velvet rocker, the cracks on her knuckles, her gentle cheeks the color of dark chocolate.

Grandma Ranjana had loved puzzles and mysteries and would have approved of Ms. Hussey. Calder grabbed the box and rushed downstairs — he would take a "rainbow bath," as Grandma Ranjana used to call it.

On late afternoons in the fall, the sun came through the leaded glass window in the Pillays' living room and threw rainbows and wavery rhombi and polygons on the floor, the walls, the backs of chairs and sofas. This parade of soft color traveled slowly up one side of the room and vanished in the corner of the ceiling. Grandma Ranjana always swore that sitting in geometry helped the brain.

Calder began to write.

The man in my hand looks toward the window, and the light lands on one arm and one cheek and the paper on his table. You know the way paper gets blinding in a bright light? Well, this paper almost makes you squint. The colors around him are blue and red and light brown. A scrunched-up rug is on the edge of the table between him and me, as if someone tossed it up there when they were cleaning the floor and forgot to put it back.

And now for weight and size. This thing is

about as heavy as a bag of chocolate chip cookies, or maybe an empty spaghetti sauce jar, or a large T-shirt. It is about as thick as a dictionary, and as long as a medium tube of toothpaste.

Calder paused, the box in his right hand, and looked at the rainbows floating on the far wall. He realized with a shiver of pleasure that the afternoon light was landing on his body in a way that was similar to the fall of light in the picture, and he wondered if he also looked like he was thinking Great Thoughts. . . .

He was interrupted by loud voices outside the front window. When he peered out, he saw Ms. Hussey and Mr. Watch, his boss from Powell's. What on earth were they doing? And then Calder noticed an old lady sitting on the ground between them.

When he opened his front door, Ms. Hussey shouted, "Water! Get some water!"

By the time he was back with a glass, the old lady was standing. Calder didn't recognize her.

Ms. Hussey said, "Thanks, Calder. I didn't know you lived right here." She explained what Mr. Watch had just told her: He usually walked Mrs. Sharpe to Powell's once a week to pick out some books. Ms. Hussey had happened to be just behind them. She'd seen Mrs. Sharpe stumble and sink to the curb.

Mr. Watch looked embarrassed. Mrs. Sharpe looked irritated. "What would I need water for?" she snapped. "Stupid! These new shoes! A grasshopper couldn't walk in them!" Was she calling Ms. Hussey stupid?

If so, Ms. Hussey didn't seem to notice. She offered Mrs. Sharpe her arm.

Calder went back inside and watched from his front window until he couldn't see the three of them anymore.

That evening, Calder got a letter. Ripping it open, he grinned. Who else?

L:1 F:1 Z:1 N:1 P:1 T:2, -
I:2 F:1 F:2 P:1 - L:2 T:1 - Y:1 W:1 N:1 -
I:2 P:1 Z:2 V:2 - N:1 L:2 L:2 T:2 - W:1 U:2 -
T:1 T:2 L:2 U:1. - X:2 F:1 I:2 W:1 U:2 V:1 P:1 N:1 -
Z:1 F:1 U:2 V:2 - Y:2 P:1 P:1 Y:1. - W:1 -
V:2 V:1 W:1 I:2 Y:1 - Y:1
W:1 N:1 I:2 F:1 N:2 N:2 P:1 N:1. -
V:1 F:1 X:2 P:1 - V:2 L:2 - U:2 V:2 F:1 F:3 -
W:1 I:2 U:2 W:1 N:1 P:1. -
F:2 L:2 F:2 - F:1 T:1 T:2 F:1 W:1 N:1. - I:2 P:1 Y:2 -
F:3 L:2 T:2 Y:1 - U:2 V:2 W:1 I:2 Y:1 U:2. -
                              V:2 L:2 F:2 F:2 F:3

He hurried up to his room to dig out the pentomino code that he'd made for himself and Tommy before his friend left:

	1	2	3
F	A	M	Y
I	B	N	Z
L	C	O	
N	D	P	
P	E	Q	
T	F	R	
U	G	S	
V	H	T	
W	I	U	
X	J	V	
Y	K	W	
Z	L	X	

Calder decoded the message. Worried, he went down to the kitchen to tell his parents the news. Everyone in the Pillay household felt bad. Moving to a new neighborhood was hard enough, but having the kid next door suddenly disappear seemed like a bad joke.

Tommy had never known his real father. During the past winter, his mom, Zelda, who worked in the university library, took a vacation with two other women. They went to Bermuda. She came back with a husband.

At first, Tommy was very quiet and didn't want to talk about "Old Fred," as he started calling him. Fred tried hard to be a dad. He played baseball with Tommy in the park. He came to school and met many of the teachers. He took Tommy and Calder to Fifty-third Street for hot fudge sundaes all the time, and let them get any size they wanted. After a while, it seemed like Tommy was starting to like him.

And then Old Fred announced, last July 4 — Calder remembered the date because it took the bang right out of the fireworks — that the family would need to move to New York. He had bought a house in the suburbs without even telling Tommy's mom. "And of course not the kid," Tommy had said when telling Calder.

And now this Frog business — what kind of a name was Frog, anyway?

Calder wrote Tommy right back.

V:2 L:2 F:2 F:2 F:3, -
U:2 L:2 - U:2 L:2 T:2 T:2 F:3 - F:1 I:1 L:2 W:2 V:2 -
T:1 T:2 L:2 U:1. - F:2 F:1 F:3 I:1 P:1 - F:3 L:2 W:2 -
L:1 F:1 I:2 - U:2 L:2 Z:1 X:2 P:1 -
F:2 F:3 U:2 V:2 P:1 T:2 F:3 - F:1 I:2 N:1 -
I:1 P:1 - V:1 P:1 T:2 L:2. - I:1 P:1 -
L:1 F:1 T:2 P:1 T:1 W:2 Z:1. -
L:1 F:1 Z:1 N:1 P:1 T:2

Tommy had always liked spying; maybe this was an opportunity not to be a mediocre kid. Calder smiled, remembering their conversation in the kitchen when he had first gotten his pentominoes. He hoped his message would help.

After writing the letter and sealing the envelope, it occurred to Calder that maybe this was bad advice. What if something horrible really *had* happened to the kid next door? Whoever was responsible wouldn't want another kid snooping around. Calder's parents had told him that the chances of it being a real kidnapping were small. He hoped they were right.

Chapter Seven

THE MAN ON THE WALL

When Ms. Hussey read the piece of writing aloud at the end of the week, there was a shuffling and a looking-around for who seemed embarrassed or who looked too pleased.

"A strange chair?"

"Modern art with things hanging from it?"

"Does the writer want to stay anonymous, or do you want to tell us what this is?" Ms. Hussey asked after several guesses had been made.

Silence.

Petra cleared her throat. "Well, it's a special book." Petra thought suddenly of the calm, intelligent woman in her dream, the woman in the yellow jacket. *She* probably never had to explain her writing. And suddenly Petra felt the woman was sort of keeping her company, whispering, *It doesn't matter what they say. I understand.*

"A book?" snorted Denise. "Berries and smelly pants?"

Petra's mouth closed in a tight line.

Ms. Hussey turned toward Denise. "Yes. Unexpected similes can carry the power of surprise. They're refreshing, aren't they?"

Denise looked as if she had smelled something bad.

Calder was impressed by Petra's writing, and wished it were his own. An hour later, in the cafeteria, he spotted Petra in a corner by herself. He decided to join her. He wanted to tell her about the threesome outside his house yesterday, and how much he liked her description. He was imagining how surprised Petra would be to have his company.

It was then that Calder's lunch box collided with the back of a chair and popped open. Petra heard the *bang* and watched his baloney sandwich, now airborne, cross the table with impressive speed.

By the time Calder retrieved his sandwich and sat down, she had begun to laugh.

"All right, all right," Calder said.

"It's just that I was reading about inexplicable loud noises and things falling from the sky, then there was this *whop!*, and then a flying —" She was gasping. "It's not you — just so perfect —"

"What're you reading?"

"The book I wrote about. I found it at Powell's yesterday."

Calder saw that it said *Lo!* on the spine. Weird title — no wonder she was trying to cover it up.

"It's by this guy Charles Fort, who spent a lot of his life looking for newspaper articles about unexplained stuff," Petra said. "You know, like weird lights in the sky, objects traveling through rooms without any visible explanation, ghosts, crazy things like that. He talks about how blind and *idiotic* he thinks a lot of our education is. And he's funny. He doesn't take anyone's thinking too seriously, including his own." She paused, surprised at herself for saying so much. "I love hearing about people who figure things out for themselves. Plus, I love to think about things that no one understands. Yet."

"Mmm." Calder's mouth was full.

"Almost anywhere you look in here, there's something amazing. Listen to this." Petra flipped to the middle of the book.

"There have been many mysterious disappearances of human beings. . . . <u>Chicago Tribune</u>, Jan. 5, 1900 — 'Sherman Church, a young man employed in the Augusta Mills (Battle

Creek, Mich.) has disappeared. He was seated in the Company's office, when he arose and ran into the mill. He has not been seen since. The mill has been almost taken to pieces by the searchers, and the river, woods, and country have been scoured. . . .

"And then:

'. . . records of six persons, who between Jan. 14, 1920, and Dec. 9, 1923, were found wandering in or near the small town of Romford, Essex, England, unable to tell how they got there, or anything else about themselves. . . .' "

Calder had stopped chewing and was staring at her.

"Tommy knows a kid called Frog, a kid in New York, who just disappeared."

"Frog?" Petra started to laugh again. "A flying frog!"

Calder kind of wanted to laugh, too, but the news wasn't supposed to be funny. What was she talking about, anyway?

"Do you believe this guy Fort?" As soon as Calder said it, he wished he hadn't. It wasn't really what he meant. Petra's face closed, and she looked disappointed.

"Well, part of what is so neat is that he worked from newspapers. I know most people would think this was completely stupid." Abruptly, Petra started to gather her things, stuffing *Lo!* into her lunch bag.

This wasn't going well. Calder *did* understand Petra's excitement; it was just that he hadn't wanted to look like an idiot again. Plus, the Frog connection had been such a weird coincidence. Before Petra could get up, he blurted, "Your writing was great, and also I saw Ms. Hussey, an old lady called Mrs. Sharpe, and Mr. Watch my boss from Powell's, outside my house yesterday. They were all there together."

Petra no longer looked unfriendly. "Mrs. who?"

"Sharpe. At least that's what it sounded like."

Petra pulled out her book again. She opened to the first page and turned it toward Calder. "Strange, huh?"

" 'Louise Coffin Sharpe,' " Calder read. "Do you think that's her? I could find out," he said as if there was nothing to it.

"Okay." Petra beamed at him. "Thanks. I'd love to know — I didn't think the first owner would still be alive."

The next day was Saturday, and Calder arrived at Powell's early. Mr. Watch was seated behind the front counter, frowning over what looked like a letter.

"Ah, yes, I need you to make a delivery." Mr. Watch refolded the letter. "I'm sending you down the street with some books. The name is Sharpe."

Calder grinned. Events were fitting together now with the precision of pentominoes. He ventured, "Would that be *Louise* Sharpe?"

Mr. Watch looked stern. "Yes, but not to you." He handed Calder a paper bag filled with books.

On the way over, Calder peeked into the bag. There were some novels in French and a new book about art by David Hockney. It looked like the kind of thing Ms. Hussey would read. There was also a small, beat-up book called *An Experiment in Time*. When Calder flipped to the table of contents, he saw that Chapter Two was called "The Puzzle." Mrs. Sharpe must not be all bad.

If she recognized Calder, she didn't let on. He decided not to remind her about the glass of water. Calder noticed that she had unusually green eyes — a sea-green surrounded by lots of wrinkles and bones. She asked him to wait in the living room while she got a check.

He looked around. He was standing on a huge Oriental carpet. Velvet cushions, naked sculpture, glass cabinets: The place was a museum. And in the corner, on a neatly organized desk, sat a large, fancy computer.

Then he saw it. Calder couldn't believe his eyes. There, hanging over the sofa, was a big version of the painting on his box.

"Do you know what that is?" Her voice made him jump.

"I was going to ask you — you see, my grandma gave me a box with that guy, I mean that painting, on the cover, and I was going to try to find out who did it — and I just did some homework that describes it — that's so strange, isn't it?"

Mrs. Sharpe sniffed and handed Calder the check. "Well, not really. That's a print of a Vermeer painting called *The Geographer*. There must be thousands of them around."

"Oh! Who was Vermeer? I know I've heard his name, but — you know." Calder, still surprised, was warming up to the situation.

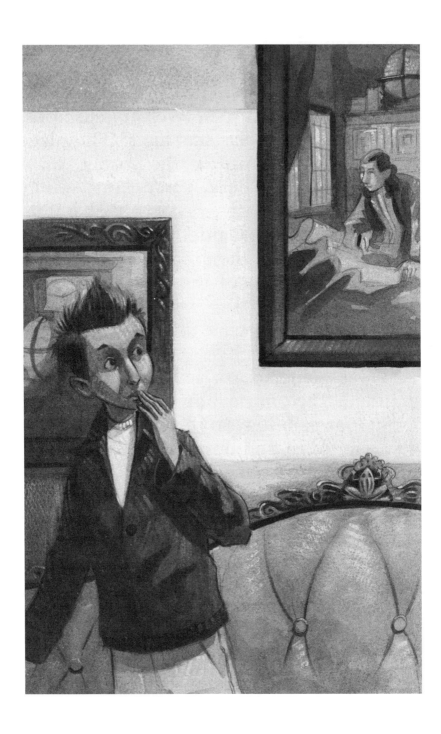

"He was Dutch, and painted in the seventeenth century." She paused, looking thoughtfully at Calder's enthusiastic grin. "I'm sure you could find a book in your school library that told you something about him."

"Wow — this is just so perfect." Calder, in his excitement, was already headed for the front door. Then he remembered Petra's book.

"Hey, Mrs. Sharpe — could I ask you a question? It's about *Lo!*, a book a friend of mine, Petra Andalee, found at Powell's, and — well, I think maybe it has your name in it."

Mrs. Sharpe was dreadfully silent for a moment. What was she thinking?

When she spoke, her voice was soft. "Do you understand the book?"

Calder looked up. He couldn't tell from her face whether this was a trick question. "Part of it, anyway," he lied. "I mean, we both really like the stuff about weird things happening that nobody understands — like people who disappear. And it's cool that he found all that in newspapers."

"I didn't think anybody read books like that anymore." Mrs. Sharpe looked almost human now.

Encouraged, Calder blurted, "Oh yes, all

the time." Oh no — he'd gone too far.

"Come for tea one day after school. Bring your friend and we will talk about Charles Fort." Mrs. Sharpe's voice was now icy. "Four o'clock." She turned to open the door, and Calder knew he was being dismissed.

"Okay, I will. Tha—" The door shut in his face. Calder walked back toward Powell's in a daze. *My friend Petra?* He hoped she would become his friend, and fast. There was no way he'd go back to talk about that *Lo!* stuff on his own. How did he get himself into this?

Monday morning was blue and white, and everything was blowing: cumulus clouds, bare branches, scraps of rubbish.

Calder stepped out his front door and saw Petra chasing a piece of paper up the block toward the Castigliones. As he watched, the paper shot skyward in a graceful loop and headed over the roof of the Castiglione's tree house and toward the train tracks.

Petra stopped. "Darn!" she said. "That letter was half-buried in your garden. I only got to read the beginning, but it said something about an old crime and art." She shrugged. "Probably just some crazy advertisement, anyway — not a real letter at all."

"I've been thinking about that Charles House book," Calder began.

"Fort." Petra tried not to smile.

"And something else." Calder took a deep breath. "Mrs. Sharpe. That *is* her book. And she's interested that we — I mean you — know about it. She wants to meet you."

Petra had stopped walking. "Seriously?"

"She wants us to have tea with her one day. She just kind of announced it." Calder looked at the tops of the trees as if they'd been invited, too. What would he do if Petra wouldn't go? Mrs. Sharpe would soon realize he'd lied about reading *Lo!*

Petra was silent for a moment. "Wait. How did you talk to her?"

Calder explained about his job at Powell's and the delivery yesterday. The rest of the walk to school they talked about coincidence, agreeing that it didn't always seem to be accidental, and Petra shared some of Charles Fort's ideas about looking carefully at things. Calder wanted to tell her about his box, and about the coincidence of seeing the Geographer on Mrs. Sharpe's wall, but didn't — Ms. Hussey hadn't read Calder's description aloud yet, and he was hoping Petra would like it.

They agreed that there was a great deal to be figured out in the world. Petra confided that she thought Ms. Hussey might be willing to let them collect strange data the way Fort did. That is, if kids like Denise didn't wreck it for everyone.

"Maybe data about art — art and unexplained stuff!" Petra blurted.

"Petra, you're amazing." How could he ever have thought that wedge of hair was anything but brainy?

Petra's mouth twisted strangely. "You'd better read that book before you agree with me. You might not be as crazy as I am."

He laughed and stirred the pentominoes in his pocket happily. This year was getting better all the time.

Calder borrowed Petra's copy of *Lo!* that afternoon. She was right: Fort was an extraordinary thinker. He looked fearlessly at occurrences that no one could explain. Even better, he looked everywhere for patterns. Calder understood the man's fascination with connecting things that didn't seem related, and he admired the way Fort challenged the experts. How could Mrs. Sharpe ever have gotten tired of such an exciting book?

Speaking of Mrs. Sharpe, he had some detective work to do.

The reproduction of *The Geographer* in his library book was clearer and brighter than the copy of the painting on his box. Behind the man was a framed map, and above that the signature **I Ver Meer**, and under that, **MDCLXVIII**. Calder counted: a thousand plus five hundred plus a hundred plus fifty plus ten plus five plus three — 1668. The artist's full name was Johannes Vermeer, also known as Jan Vermeer, and he was from the Netherlands, in northern Europe.

The book explained that no one knew for sure who the Geographer was, but that the area where Vermeer lived was a center for mapmakers. It talked about how people with money liked to hang maps on the walls of their houses to show that they were wealthy and that they thought about the world. Mapmaking was a respected profession, something between a science and an art.

Calder flipped back and forth in the book, looking at some of the other Vermeer paintings. Most of them showed people in front of a window; the Geographer's rug appeared in many of the paintings, and the same yellow jacket turned up in a number of places. The pictures made you feel as though you were peeking in at someone else's private moment. The light that came from outside made ordinary objects seem important: a quill pen, a pitcher with milk, an earring, the brass buttons that were part of a straight-backed chair. It occurred to Calder that there could be hidden information here — after all, codes involved repetition, and the same objects appeared again and again in Vermeer's work. There was the obvious geometry of windowpanes and floor tiles, and then all the pearls, baskets, pitchers, and framed maps. There was symmetry, both complete and carefully broken.

Calder read more. The book said that Vermeer died penniless when he was in his forties, and that almost nothing was known about his life. No one understood why such a fabulous painter had made only thirty-five works of art. No one knew who the people he painted were, or why he painted the things he did. No one knew how he became an artist.

Vermeer had left behind more questions than answers.

Chapter Eight

A HALLOWEEN SURPRISE

On the morning of Sunday, October 31, Petra overheard her dad telling her mom that he just wasn't up for Halloween.

"Frank, think of the kids." Her mom sounded tense.

Then Petra heard her dad's rumble and parts of what he said: "Sorry, honey . . . letter in the mail this week . . . you'll see . . . be over before we know it." He'd given her mom a hug.

What letter? And what had happened to the one that was torn up? *What* would be over? Did their family need money? Would they have to move? Petra suddenly longed to tell Ms. Hussey what she'd just realized: Important letters *couldn't* be talked about because they always held secrets. Ms. Hussey must never have gotten one or she'd know that.

Harper Avenue was in its element on Halloween. People came from miles around to walk down the block where Petra and Calder lived, and families took pride in becoming as frightening as possible. Graves sprang up in front yards, complete with scattered bones, headstones, and shovels. Tarantulas looped from gutters, and pumpkins flashed and growled. Corpses hanging from second-story windows swung gently in the darkness. Chocolate eyeballs rolled underfoot. A mesh of webs covered bushes and porches, and crackly voices and organ music came from flower beds. For the kids who lived on the block, costumes were a big deal.

At 4:00 that afternoon, Petra was struggling to tie ribbons in her hair. Bouncy and curly, it didn't like the idea of being pulled back so tightly. Petra finally yanked out all of the ribbons and made a tight ponytail and a tidy bun. She then fastened the already-tied ribbons on with bobby pins.

Next she put on her homemade earrings. They were large white beads that hung on a hoop. She looked different, quite definitely. The train roared by outside the window, and Petra stood still, watching her earrings tremble with the vibrations.

She put on her jacket with the fake-fur collar and cuffs — she had sewn carefully

trimmed pieces of an old Dalmatian costume onto a yellow sweater. She was ready.
Lowering her lids a fraction of an inch and
smiling a smile that was more an idea than a
movement, she looked at herself sideways in
the mirror. She felt filled, at least for that
moment, with the easy elegance of the writer
in her dream.

When Petra opened the door, there was
Calder on her front porch wearing a large
red letter made out of taped-together cardboard squares.

"Hi, Calder!"

"Petra —"

She suddenly wished she hadn't done all
that stuff to her hair, and instinctively
pulled back out of the light.

"You look like something I've seen, I
mean, just like a painting —"

"I do?" Petra mumbled.

"How did you think of dressing up like
her?"

"Like who?" Petra looked at Calder directly now, frowning slightly.

"The lady with the feather pen, the lady
at the desk!"

Calder tried to protect his pentomino costume as Petra pulled him into her front hall.
"Tell me *exactly* what you're talking about."

"Look out! Now you've bent my F," Calder said crossly. "What're you so upset about?"

"I'm sorry. It's just that you recognized my costume. You see, I dreamed about it."

"What do you mean you dreamed that painting?"

"I didn't say it was a painting. I don't know what it was."

"Weird. I have your picture at home — come over and see for yourself."

They were down Petra's steps and up Calder's in seconds.

Once inside, Calder ducked out of his F and flew up the stairs. When he reappeared, he was carrying an oversized library book. He sat on the floor and leafed quickly through the reproductions. Petra knelt beside him.

"There!"

Petra's stomach gave a sickening lurch. It was not only her costume, it was the woman in her dream. She touched the reproduction with her hand, as if to be sure it was really there. The caption next to it read: JOHANNES VERMEER, A LADY WRITING, 1665.

Chapter Nine

THE BLUE ONES

Calder and Petra found three other paintings of the woman in the yellow jacket. In one, she was wearing a pearl necklace and looking into a mirror. In another, she was playing a lute. In the third, she was seated at a writing table and a maid was handing her what looked like a letter.

"You've never seen any of these before?" Calder looked worried.

"Never." Petra had taken off one of her earrings and was rolling it around on the floor.

"So how did you dream about something you didn't know existed?"

"I wonder," Petra said slowly, "if paintings that float into your mind on their own are kind of like flying frogs or disappearing people."

"Mmm . . . you mean your dream might be part of something bigger." Calder jumped up and got a piece of paper and pencil. He handed them to Petra. "Maybe we should start keeping a record of unexplained stuff."

Petra ducked her head happily over the paper. "Fine."

She began with:

Charles Fort: chief questioner, philosopher, guide

"Hey, here's something else. Did you know I made that F costume because I was thinking 'F for Fort'?"

"We'll include that."

Calder told Petra about his box, explaining the reason he happened to be looking at the book. "I wonder what made me remember that old thing, anyway? If it hadn't popped into my mind, I wouldn't have recognized *The Geographer* at Mrs. Sharpe's, and then I would never have read about Vermeer or recognized your costume."

"It's Ms. Hussey's fault," Petra said, delighted. "It all started with her find-some-art assignment. We found it, all right."

They spent the next ten minutes trying to figure out what happened when. Petra wrote:

1. **Calder writes about box with Geographer on it, same day that Petra finds Lo!, writes about it, then dreams about woman.**

Calder was flipping back and forth in the book. "This doesn't tell you too much about Vermeer's life. Do you think we should do some research? I've been wondering if there's some kind of secret code that no one's ever noticed before — I mean, why so many pearls and pens and button thingies?"

"Good thinking." Petra grinned.

"And maybe there's some other crazy connection with Charles Fort," Calder went on. "Some facts we might be missing."

"We could look in the high school library tomorrow."

"Great." Calder stood up and reached into his pocket. He stirred the pentomino pieces around and pulled one out.

"V for Vermeer." He smiled in a distracted way at Petra, who looked puzzled. "A one-in-twelve chance. Think it's coincidence?"

On the way to school the next morning, Petra asked Calder about the V for Vermeer business. "I told you about the woman. Now you can tell me about these pentominoes. And don't say they're just for making rectangles."

"They help me figure things out," began Calder. He looked sideways at Petra. "Promise you won't laugh."

"Why should I? What could be weirder than my dream?"

"Well, it seems like the pentominoes kind of talk to me. I'll get the feeling that they want to tell me something, and so I'll grab one, and a word will just pop into my head."

Petra was looking at Calder with interest.

"I know. It sounds like a superstitious game. And it probably is. But you're right about Charles Fort. He makes you look carefully at stuff you might have ignored before."

"I think it's cool."

Calder smiled gratefully at Petra. He should have known she'd understand.

At 3:30 that afternoon, they were sitting behind a stack of books in the library.

"Let's begin with dates, okay?" Petra, writing in neat purple ink, started a new page with the heading "Facts about Vermeer."

Calder looked at the book in front of him. "Whoa! Petra! Get this: Vermeer was baptized on Halloween in 1632. That's the first fact about his life."

"Kind of spooky, don't you think? We started writing about him on the same day that his name was first recorded. There are more than three and a half centuries in between. . . ."

"Here it is," Calder went on. "Johannes, son of Reynier Jansz and Digna Baltens —"

"Wait. Spellings."

Calder paused for a moment while Petra copied the names. He went on: "His father was an innkeeper in Delft, but was also a weaver who manufactured a fine satin cloth called 'caffa.' Vermeer was an innkeeper, too, and then an art dealer. Let's see. . . . When he was twenty-one he married Catharina Bolnes. Later that year he was registered as a 'Master Painter' in the Guild of Saint Luke . . . became a director of the same guild several times . . . had eleven children. He died in 1675, at age forty-three."

Petra was writing madly.

Calder turned the page. "It looks like he died owing money, and that he wasn't really famous until about a hundred years ago. Huh. He's mysterious, I mean everything about his life is. There aren't any records of how he got started, or of what money his family lived on. Historians don't know where he worked, or who the women and men in his paintings were, whether they were friends or family or what. I read that before — almost nothing at all is known about him as a person." Calder looked up. "That's so strange, don't you think? I wonder if someone destroyed his notebooks or letters?"

Petra glanced at Calder. "It does seem suspicious. And sad, don't you think? These magical scenes that no one will ever know more about."

Calder was reading again. "You know what else? He only signed some of his paintings. I wonder why?" Calder turned the page. "I'd never have done that," he muttered under his breath.

"Let's find out more about the painting in your dream," he went on. "Here it is: *A Lady Writing*, and it's in the National Gallery of Art, in Washington, D.C. The thing she's wearing is a morning jacket, and it has white fur around the collar and sleeves. Those big earrings are either some kind of fancy glass or pearls, can you believe it? The oyster that made those would have to have been the size of a football. That's a quill pen, of course. The same chair with the lion's-head knobs turns up in other images . . . and the same jewelry, furniture, even maps and paintings on the walls. I wonder if this is Vermeer's home."

"Must've been hard to work with so many kids." Petra was thinking about how noisy just five could be.

"Is anything making sense here?" Calder asked.

"Well, there's the Halloween thing. That's a pretty weird coincidence."

"But is there anything else we're missing? A pattern? Numbers?"

"It seems like there's too much connection here," Petra said slowly. "Like Mrs. Sharpe knowing about both Vermeer and Charles Fort, you knowing Mrs. Sharpe, me reading Mrs. Sharpe's book and having that dream right when you were reading about Vermeer, and then the costumes we both made. . . . Do you suppose that ideas overlap like this all the time, and people just don't realize it?"

"Maybe."

Outside the library, they walked several yards in silence. Calder pulled two packages of peanut M&M's out of his coat and passed one to Petra.

"Thanks," she said, surprised.

"What's your favorite?" he asked.

"The blue ones."

"Hey, how about the blue M&M symbolizes secrecy? We can start a collection and each eat one at special times as a sign of our determination to figure this out. It'll be kind of our own private thing —" Hearing himself, Calder stopped.

Petra added quickly, "It'll represent us, Charles Fort, and Vermeer. Perfect."

They decided to save the blue M&M's in Calder's box and keep it under his bed. Petra would hold on to the notebook.

At the end of Harper Avenue they stopped and both ate an M&M, agreeing that the color blue had a rare and mysterious taste.

Chapter Ten

INSIDE THE PUZZLE

Calder felt restless as he stood in front of the living room window on Wednesday afternoon. It had been two days since their trip to the library. Not knowing what to investigate, neither Calder nor Petra had done any further research.

Outside, it was pouring rain. The water was running and puddling. As Calder absentmindedly watched the droplets forming and re-forming in shape after shape, an idea came to mind. Of course! It was the obvious next step. He bounded up the stairs, away from his parents talking in the kitchen, and picked up the phone.

When Petra answered, he said, "Listen, I think we should call the National Gallery and ask if *A Lady Writing* is there. You know, to find out if the painting is safe and all that."

"Why wouldn't it be there?"

"Well, I just want to be sure. Maybe Charles Fort's warping my brain, but

stories about teleportation and people vanishing into thin air . . . we should check."

"I'll be right over."

Neither Petra nor Calder had ever called a museum before. They flipped a penny about who was going to speak, and Petra dialed. There was a recording, with museum hours and information about shows and tours, and then finally a chance to talk to an operator. Petra held the phone at an angle so that Calder could hear, too.

"National Gallery of Art." The voice was silky, not young, and very official.

"Umm, we're calling to find out if a certain Vermeer painting is on the wall right now."

"Oh? What picture are you looking for?" Petra made a face at Calder; the voice now had that half-fake cheeriness that some adults get when talking to kids.

Petra continued, trying to sound as businesslike as possible, "*A Lady Writing.*"

"Let me check my computer. If the painting is on loan, I can tell you."

Petra and Calder waited, silent, for her to come on again.

"Well, yes, the painting is traveling just now. It's in Chicago. There's going to be a show called 'Writers in Art' at the Art Institute."

Petra's and Calder's eyes widened. Calder grabbed the phone, pulling Petra's hair in the process. There was a fierce, whispered "Ow!" followed by a muffled "Sorry!"

"Excuse me?" The woman's voice came on again.

"Do you know whether the painting is in Chicago now?" Calder was squeezing the phone receiver so hard that his knuckles stood out.

The woman on the other end hesitated. "Well, that's what the computer said. I assume so. It left Washington several days ago, and the show opens next week."

Sensing that the woman was going to ask them what they were doing, or whom she was speaking with, Calder said a quick "thank-you-good-bye" and hung up.

"Holy smokes, Petra!"

Petra nodded, silent.

"Are you thinking the same thing I am?"

She nodded again. "I'm calling the Art Institute. And this time, Calder Pillay, you're not grabbing the phone and ripping out my hair."

After a great deal of waiting and transferring to other lines, the second call told

108

them only that a new show was going up the following week.

"Well, it could just be that we're thinking about this stuff because the painting is part of a show here, and . . . and we're just picking it up, that's all. . . ." Petra's voice trailed off.

"Yeah, but I still feel funny knowing she's traveling, don't you?" Calder said.

"Paintings travel all the time. And now we'll actually be able to see her."

"Time for a blue one."

They sat cross-legged on the floor with the Geographer between them, arguing about whether the M&M's they'd picked were the same size. They played a half-hearted game of Monopoly. Calder's mom brought them cookies on dark blue napkins covered with green frogs.

"Hey, where did these napkins come from, Mom?"

"I don't remember, but they're fun, aren't they?"

After she left the room, Calder and Petra looked at each other.

"Maybe the rain gave the frogs an excuse to drop in," Calder grinned.

"Right. Speaking of frogs, any news from New York?"

Calder had called Tommy the night before. He'd told Calder he was beginning to wonder if there was a *reason* that everyone in his neighborhood was so unfriendly — like there was some huge secret he hadn't figured out. Frog was definitely not around, and no one wanted to tell Tommy why. He admitted to Calder that he might have been a bit dramatic with the kidnapping stuff, but facts were facts: Frog was there one day and gone the next. And no one was talking.

"I feel bad not being able to help," Calder said to Petra. "Must be creepy, wondering if you'll be the next kid to go."

"Maybe your pentominoes will say something," she suggested.

Calder stirred them around. He pulled out an N. He frowned. "N for what?" Calder thought aloud. "New York? No. National Gallery? Forget it — a serious case of Vermeer on the brain."

"Yeah, it's hard to think about anything else."

After school the next day, Petra raked leaves with her dad, who seemed to be in his own world lately. He never passed the food at meals. He had forgotten to turn off the bathtub a couple of days ago. He tried to put on tiny socks from the socks basket and just looked puzzled when they didn't fit.

Now he raked over and over the same spot on the lawn. The grass was pulling up, leaving patches of bare dirt.

"Dad?" Petra had stopped working.

"Yes?"

"You okay?"

Petra's dad looked at her as if she were on the other side of a closed window. He lifted his hand in a stiff wave. "Fine!"

But Petra didn't believe him. What had happened to him? He still went off to work, but he was always distracted. She wished with all her heart she had found the letter that had started this, the one her parents had been arguing about weeks ago. There might have been something she could have done.

As her dad headed inside, she heard him mutter, "A loan. Insane."

Petra's eyes opened wide. A loan . . . The first thing she thought of was *A Lady Writing*. What was her dad talking about? Had he meant money? Or had she heard wrong? Maybe he'd said "alone." Either way, it sounded bad.

Calder made two pumpkin pies that afternoon with his mom, and played three games of solitaire. He helped his dad fold the laundry.

"Calder, I need you for something else. Come outside." Calder's dad was already in his jacket.

Calder followed him onto the front walk, noticing with interest all the papers that had collected under the dead plants in their yard. He was remembering the letter about crime and art that Petra had found there and then lost.

His dad was squinting up at the outside of the house. "It's time we repainted. Think we should keep the same color?"

"Yup," Calder said. "That's Grandma Ranjana's color, isn't it? Too bad she can't know we're keeping her choice. Why did she like red so much, anyway?"

Calder's dad laughed. "It's a long story. Something about the artist Vermeer . . . she wished he'd used more red, because she thought he was the best, but red would have made him perfect."

"Weird," Calder said quietly.

He glanced down the block and saw Petra in her yard. She had on a red hat, a smudge of bright color against the November gray.

Sometimes he wished he'd never heard of Fort or Vermeer. Events that were purely accidental were beginning to feel like they fit together, but not in a way he understood or even knew how to think about. It was one thing if you were using a handful of plastic pieces to find solutions to a puzzle; it was another if you felt like you'd fallen inside a puzzle and couldn't get out.

Chapter Eleven

NIGHTMARE

At 7:30 on the morning of November 5, Calder was hunting for his sneakers. Petra was looking under the living room sofa for the hairbrush. Both reached their kitchens at the same moment.

In the Pillay household, Calder's parents were pouring juice, pulling out cold cereal boxes, and talking. Calder caught the words "tragic" and "shocking."

"What's the matter?" he asked.

In Petra's kitchen, her mom was making cheese sandwiches and talking to her dad. Petra heard her mother say, "How could a thing like this happen? I mean, whose fault is this?"

Petra read the headlines. On the front of the *Chicago Tribune*, in giant letters, were the words "VERMEER VANISHES: IRREPLACEABLE TREASURE DISAPPEARS BETWEEN WASHINGTON AND CHICAGO." Petra sat heavily on a kitchen chair and began to read:

114

A 1665 Vermeer painting entitled <u>A LADY WRITING</u> was stolen this past weekend when in transit between the National Gallery of Art in Washington, D.C., and the Art Institute of Chicago.

The painting was to be the centerpiece of an exhibit to open next week at the Art Institute. <u>A LADY WRITING</u> is, according to curators at the National Gallery, of "absolutely incalculable worth." One of thirty-five known works by Dutch artist Johannes Vermeer, it is without doubt one of the most valuable paintings to have been stolen in the twentieth century.

In an emotional telephone interview, N. B. Jones, the curator in charge of arranging the loan, said, "This is every museum's nightmare. This is an exquisite and fragile painting that needs to be kept in certain atmospheric conditions. It is easily worth millions of dollars, but could never be sold on the black market. It must have been targeted for theft by an individual collector. This is a tragedy of indescribable proportions."

ACCORDING TO SOURCES AT THE ART
INSTITUTE, THE PAINTING ARRIVED WITH
ARMED GUARDS LATE YESTERDAY AFTER-
NOON. WHEN IT WAS UNPACKED WITH
GREAT EXCITEMENT BY A GROUP OF CON-
SERVATORS AND CURATORS, THE CASE WAS
FOUND TO BE EMPTY. A PRINTED NOTE WAS
TAPED TO THE PACKING MATERIALS. IT
READ: <u>YOU WILL COME TO AGREE WITH ME.</u>

EVERY ATTENDANT AND ARMED GUARD
WHO WAS NEAR THE PAINTING FROM THE
TIME IT LEFT WASHINGTON HAS BEEN
IDENTIFIED AND IS BEING HELD FOR
QUESTIONING.

Petra could hardly breathe. She had to find Calder.

Calder listened to his parents read parts of the article aloud. "I knew it, I knew it," he muttered to himself.

"What's that, Calder? It's upsetting, isn't it?" Calder's dad peered at him over the paper. As Calder ran down the hall, he heard his father remarking to his mother, "Must have Spelling today."

Calder was down the steps in one leap and running toward Petra's house. He arrived just as she stepped out. One look at each other and both knew it wasn't necessary to break the news.

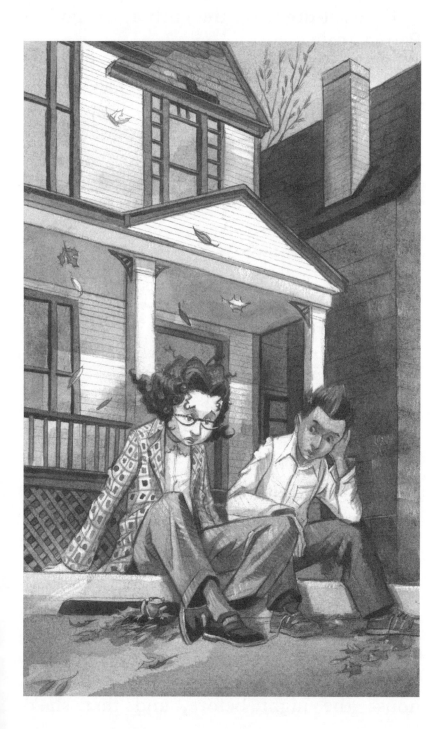

They sat down on the curb at the end of Petra's walk.

"We knew it, right? We knew ahead of time!" Calder began fiercely tearing up fallen leaves.

"Yeah, but we didn't *really* know." Petra's voice was strangled-sounding. "Besides, who would've paid any attention to two kids talking about what sounds like a few coincidences?"

"There's no question now that there's something really creepy going on here, and that we're somehow mixed up in it." Calder looked at Petra directly for the first time. "I mean, how could we have just stumbled on all this stuff?"

Petra didn't disagree. "It sounds nutty to say, but I think the Vermeer woman is depending on us — kind of like she's been waiting for us to catch up."

They were both silent for a moment.

Calder stood up. "So what do we do now?"

"What Charles Fort would do. Pay attention and keep our heads."

Ms. Hussey turned up at school that morning with her arm in a sling. She explained that the lights had gone out in her house the night before, and that she'd fallen. What had seemed intriguing just a couple of days ago suddenly felt sinister to both Calder and Petra: Petra's dream painting had been stolen, Petra's dad was acting weird, Calder was worried about Tommy, and now Ms. Hussey was hurt. Petra and Calder looked at each other, silently running through all the things that were going wrong. Who or what would be next?

Ms. Hussey had the newspaper under her arm, and the first thing she did was read aloud the article about the Vermeer painting. This started a discussion about art theft, and about how thieves sometimes cut canvases out of frames. Ms. Hussey told them about a theft in 1990 at the Isabella Stewart Gardner Museum in Boston. Thieves had dressed as police and had gotten the night security guards to let them in. Then they tied up the guards, turned off the alarms, and stole at least ten paintings, including a Vermeer and a Rembrandt. Those paintings were still missing. She told them a number of other stories about art thefts, some of the plottings ingenious and some a mess.

"We just have to hope," Ms. Hussey said, "that this thief is not a professional."

"You mean that he'll do something

stupid?" Calder asked. "Something that will give him away?"

"Or that he or she will crack under the strain of it all," she said, her voice sounding tired. "I'm giving you free work time this morning — I don't feel very well."

Most of the class whispered happily or read, seeming to forget about the Vermeer. All day, a book with a full-page reproduction of the Lady was propped open against the blackboard. Calder walked by it and was surprised to realize that it was the same book they'd seen Ms. Hussey pay for at Powell's a couple of weeks earlier. The word Calder had seen on the cover hadn't been "Never" — it was part of "Netherland." Netherlandish Painting.

When he told Petra, she got very quiet. "Another coincidence," she said, her voice barely audible. "I didn't like the way Ms. Hussey said that thing about cracking under the strain — she looks like *she's* cracking."

"Think we should tell her we've been studying Vermeer, too? It might cheer her up," Calder suggested.

Petra thought for a moment. "No," she said slowly, "and I'm not sure why. I think she's in some kind of trouble, and I don't want her to think we've noticed. Otherwise, we won't be able to help." Petra looked at Calder.

"Right. She wouldn't want us to get hurt, too," Calder finished. Suddenly he remembered the pentomino Denise had kicked under Ms. Hussey's desk. It had been T — T for trouble.

Walking home that day, Calder and Petra saw Ms. Hussey cross Harper Avenue and head toward Powell's. They knew exactly what to do.

Hurrying to the corner, they looked both ways. There was no one in sight; she must have gone inside.

"Maybe we can see something through the front window — Mr. Watch is usually facing the other way. If we walk in the door, she might be right there," Calder said.

Petra nodded.

They crept under the window and stood up just enough to peek over the display shelves. Ms. Hussey and Mr. Watch were talking intently, their heads close together.

It was frustrating, being so close to them and not being able to hear. Petra's and Calder's minds were racing, but in different directions. Calder was going over everything he'd seen Mr. Watch ever do that was puzzling — why did he spend so much time in the art section of the store? It seemed like he was always straightening books over there. Why had he been so friendly to Mrs. Sharpe, walking her to the store before Calder started her deliveries? And were he and Ms. Hussey friends?

Petra was wondering what had made Ms. Hussey buy that art book weeks ago, and whether it was just a coincidence. Ms. Hussey was very adventuresome. Had she gotten herself in over her head somehow? Had she really just fallen the night before? Did her injuries have anything to do with *A Lady Writing*?

Heading back down their block, Petra and Calder shared their worries. If they had turned around, they would have seen Ms. Hussey and Mr. Watch leave the store together.

Ms. Hussey was carrying a thick package under her good arm.

The *Chicago Tribune* editorial board printed this unsigned letter the following morning:

Dear Concerned Art Lovers,
I am the one responsible for the temporary disappearance of A LADY WRITING. *She remains in her frame, and no harm will*

come to her. She will be returned when the lies that surround the lifework of Johannes Vermeer have been corrected. I have committed a crime, but in my heart I know that my theft is a gift. Sometimes bold steps must be taken to uncover the truth.

Here lies the problem: The great master known as Johannes Vermeer painted, in truth, only twenty-six of the thirty-five paintings we now attribute to him. These "real" Vermeers were done between 1656 and 1669. How do I know this? Look for yourselves. His touch is unmistakable, his vision and originality impossible to truly reproduce.

Now tell me why we have no papers, no printed materials written by this great artist about his lifework? Why do we know so little about the man?

I believe that this is the answer: Vermeer's followers and perhaps even members of his family, those he taught and those who so greatly admired him, got hold of and destroyed his papers after his death. Then, a number of works done under his direction or influence were sold as paintings either executed by an immature Vermeer at the start of his career or by the ailing artist in his last years. Centuries went by, and Vermeer fell into obscurity.

As the master's works became more and more valuable in the twentieth century, those who owned these "earlier" and "later" paintings were, of course, uninterested in the idea that they might be in ownership of a painting done by someone else. These paintings are currently in a number of big and powerful museums, including the Metropolitan Museum of Art in New York and the National Gallery in London. Who is now brave enough to correct these errors? Who but the public at large, those with nothing to lose?

What should you do? First you must simply go and look. Look at the reproductions in books about Vermeer if you cannot get to the museums. Ask yourself, after studying the great paintings of genius done by Vermeer during the 1660s and just before, whether these other works have the same magic, the same luminous glow, the same secretive, dreamlike power. Well, do they?

The greatest art belongs to the world. Do not be intimidated by the experts. Trust your instincts. Do not be afraid to go against what you were taught, or what you were told to see or believe. Every person, every set of eyes, has the right to the truth. These paintings will speak to you as they have to me.

When you have looked as you have never looked before, you will come to agree with me. And then the record must be set straight.

To do this, you must protest. You must be difficult and impossible to ignore. I hope you will write, by the thousands, to museum officials, to newspapers, to those in power. When the surviving lifework of this great painter has been correctly identified, I will return A LADY WRITING.

I eagerly await your involvement. I will be setting up a Web site where you may post letters on a computerized message board. They will be kept by me, and they will be read by the world.

As for the three people who received a letter from me in October, you know who you are. I cannot thank you enough. The part you have played has been invaluable.

I congratulate you all on your pursuit of the truth.

The uproar was instantaneous and dramatic.

Chapter Twelve

TEA AT FOUR

The unsigned letter was reprinted in a number of major newspapers around the world. This was a first: An art scholar had become a thief and was asking the public for help.

Overnight, Ms. Hussey's classroom became a combination of museum and laboratory. The walls were soon plastered with reproductions of Vermeer paintings, and library books were piled on every surface. The kids borrowed powerful magnifying glasses from the science department, trying to see how the floor tiles Vermeer painted in the 1660s compared with those in the 1670s, or whether a hand in one painting was similar to a hand in another. They studied wrinkles, reflections, shadows, wood, glass, and fabric. In the process, they discovered how blurry most reproductions can become when examined through a magnifying glass. Ms. Hussey seemed happy with the noise and argument and made everyone defend their opinions. Calder's job was to organize the data the class collected into a giant chart. Petra's was to record some of the conclusions about which paintings were "real" and which were not. Other kids set up a voting system and tallied the results, or worked on letters that they would post on the Internet.

Talk that felt exhilarating in Ms. Hussey's classroom was nerve-racking elsewhere. Behind closed doors, those in museums or in positions of authority in the art world were deep in complicated, sometimes angry discussions. Everyone agreed that the most important issue was how to get back *A Lady Writing*. Her safety came first. They also agreed that a scholarly terrorist should not be allowed to blackmail the art establishment and endanger one of the world's greatest treasures simply to have his or her way. How could museums consider the thief's demands?

Another problem was that the letter had fired the public's curiosity and imagination. The press had, of course, fed the flames. Suddenly everyone from sports stars to taxi drivers felt entitled to share their thoughts on which work was a "real" Vermeer painting and which wasn't. There were interviews every day on the news. People talked confidently about Vermeer — in fancy restaurants, in subways, in doughnut shops, in elevators. There was a wave of rebellious feeling against those who were experts in the field. After all, if art wasn't for the people of the world, who was it for? And, as the thief had pointed out, wasn't one set of eyes as good as any other? What did an education and a fancy degree have to do with seeing? The letters that swept over the Internet were adding up in the thousands.

Many were siding with the opinions of the thief. Some even forgave him or her in the interest of truth, feeling that the thief had a very important mission that would have pleased Vermeer himself.

On the day her class voted on the attribution of each of the thirty-five paintings, Ms. Hussey was oddly quiet. The majority of sixth graders sided with the thief, concluding that Vermeer's early and late works were indeed suspicious.

Impatient to know what Ms. Hussey thought, Calder asked his teacher the question she usually asked them: "Well, do you agree?" He thought she'd be pleased.

"We'll see," Ms. Hussey said in a flat, grown-up tone. It wasn't like her at all.

As she turned away, Calder thought she looked frightened.

Several long weeks had gone by since Mrs. Sharpe had invited Calder and Petra to tea. In that time, *A Lady Writing* had vanished. She was gone, but she was everywhere — she was still Petra and Calder's secret, but she was now a familiar face to many thousands of others.

Mrs. Sharpe had left a message for Calder at Powell's. He and "his friend" were expected for tea on Monday, November 22.

As they walked slowly toward the house, the kids agreed that Mrs. Sharpe was a good person to be seeing. If she liked both Fort and Vermeer, she might have some insights on the theft.

Calder noticed the top of Mrs. Sharpe's head, just the crescent of a tidy white bun, in one window. It was getting dark outside, and the lighted interior looked like a painting. Through the wobble of old glass they could see the edge of *The Geographer* over the sofa, a fan of rosy light on the ceiling, a lace curtain — and then abruptly, as if in response to their curiosity, a hand reached up and released the blinds.

"Calder? Something's funny here."

"What do you mean?"

Before Petra could answer, Mrs. Sharpe

opened the door. "So you're the young woman who has my book. Hurry up, you're letting in the cold air. We're having tea in the kitchen. I hate any kind of mess, so that is where we will eat."

Mrs. Sharpe ignored Petra's murmured comments about how nice the house was, saying only, "Watch your step, and don't touch anything."

Calder was thinking to himself that Mrs. Sharpe was rude. For someone who was so proper, it seemed odd. She had barely said hello.

The kitchen walls were decorated with Delft tile, and the plates in the glass cabinets were also blue and white. An old wooden table filled the middle of the room. Its surface, worn with age, glowed a buttery yellow. The chairs were large and heavy and had lions' heads carved on the tops of the backs. On the table sat a tray with a teapot, cups and saucers, and a plate with tiny chocolate cakes. There were embroidered napkins. In the center of the table, in an earthenware jug, was a bunch of red tulips.

"Why, it's Vermeer's world!" Petra was touching the tile on the counter, running her fingers over the cobalt glaze with obvious delight.

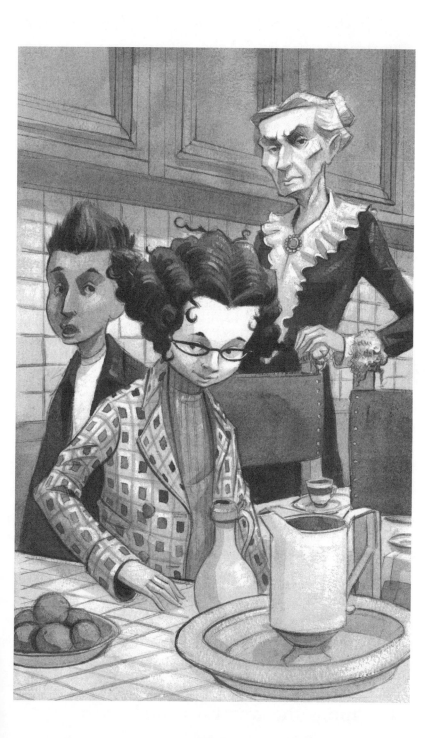

"Sit down, both of you. You're not here to admire things." Mrs. Sharpe's voice was true to her name. Perhaps realizing how harsh she sounded, she went on in a softer tone, "We're here to talk about Charles Fort. This young man tells me you picked up my copy of *Lo!* at Powell's. But don't say anything until you've finished eating."

Calder and Petra sat down and sipped obediently on tea served in cups so thin that you could see the shadow of your finger on the other side of the china. Calder's swallowing made a loud noise in the silence. Petra wanted to giggle, but instead choked on her cake and had to wash it down with a scalding gulp of Earl Grey.

"So. Charles Fort. What do you two make of him?"

Petra cleared her throat. "He believes in figuring out the truth, no matter what anyone else says. Calder and I like that. I mean, he's such a fearless thinker."

"Yes . . ." Mrs. Sharpe was looking at Petra with an intensity that wasn't at all comfortable.

Petra looked over at Calder for help. "Calder and I have been pretty inspired by — well, by his way of seeing. It seems like most people aren't brave enough to question things the way Fort did."

"Yes. His ideas have meant a great deal to me." Mrs. Sharpe looked coldly at her teacup as if it had spoken instead of her. It occurred to Petra that maybe the old woman had said more than she'd meant to. But before Petra could think up an appropriate response, Calder blurted, "Then why did you get rid of your book?"

As soon as he'd spoken, he knew he'd made a mistake. Trying to chat with Mrs. Sharpe was not easy. It was kind of like playing with a dangerous animal.

"I was finished with it." Mrs. Sharpe's tone made it clear that she could soon be finished with Calder, too. There was another silence. "It has a dreadful stain on it, if you haven't noticed. All of Fort's books have just been beautifully reprinted in one volume, so I now have that."

Calder remained judiciously silent.

Petra stirred more sugar into her tea. "You must like Vermeer. Horrible news about the theft, isn't it?"

Mrs. Sharpe's face was masklike. "Charles Fort would have been pleased."

Petra looked shocked. "Why?"

Calder thought he understood. "You mean pleased about all the *questions*, right?"

Mrs. Sharpe made a noise kind of like a snarl. Calder, aware that he had trespassed again, looked down at the table. He was moving too fast — what was wrong with him?

Petra tried to make things better. "Pleased about how people are thinking for themselves?"

Calder pulled a pentomino out of his pocket and began tapping it nervously against his knee. For a long minute, everything was silent.

"I think the thief is very intelligent," Mrs. Sharpe said.

Both Calder and Petra looked at her.

Calder couldn't restrain himself. "Sure he's smart, but so what? Does that make the theft okay?" There was a long silence, and Calder could feel Mrs. Sharpe's eyes drilling into his head.

"I think, as Charles Fort does, that people don't look carefully enough at what is around them." Mrs. Sharpe stood up, signaling that tea was over.

As they followed the old woman silently through the house, Petra and Calder absorbed as much of what was around them as they could. A pewter pitcher . . . several tapestries . . . goblets made of green-and-bubbly glass.

"We must talk soon. I'll leave word with Mr. Watch." The door was shut before Calder and Petra could reply.

They stood outside in the twilight looking at each other. Calder was still holding what he now realized was the F pentomino.

"For someone who obviously loves Vermeer, she didn't seem too upset," Petra said.

Calder frowned. "You know what my pentomino just said? *Fooled.* If she wasn't so old, I'd wonder if *she* had something to do with the painting disappearing."

"What reason would she have for stealing it?" Petra asked. "Plus, can you imagine her hiring a bunch of criminals to do the dirty work? But what she said about people not seeing what was right in front of them — that did feel almost like a hint."

They walked several steps in silence.

Calder was scratching his chin with the F pentomino. "You think that it's Mrs. Sharpe who's fooled, or us?"

Calder got another letter from Tommy that evening. Something else had gone wrong, something besides Frog's disappearance:

L:1 F:1 Z:1 N:1 P:1 T:2, -
T:1 T:2 P:1 N:1 - L:1 F:1 W:2 U:1 V:1 V:2 -
F:2 P:1 - Z:1 L:2 L:2 Y:1 W:1 I:2 U:1 - T:1 L:2 T:2 -
L:1 Z:1 W:2 P:1 U:2 - L:2 I:2 - T:1 T:2 L:2 U:1. -
U:1 L:2 V:2 - F:2 P:1 F:1 I:2. - V:2 L:2 L:2 Y:1 -
F:2 F:3 - I:1 W:1 Y:1 P:1. - F:2 L:2 F:2 -
F:1 I:2 N:1 - T:1 T:2 P:1 N:1 -
T:1 W:1 U:1 V:1 V:2 W:1 I:2 U:1. -
V:2 L:2 F:2 F:2 F:3

Calder felt partly responsible — it had been his idea that Tommy do some detective work, and now his buddy had gotten in hot water because of it.

Suddenly Calder felt guilty that he and Petra were sharing secrets while Tommy was on his own. He'd always told Tommy everything. It wasn't that he'd meant to leave Tommy out. It was just that so much had happened without him.

He decided to call his old friend. There wasn't the same privacy on the phone as in their letters, but at least they could make a few jokes.

Calder got a recording saying that Tommy's number had been disconnected. A shiver of fear ran down his spine.

He dialed Petra's number and told her the news. "I can't help remembering Fort's stories about people who vanished into thin air, sometimes from the same area. You don't think this could be anything like *that*, do you?"

Petra's voice was subdued. "No, but guess what? My dad just left on a business trip and wouldn't tell my mom where he was going. He wasn't mad or anything, but said he couldn't tell her right away. He hasn't been acting like himself at all lately. He kind of disappeared, too."

Both were silent for a moment. Calder was the first to speak. "Got the Vermeer notebook?"

"Of course."

"Can you add something about our tea with Mrs. Sharpe? And maybe even Tommy's letter and the disconnected phone, and your dad's mysterious trip? You know the way writing things down sometimes makes stuff clearer."

"Good idea. Come over, okay?"

Before Calder got there, Petra looked at their last entry in the notebook. It said, **Unknown: Do objects and people repeat because V. painted at home?** Then she remembered. They'd been wondering if the women who kept turning up in Vermeer's paintings were his family, surrounded by the everyday stuff of their lives.

Absentmindedly, Petra underlined "objects and people repeat." People repeat. Who was the woman in *A Lady Writing*? Suddenly, it all felt so sad, not only the theft but the thought that the woman didn't have a name. Unknown. She was hidden somewhere in the dark, in danger and alone. Petra shut her eyes. As the first tear rolled down her cheek, she could suddenly picture the woman looking at her, her earrings shimmering in that clear light. *Don't worry,* she seemed to be saying. *I remember you, and I'm right here.*

Petra opened her eyes and sat up straight. She blew her nose. But where are you? she asked silently, feeling excited but kind of silly. Imagining a safe place to hide a small painting, she thought of drawers, cupboards, cabinets, closets, blanket chests. . . . Everything she pictured was wood. And then Petra felt an odd certainty: It was dark wood they were looking for.

By the time Calder turned up, she was writing madly in the notebook.

"Calder! I think we just might have a clue!"

She explained that the Lady had kind of helped her think of it. She wanted Calder to understand that.

Calder shrugged. "It's a logical idea, you

know? Dark wood equals fancy places. The thief is an educated person, maybe with a lot of money — he or she could easily live in a mansion with old cabinets or something. Good thinking."

Petra wrote: **Look for wooden storage places in Chicago.**

Of course, there was Mrs. Sharpe's house, but neither remembered seeing anything that might fit that description in the living room or kitchen.

"Maybe we can get a look at more of her house when we go back. I'll make up an excuse about using the bathroom and run upstairs," Calder suggested. "Or maybe she'll want something from Powell's before then."

They laughed nervously about how furious Mrs. Sharpe would be if she caught them spying. "We'd be the next to vanish, you can count on it," Calder added.

Both felt better by the time they had a blue one and closed the notebook. There was comfort in making plans.

Chapter Thirteen

X THE EXPERTS

The next morning, they had another surprise. This one came from Ms. Hussey.

She asked her students to think about what they might have done if the thief had written them a personal letter before the theft took place, a letter delivered to their home.

"You mean like one of the three letters the thief talked about?" asked Calder.

"Not necessarily. We're just inventing a situation," Ms. Hussey answered, with some of her old *we're-in-this-together-and-it-might-be-dangerous* tone.

Hearing the undercurrent of excitement, her class grew quiet.

Ms. Hussey went on to explain that this letter would have asked anonymously for their help. Say the thief had offered lots of money, promised that the cause was honorable, and — last but not least — threatened their life if they showed the letter to anyone else.

Petra scribbled Calder a quick note: **The letter that blew away from me that day on Harper Avenue — it sounded just like this! Except I didn't get to finish it and don't remember the threat.**

As Calder read Petra's note, Ms. Hussey was saying, "This is a question of judgment. It's not clear, in your letter, if the thief is good or bad. I'm interested in what you might do. And Calder, could I keep that, please? You know I don't allow those kinds of communications during class."

Calder flashed an *uh-oh* look at Petra, who had slumped down in her seat. He stepped carefully over Denise's outstretched foot as he handed Ms. Hussey the note. She popped it in her pocket.

Although she knew Ms. Hussey wouldn't be angry, Petra had a queasy feeling. How could the letter Ms. Hussey was asking them to imagine sound so similar to that one about art and crime? But maybe this was just another coincidence, pure and simple — there had been so many lately. Or maybe Ms. Hussey had found the letter blowing around, too! Of course — the thought was a relief. Petra sat up.

Ms. Hussey wrote some of their responses on the blackboard:

— *Go directly to the police and get protection.*

— *Hide the letter and try to figure out who the writer was.*

— *Change the locks on the doors.*

— *Do what was asked, have an adventure, and hope you weren't breaking the law.*

— *Tell a friend and make them promise not to tell, and then talk about what to do.*

Ms. Hussey listened closely to what the kids were saying, as she always did. At the last suggestion, her eyes suddenly filled with tears. Then, just as quickly, they were gone, and she was muttering something about dirt in her eye.

Out in the hallway, Calder looked upset. He said to Petra, "Do you suppose Ms. Hussey got one of the three letters, and dropped it or something and you picked it up? What if she's kind of looking for help by asking us what we think?"

"But why would the thief ask *her* to help him? I mean, she's just a sixth-grade teacher." Petra's voice sounded unsure.

"Good people sometimes get caught in

142

bad things." Calder was thinking now about Tommy, about Frog, about Petra's dad, about Vermeer himself.

Should Ms. Hussey be added to the list?

As if he or she were playing on Petra and Calder's fears, the thief resurfaced the next morning. A full-page ad appeared in newspapers around the world.

After the thief's first published letter, the fuss over *A Lady Writing* had been tremendous. The catchy phrase *You will come to agree with me,* the message found inside the packing box after the painting was stolen, had been picked up everywhere. It appeared spray-painted on subway cars, on walls, and on the sides of buildings in New York City, in Chicago, in Tokyo, in Amsterdam. It turned up on cheap T-shirts in English, Dutch, French, Spanish, even Japanese. Demonstrations were organized outside several museums, and protestors were photographed marching and shouting. There was footage on the evening news of signs that said things like: TELL THE TRUTH! GET HER BACK! Or X THE EXPERTS! Or ¡VIVA VERMEER! ¡SOLAMENTE LA VERDAD! Museum officials had days when they had to scurry, protected by police, through noisy crowds to get to work.

It was after this first wave of passion began to die down that the first full-page ad appeared.

It said simply: *You are doing the right thing.* Sure enough, the response from the public was instantaneous. There was more mail, there was more publicity.

The next time the public seemed to be losing interest another message appeared, saying: *Be patient. Do not give up.* This also was followed by a flood of letters.

The ad that Calder and Petra read before school that morning in the *Chicago Tribune* said: *You have come to agree with me. They will come to agree with you.*

In tiny print below the letter, newspaper editors, under pressure from the FBI, the police, and a committee of museum directors, explained that they would not publish any more of the mysterious advertisements. This was the last. The first advertisement was mailed from New York a week after the theft, the second from Florence a week after that, and the third from Amsterdam. The thief almost seemed to be showing off, thumbing his nose at the authorities.

Ms. Hussey said nothing to Petra that morning about the note she had pocketed the day before. Maybe she hadn't even read it, Petra thought with relief. Class began with a discussion about the thief's latest ad.

Ms. Hussey asked, "Why do people assume the thief is just one person? I mean, couldn't this be a group?" She was absent-mindedly twisting her ponytail around and around one thumb.

Calder raised his hand. "Don't the police think three other people are helping?"

"I don't know," Ms. Hussey said. "Do they? I guess it depends on what is considered helping. And whether those three letters even exist."

She looked so genuinely concerned that Petra and Calder began to wonder if they had jumped to silly conclusions the day before.

One thing was clear to the sixth graders: In spite of their discussions earlier in the year with Ms. Hussey, the letter as a form of communication was very much alive.

Chapter Fourteen

FLASHING LIGHTS

Calder arrived at Powell's that afternoon just as Mr. Watch was folding the top closed on a large paper bag. He nodded to Calder and began lettering **S-H-A-R** with an indelible marker on the outside.

Before Calder could say anything, Mr. Watch pointed toward a massive pile of children's picture books. "Need to be shelved." He turned back toward the bag and added **P-E**.

"But I'd like to deliver that," Calder blurted. "I mean, she's nice," he added lamely. Nice? he thought to himself. Hardly.

Mr. Watch stood up and adjusted his suspenders. "I can drop them off myself after work."

Calder looked miserably at the picture books. When Mr. Watch went to use the bathroom, Calder rushed over to the bag and peeked inside.

They didn't look like the kinds of books

147

most people would bother with. There were several on the history of mathematics, a book called *On the Plurality of Worlds*, and another called *The Roots of Coincidence*. Calder heard the toilet flush and hurriedly closed the top of the bag. Funny that Mrs. Sharpe was also thinking about coincidences.

He worked extra quickly on shelving the picture books and returned to the front desk. Mr. Watch was surprised and gave him a smile that revealed a row of small, pointed teeth. No wonder the man usually kept his mouth closed.

"Need that delivery now?" Calder asked.

Mr. Watch shrugged. "Fine," he said, then reached into his pocket as if to find something. "Wait — no, never mind. Go ahead."

Calder hurried south on Harper Avenue. Should he stop at Petra's and let her know where he was going just in case something happened? No, that was ridiculous.

When the door opened, Calder was surprised to see Mrs. Sharpe looking almost friendly. The wrinkles in her face were arranged into something that resembled a smile.

"Come in while I get a check for you, boy."

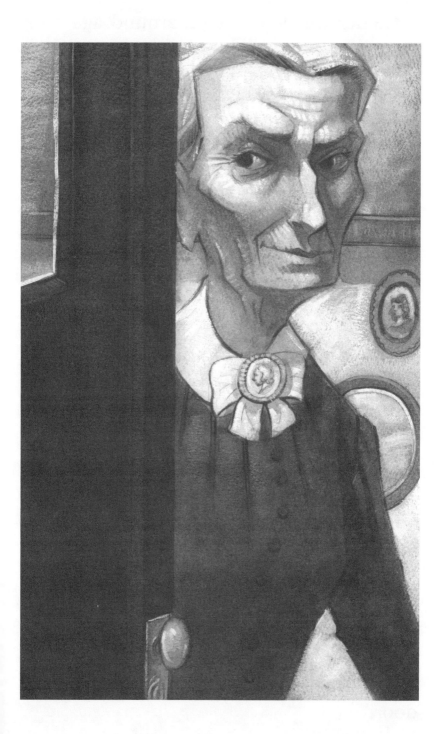

Calder was left to look around again for several moments. This woman had money, no doubt about it. What did she do all day? Calder noticed a hefty pile of papers next to her computer. They were too big to sit on her desk and had their own foldout table. Maybe she was a writer. A writer and a thief?

When Mrs. Sharpe returned, Calder shifted his weight from one foot to the other, hoping she'd get the hint. She paused to look at his feet, as if there were something wrong with them. Calder took the plunge. "Mrs. Sharpe, would it be possible for me to use your bathroom? I'm not feeling well."

Mrs. Sharpe waved a bony hand behind herself. "Up the stairs, turn left." Then she gave Calder a hawklike glance, as if to say, *I'm old, but not that old.*

Calder, sweating already, scurried up the stairs. They creaked horribly under his boots. Once at the top, he paused, trying to take in as much as possible. Sure enough, to his right, he saw a large standing wardrobe. A perfect storage place, it looked almost identical to the one behind the Geographer in Vermeer's painting.

Mrs. Sharpe's voice came from downstairs. "The switch is high, inside the door."

"Got it," Calder called back, fumbling on the wall inside the first room he came to. The light went on in a huge bedroom. There was another wardrobe with carved panels, this one covering most of the far wall.

"Oops," Calder called down, trying to sound lost. He was back out in the hall, the bedroom light off. Ah — the bathroom. Calder shut the door, flushed hurriedly, and took several deep breaths.

On his way down the stairs, he noticed a built-in cabinet with heavy doors beneath an old bench on the landing. The house was nothing but wooden storage places.

"Thanks, Mrs. Sharpe," Calder said, realizing he probably didn't have to overdo it on not looking well. He stuffed the check in his pocket. "See you soon."

The front door was closed almost before he was out of it. The old woman clearly wasn't big on good-byes.

Calder went directly to Petra's and invited her back to his house. It was quieter there, and they had to get his discoveries written down. Petra carried the Vermeer notebook.

On the way over, she said happily, "My dad just got home. He was doing some kind of research for his department.

Strange it had to be so secret, isn't it?"

"Not so strange," Calder mumbled. "Secrets seem almost normal these days."

Together they sat on the floor in Calder's room. First, Petra wrote down the titles of the books Calder remembered from Mrs. Sharpe's bag, then Calder sketched the standing wardrobes. They each ate several blue ones before there was a knock at the door.

"Calder, a letter for you." His dad gave them a quick smile. "Looks like another one from Tommy."

Calder tore it open and began decoding as Petra watched, fascinated. "How did you learn to do that?" she asked.

"I made it up," he said, glad she'd happened to see. Then he began to understand what he was reading. It said:

L:1 F:1 Z:1 N:1 P:1 T:2, -
T:1 T:2 P:1 N:1 - F:2 L:2 X:2 P:1 N:1 -
L:2 W:2 V:2. - Y:2 P:1 - Y:2 F:1 I:2 V:2 - V:2 L:2 -
L:1 L:2 F:2 P:1 - V:1 L:2 F:2 P:1. - I:1 W:2 V:2 -
I:2 L:2 - F:2 L:2 I:2 P:1 F:3. -
V:2 L:2 F:2 F:2 F:3

"Whoa! Petra, there's something else we've got to do — we've got to rescue Tommy."

Calder and Petra spent most of the weekend baking brownies and selling them on Harper Avenue. They explained to the neighbors that they were raising money for Tommy Segovia and his mom, Zelda, to come home because Tommy's new stepfather had deserted his family in New York. "There one day, gone the next," was Calder's way of putting it. Everyone was sympathetic, and everyone bought.

Late Sunday afternoon, as the grand total of $129 was being stuffed into several coffee cans to go to the bank, there was news about the theft.

The news was local.

According to the evening broadcast, an elderly woman in Chicago had just notified the authorities about receiving a strange delivery. That delivery was a letter that arrived back in October, and that woman was Louise Coffin Sharpe. She was asking for police protection.

"WHAT?" shouted Petra and Calder together. They dropped the jar of quarters they'd been counting and rushed around the corner to where Calder's parents were watching TV in the next room.

The broadcaster read the letter aloud. Petra and Calder stared at each other. It

153

sounded exactly like the letter Ms. Hussey had described to her class. The broadcaster explained that "For an older woman living on her own, it had required an act of great courage" to finally take the letter to the police. The broadcaster clearly had never met Mrs. Sharpe.

"Oh my God — the letter was delivered right down the block." Calder's mom clapped her hand to her forehead. "And Calder, you were just over there!"

"Mrs. Sharpe *is* involved," Calder said to Petra in a low voice. "Do you think she was waiting all that time for the thief to get back in touch with her?"

"Who can tell? And think of Ms. Hussey's letter — this can't be pure coincidence," Petra said. "It's too close."

"Do you remember that Louise Sharpe's husband was a Vermeer scholar?" Calder's dad said to his mom.

"*What?*" Calder and Petra asked in one voice.

Calder's dad said he remembered hearing that Mrs. Sharpe's husband had been murdered in Europe many decades ago, and that he had been doing research on Vermeer at the time of his death.

Calder and Petra stared at each other.

"Murdered how, Dad?" Calder asked.

"I don't remember, but I think it was considered a random street crime, a horrible case of being in the wrong place at the wrong time. They never arrested anyone."

"Poor Mrs. Sharpe," Petra said. "Well, that could explain some of her odd behavior."

"And maybe more," Calder added.

The phones rang nonstop all over Hyde Park that night. Looking out his living room window after Petra went home, Calder could see the blue flash of police cars and knew they must be stationed outside Mrs. Sharpe's house. She'd be safe, no question about that. A nagging doubt crept into Calder's mind: Could Mrs. Sharpe be so clever that she had framed herself? He wouldn't put it past her. Even though her husband had been killed, it was hard to picture her being afraid so many years later. And Ms. Hussey . . . what was going on with her? The pieces just didn't fit.

Petra, three houses away, followed the flashing lights on her ceiling, her thoughts falling into rhythm with the pulse of blue.

What about the letter she had picked up that day on Harper Avenue — had that been one of the original three? Was Mrs.

Sharpe really a victim now? Was Ms. Hussey?

Petra's thoughts swirled in circles, refusing to make sense.

Chapter Fifteen

MURDER AND HOT CHOCOLATE

The University School was buzzing the next day. Ms. Hussey was not there, and word had leaked to the papers that she had been arrested the night before as a suspect in the theft. Her class was out of control — it took the substitute half the morning to stop the accusations and shouting.

"A *suspect!* She'd never help a criminal!"

"How do you know? Maybe she was forced into it. Remember when her arm was hurt?"

"She would have called the police right away — I know her."

"We all know her, dummy. What we don't know is what's going on."

"Somebody in this room must have called the police last night."

"No way!"

"That rat is dead meat!"

"Yeah — a memory!"

Even when they'd finally quieted down, the sixth graders glowered at one another suspiciously. There was clearly a traitor in their midst. The substitute handed out sheets of word problems to keep everyone busy.

At lunchtime, Petra and Calder sat next to each other as usual.

"I'm worried that the letter I picked up in your garden was Ms. Hussey's, from the thief. If it was, then she wouldn't have any proof that she'd been one of the three — and who would believe me if I said I'd found it and lost it again?" Petra was pushing her grilled cheese back and forth across her plate.

Before Calder could reply, Denise leaned over. "Something the rest of us don't know about, Petra? Something you'd like to tell the police? No more secrets, now. And hanging out in Calder's garden — *really.*"

Petra moved away angrily, bumping Denise's elbow by mistake as she picked up her lunch tray. Denise lost control of her butterscotch pudding, and it slithered down her leg. Slipping on the pudding, she lost her balance and landed heavily on the substitute teacher, who was sitting nearby. Petra smiled. Other tables began to giggle, and Denise told the substitute that Petra had pushed her.

Calder and a number of kids turned on

Denise, and soon they were shouting. Denise turned crimson and yelled, "I hate all of you!"

The class had to stay inside during recess as punishment for bad behavior.

It was a horrible day.

Hyde Park continued to make the papers. The *Chicago Tribune* had pictures of both Mrs. Sharpe and Ms. Hussey on the front page the next day, as well as the happy news that Ms. Hussey had received the same letter as Mrs. Sharpe. Ms. Hussey was released. She made a statement about having been terrified, as was Mrs. Sharpe, to do anything about the letter. Both women were given round-the-clock police protection.

There were many questions. Why would a professional thief ask an old woman and a young schoolteacher to help him or her? Why hadn't the first letter been followed by another? And who had gotten the third?

Then a reporter added to what Petra and Calder already knew: Louise Sharpe was the widow of Leland Sharpe, a Vermeer expert who had died in Amsterdam thirty-one years ago. He had written to his wife that he had made a breakthrough discovery about Vermeer's work and was then silenced before he could share it.

The possibility of his death being connected to a discovery about Vermeer changed everything. Mrs. Sharpe *could* be genuinely afraid. Petra and Calder admitted to each other that she just might be innocent. Or at least partly innocent — things with Mrs. Sharpe were never simple.

"Ms. Hussey!"

When she returned the next day, her sixth-grade class crowded around, giving her hugs and stepping on her sneakers.

"How was jail?"

"Were you really scared?"

"How come you didn't tell us that was your letter?"

"We were so worried about you!"

The questions poured out, but she wouldn't talk about either the arrest or the letter. She looked happy to be back, but nervous. Every time someone dropped a book or bumped into a desk, she jumped. She glanced into the hallway a number of times, as if afraid that the policeman on duty might have left.

She took down all of the Vermeer posters and all of the newspaper clippings. The classroom looked bare and dismal.

She asked the class what they wanted to study, but when they suggested ideas, she didn't seem to be listening. Petra thought about bringing up Charles Fort's research, but could tell it wasn't the right moment.

The day after Ms. Hussey came back, Petra left science class and went to her homeroom to get a book she'd forgotten. She found Ms. Hussey standing alone, her back to the door, talking on a cell phone.

Petra took two steps into the room and froze. She overheard "mistake . . . but why . . . it *is* here . . . but I can't do that!" And then her teacher began to weep. Not wanting her to know that she'd heard, Petra crept out.

Petra felt suddenly outraged for Ms. Hussey. She was a wonderful person. Who or what was hurting her? And were Mrs. Sharpe and Ms. Hussey really so protected now?

Petra didn't think so. Something was very wrong with Ms. Hussey.

"Come on, Calder," Petra said when school ended. "Let's go someplace we don't usually go, someplace on the campus. How about Fargo Hall? I've got money for hot chocolate."

Petra's hat was pulled down almost to her eyebrows, and her hair fanned out in a black halo around the bottom. She was walking a couple of steps ahead of Calder.

"You remember what Mrs. Sharpe said about people not looking carefully enough at what is around them?"

"Of course," Calder said.

"I think we should be careful, that's all."

"What's the matter? Something happen?" Calder was looking curiously at her.

"I'll tell you when we get there."

They plodded quietly through the dim afternoon light, heading two blocks north on University Avenue. Fargo Hall, close to a century old, had stone gargoyles and carved human heads on every turret and ledge. A tangle of leafless ivy clutched at the limestone walls.

As they pulled open the heavy doors on Fifty-seventh Street, there was a comforting blast of heat and student messiness. Petra bought two hot chocolates with whipped cream, and they headed through French doors into what looked like a giant living room. There was a fire in the fireplace, and students were scattered around in armchairs, talking quietly or reading.

They sat down on huge leather chairs in a corner.

"Here's what I'm thinking," Petra began. "You and I know some things other people don't. There're all the coincidences that have led us along, the possible storage places in Mrs. Sharpe's house, and my feeling that the painting might be hidden behind dark wood."

"Right." Calder nodded toward the walls in the room they were sitting in. "It's everywhere."

"I think we need to go into high gear and start actively hunting." Petra told Calder about overhearing Ms. Hussey's conversation. "I have a feeling that she may be in real danger. We may not have much time."

Calder put down his cup and started running his fingers excitedly through his pentominoes.

"Shh," Petra said, aware of someone glaring at them, someone in a dark armchair across the room.

Calder pulled out one of the pieces. "It's the U. U for understand . . . no, that's not right. It's U for under. Under — maybe the painting is hidden beneath something."

"What else do we have to go on?" Petra asked.

"Well, what you heard today."

". . . it *is* here . . ." Petra repeated Ms. Hussey's words.

"Here!" said Calder. "Imagine that Ms. Hussey, being adventuresome and wanting to do the right thing for art, did help the thief. Or how about this: Imagine that she and Mrs. Sharpe are working together. They do know each other. Imagine Ms. Hussey hid the painting and Mrs. Sharpe knows where it is. Imagine they picked a spot they both knew. What would be a logical place?"

"Maybe it's also U for University School! What a brilliant place to hide something — around hundreds of kids!"

Calder was jabbing the U pentomino into the arm of his chair for emphasis. "Great — and imagine that we *found* the painting, and no one ever had to know that Ms. Hussey was involved? Except you and me, and we'd never tell. We'd be rescuing all three of them: the Lady, Ms. Hussey, and Mrs. Sharpe."

"How about the third person? The person who got letter number three?"

Petra glanced over to see that the armchair in the corner was empty.

"The dark horse — the difficult piece in any puzzle that doesn't seem to be there at all until you need it." Calder popped the U back into his pocket.

Both tried not to get too excited. Charles Fort, as Calder reminded Petra on the way home, collected "294 showers of living things" without knowing why.

Chapter Sixteen

A MORNING IN THE DARK

The University School was built around a central courtyard. Gracie Hall, now the Lower School, had been built in 1903 as a home for John Dewey's radical new school. Forming the west side of the quadrangle, King Hall had been built almost thirty years later for the University of Chicago's education department. The idea was to be able to observe what was going on in Dewey's now-famous laboratory. A new middle-school building, built in 1990, was on the east side, and the high school, built in 1960, on the north. Poppyfield Hall, tucked behind the high school, dated back to 1904 and had music and art rooms.

The following morning, Calder and Petra sat down on a bench in the Gracie Hall lobby. They were facing a stone fireplace that had a bust of Francis Parker on the mantel. Parker, a colleague of John Dewey's, had a University High baseball cap on and a red scarf around his neck.

"The painting is small, remember? The canvas is only about a foot by a foot and a half." Calder was fiddling with his pentominoes.

"Think — hundreds of kids and grown-ups go in and out of this building all day. There are cleaning people in here at night. What's a place that no one would disturb?"

Calder pulled a pentomino out of his pocket and looked at it.

They both stared at the T in Calder's palm. "T for twelve. There aren't twelve floors . . . hmm. I don't get it." Calder shrugged.

Petra sat up straight, her knees cupped in her hands. "Let's try to think like Ms. Hussey. She'd find a place with no leaks or mice or anything."

Calder was scraping the T back and forth on the wooden bench. "Twelve . . . does Ms. Hussey have twelve of anything?"

"She wears all those earrings — there's a key, a pearl, a high-heeled shoe . . ."

Calder was muttering now. "Key-pearl-shoe . . . shoe-pearl-key . . . pearl-shoe-key . . . heel-key-pearl . . . key-pearl-heel . . ."

"Hey! That sounds like 'keep her here,' doesn't it?" Petra laughed. "Now you've got *me* thinking like a pentomino. Maybe this means she's in Gracie Hall!"

Calder, in his excitement, gave Petra a quick bear hug. "Good thinking," he said.

Straightening her glasses, she tried not to look too pleased.

He and Petra agreed that they should pretend to make a master map of the school. This would give them an excuse to poke around during lunch. None of the classes aside from their own would know that it wasn't an assignment.

At lunchtime, armed with measuring tapes, clipboards, and pencils, they'd covered the first floor, checking even unlikely places. They looked in storage closets, behind file cabinets, under the beds in the nurse's office, inside old paper towel dispensers in the bathroom, around the coatrack in the director's boardroom, and beneath hats and mittens in the Lost and Found.

On day two, they covered the second floor, although it was hard to be thorough. Most of the classrooms had hundred-year-old built-in cupboards and drawers and bookshelves, and it was awkward explaining why they had to look into those to measure the room. Petra got bitten by a hamster, and in the science room Calder accidentally allowed a box of hissing cockroaches to escape down a heating grate.

Petra dropped a hunk of limestone being examined by fourth-grade geologists on her toe, and Calder got a third-grade teacher angry by trying to look behind her bulletin board and knocking off some drawings of the Great Chicago Fire.

They had worked their way through Gracie Hall except for the basement, which was locked.

They decided to talk with Mrs. Trek, the Lower School principal, about letting them in. Always enthusiastic about kids' projects, she could be counted on to help. They explained about the map, and she agreed to take them down there the next day.

"That defeats the whole purpose." Calder was digging in his locker for his math book. He didn't realize that Petra had walked ahead.

A voice behind him said, "Talking to yourself? Where's your girlfriend?" It was Denise. Calder felt his face get hot and slammed his locker door. Someone ought to hide *her* somewhere — permanently.

On Monday morning they met up with Mrs. Trek, as planned. Reminiscing about the kindergarten field trip to the basement, a tradition in the Lower School, Calder and Petra watched as the principal struggled with the bolt.

They had forgotten how weird the place was, the walls were fieldstone, and the floor went uphill and down. Right angles had clearly been abandoned below ground level. They saw piles of rolled rugs, broken benches, a tangle of plumbing pipes, even a claw-foot bathtub. There were spidery shapes made out of old desks stacked top to top. Mrs. Trek had just unlocked the supply room when her cell phone began to ring. A parent needed to speak with her in the office.

"Oh dear — will you be okay down here for just a minute? I'll be right back."

As soon as she left, Calder and Petra opened the supply room door. Reaching bravely into blackness, Calder groped around for the light. It wasn't on the wall by the door. He took a couple of steps into the room, ran into a string hanging from the ceiling, and pulled it. Shelves of construction paper and boxes of pencils and rulers jumped into focus. Teachers were allowed down here for supplies. Both kids could imagine Ms. Hussey using it as a hiding place.

There was no time for talking. Quickly they ran their hands along shelves, looked behind cartons, tried to lift crates. On one side of the room were several old picture frames. Behind them, leaning against the wall, was a small package wrapped neatly in brown paper. It wasn't as dusty as the others, and was the right size, no doubt about it.

They heard steps coming down the stairs and Mrs. Trek calling their names. By the time the principal reached the supply room, Petra was alone.

Petra told Mrs. Trek that Calder had needed the bathroom and had gone back up. As they walked toward the stairs, Petra asked if they could return in the middle of the morning.

"I'm afraid I won't be free again until tomorrow." The principal smiled kindly as she locked the heavy metal door. "Think you can wait?"

"Sure," Petra said, her mind racing. "No problem."

As soon as she got to the classroom, Petra told Ms. Hussey that Calder had a morning dentist appointment, and slipped into her seat. She tried, but it was just about impossible to pay attention in class. She excused herself to go to the bathroom more than once, tore down to the basement door each time, and knocked softly.

There was no sound from inside.

Calder stayed crouched for what felt like hours. This was the darkest dark he had ever been in. The basement didn't seem to have any windows. At one point, he heard a scurrying sound. He knew that Gracie Hall, like most old buildings in Hyde Park, had mice. And there were also those hissing cockroaches that had disappeared down a vent. He stood up.

Holding the painting carefully, he took two steps, then two more. What if there was some monster living in this basement? Someone who had snuck in when the janitor wasn't looking?

Humming tunelessly, he felt his way up the stairs. When he got to the landing, he tried the door to the first floor. The handle turned, but the door was bolted. He crept back down, trying not to touch the walls. Better to stay out of sight. Maybe, if he was lucky, someone would come down to get pencils and leave the door open long enough for him to slip out.

He reminded himself that he was probably holding one of the greatest treasures of the art world. What were a few hours of his life next to all the adventures the Lady must have been through in her three hundred–some years? Besides, now

he and Petra would be famous. They'd be interviewed on TV. They'd be in the *Chicago Tribune*. . . .

Groping his way along, he found a chair and sat down slowly. He'd better stop daydreaming. A number of things had to happen before the painting was safe — if it *was* the painting. To occupy himself, he worked on some puzzles in his head.

First he made three different twelve-piecers. Then he tried writing to Tommy, but without the code, it was tough.

Soon Calder felt himself wanting to doze. It was so quiet, and so dark.

Petra hurried down to the Lower School office at lunchtime.

"Mrs. Trek isn't here, dear. She's gone for the rest of the day." The secretary looked irritated.

Petra felt a rush of determination. "The basement — my friend Calder and I need to finish an assignment by today — is there some one who could let me in?"

"We don't allow kids down there alone, you know that."

"Mrs. Trek said it was fine for us to finish our research, though," Petra lied. "She said she'd make an exception. Please. Plus, we're sixth graders."

The secretary looked at Petra and sighed. "All right. Just let me get my lunch."

While the secretary was gone, Petra looked carefully at the top of her desk. Maybe the keys were inside the drawer. If she found them, should she race down and let Calder out? If the secretary came with her, she'd discover Calder had been there all morning. It'd be better to get blamed for taking the keys.

She stepped quickly over to the desk, jerked open the drawer, and found — sure enough — the fat ring of master keys. Stuffing them into her pants pocket, she headed toward the basement entrance as fast as she could go without looking conspicuous.

She waited outside the basement door, pretending to use the pay phone until there was no one in either direction. Her hands were fumbly and damp. First one key . . . no. Then another . . . no. Someone was coming. Petra picked up the phone again, her heart pounding wildly. She felt sure the person walking by would hear it, but they didn't stop.

The third key turned easily. Pulling open the basement door, she clicked on the switch and slipped inside.

"Calder! *Calder!*" she whispered at the foot of the stairs.

There was no answer. It was too quiet. Couldn't he hear her? As her eyes adjusted to the dark, she made out a small figure slumped in a chair. The package was still held tightly in his arms. Her first thought was that he'd died of fright.

She hurried over and gave him a prod.

He popped upright. "Jeesh, Petra! I ought to get ten pounds of blue ones for being down here all this time."

"I'm glad you're all right, but hurry up, Calder! I had to steal the keys. Hurry!"

They were up the stairs, peeking out the door, and in the front hall in seconds. They clicked the basement door shut behind them. Petra grabbed a jacket from the Lost and Found box in the lobby and covered the package with it just as the secretary came around the corner carrying her lunch.

"Well, hello, you two. I'll be right back to let you in. It won't take long, will it?"

Silent, both shook their heads.

As soon as she headed off toward the office, Petra looked at Calder in a panic. "Now what? What do we do about her keys?"

"Leave them in the door to the basement. She'll think Mrs. Trek left them there."

Petra and Calder were too nervous to talk on the walk home from school. They raced up Calder's front steps and straight to his room.

Both struggled with the zipper on Calder's backpack. In the rush at school, he had pulled it closed on the fabric.

"Stupid thing!" Calder grabbed scissors from his desk and cut open the backpack.

They pulled off the tape wrapped around and around the brown paper. The edges of a dark wooden frame emerged, and then an old backing. They turned it over.

Someone with an eager, pear-shaped head and a green bun sat writing at a table. Her one visible ear was graced with what looked like a dangling Ping-Pong ball. There was an orange moon behind her, and a melting castle. The painting might have been done by a second grader, a second grader who was now a grandparent.

It was not the Lady they'd been looking for.

Chapter Seventeen

WHAT HAPPENS NOW?

Calder was home with a cold the following day, and Petra walked home from school by herself.

It was early December, and patches of ice alternated with drifts of brown leaves. Petra scuffed along, thinking about Charles Fort. *He* wouldn't be feeling discouraged. He'd have his eyes wide open. With that in mind, she picked up a scrap of graph paper off the ground and read,

corn oil
butter
tea bags
onions
green grapes
bacon

She popped it into her pocket. Was there poetry here, in these accidental combinations of words? Would Fort have seen an interesting pattern or a secret of

the universe in grocery lists?

Hey — this might be something they could get into with Ms. Hussey one day: accidental combinations of sounds and ideas. Why did some words seem more elegant, more graceful than others? Why were some words peanut butter and jelly sounds, and others caviar? What made the words "onion" or "tea bag" so plain? Why did a word like "ice" or "exquisite" sound so lacy?

Inspired by the idea, Petra spotted another piece of paper. It was tucked into a thorny hedge near Mrs. Sharpe's house, and torn along the bottom. Folded in four, it looked worn.

She opened it carefully and began to read:

Dear Friend,
I would like your help in identifying a crime that is now centuries old. . . .

Petra ran straight over to Calder's house. "Did anyone see you pick it up?"

"I looked around — only one person crossing the street."

Calder blew his nose vigorously. "Do you think it's the same letter you started to read, the one that blew away?"

"How could it be? Maybe there's a *fourth* letter." Petra groaned.

Calder reached for his pentominoes. "It's creepy to think of someone sticking that letter carefully in Mrs. Sharpe's bushes."

"Do we tell the police? It'll make it harder for us to keep looking."

"Good thinking. But neither one of us should walk around here on our own. We could end up like that Frog kid."

They refolded the letter, placed it neatly inside a sandwich bag, and tucked it into the Geographer's box.

They each ate a blue one. Then they each ate two more.

Calder was holding the P pentomino. "P for pray," he said, trying to grin.

Petra looked horrified. "Prey?" she said. "Us? You mean we're being hunted?"

"No, I meant *pray*, as in hoping to stay safe," Calder said.

"Maybe it's *pray* we're not *prey*," Petra added, scaring them both.

The next day, more news broke. A book appeared in the stores that morning called *The Vermeer Dilemma: What Happens Now?* Easily a fifty-dollar art book, it was being sold for an unusually affordable $1.50.

This was less than the price of a Big Mac. An anonymous gift had made it possible for "everyone with an interest in Vermeer and in this painful situation" to buy the book. Written by a respected art historian, it included an excellent color plate of every painting attributed to Vermeer.

Thousands of copies changed hands across the United States on the first day, and countries around the world reported similar sales.

The book was about all the positive things that had come out of this terrible crime. People were looking at and talking about paintings as they never had before. They were comparing furniture, tile work, the structure of a leaded glass window, the folds in a satin skirt. They were comparing details, like the way light struck a fingernail or a wrist bone, the look of a woven basket handle or a curl of hair. They were examining works of art with a toughness and intensity usually seen only in the buyers of new cars or electronics. Groups of people pointing and arguing energetically in front of a Vermeer had become a common sight. Museums were busier and livelier places.

It was the first time that many "untrained" people had felt that they could say something of value about a work of art, something that might make a difference. It was the first time that many people had realized how murky and changeable the waters of history can be. When an artist leaves behind no personal papers, when hundreds of years go by, who is to say that followers or forgers didn't use his or her name to make some money? And, of course, the idea of correcting a centuries-old mistake, of pointing out that the experts in museums and universities weren't really as expert as they'd thought they were, was irresistible.

Children were thinking about Vermeer, too. They were comparing, writing, and visiting museums with friends. Many said that they hadn't realized how cool old pictures could be. They also hadn't realized that the art in museums can be mysterious, that grown-ups don't always know what it means or where it came from.

The author talked about how this uproar was probably also good for art historians and museum curators. It was forcing them to question views that had been accepted for decades, to look carefully at what they had been taught. Was the thief right? Was the public right? Why *didn't* the so-called "early" and "late" Vermeers have that luminous, haunting touch?

The book ended by stating firmly that while what the thief had done to get the attention of the art world was wrong, the public's relationship to Vermeer and to other great masters had, as a result, changed drastically. People around the world had developed a comfort with great art that they had never had before. The theft *was* a gift.

The last page carried a message to the thief. Whether or not museums chose to change the wall labels next to some of Vermeer's paintings, the public had done an amazing job of spotlighting any possible fraud. Everyone was now looking. It was only a matter of time, the author suggested, before museums would respond to the public's thinking. In the meantime, *A Lady Writing* should be returned. The thief could consider his mission to have been successful.

Chapter Eighteen

A BAD FALL

Petra and Calder talked about the book on the way to school the next morning.

"All these questions being asked by people around the world," Petra said, still excited by what she'd read. "It does make the theft seem partly good."

"Yeah, but what if the thief turns out not to be as moral as he sounds — what if he's a real sicko?"

"Someone on the radio was talking about that this morning." Petra looked sideways at Calder. "But don't you think I would sort of know if the Lady had been hurt?"

They walked several steps in silence. Calder kicked at a snowbank. "Maybe. And maybe not — I wish she'd say something else to you. Like, 'Down this street, up those steps, in this cupboard, and presto'!"

They were laughing when they turned the corner near Mrs. Sharpe's house. To their horror, they found themselves facing the flashing lights of an ambulance. The children stood, mouths open, as a stretcher appeared at Mrs. Sharpe's door. The old woman was neatly strapped in under a mound of blankets. She looked tiny and pale. Two policemen followed the emergency technicians.

"Mrs. Sharpe! Are you okay?" blurted Petra.

Calder called out, "What happened?"

At the sound of their voices, the old woman turned her head. "Oh good. It's you two. Close your mouths before your tongues freeze." Mrs. Sharpe struggled to get her hand out from under the blankets. "Stop, you carriers! I want to speak with the children. I know them." Mrs. Sharpe's imperious tone brought everyone to a standstill.

"I slipped and cracked something in one leg — very stupid of me, I must say. Never broken anything in my life. I was planning to take this letter to the post office today. I could have someone in the hospital mail it, but I would prefer giving it to the two of you."

"No problem." Calder reached for the letter in Mrs. Sharpe's hand. She watched with something of her old fierceness while

Calder put away the letter.

"Now, don't forget and don't lose it, boy." Mrs. Sharpe was eyeing the duct tape on Calder's backpack. "The two of you can visit me at the hospital later if you'd like. I'm sure by then I'll be stuck in some dreadful room."

"Don't worry, Mrs. Sharpe. We'll mail your letter. Want us to bring you books or anything?" Petra asked.

"No, no . . . oh, the pain of this darn leg! Stupid, stupid!" Mrs. Sharpe collapsed back on the stretcher.

"All set, ma'am?" one of the EMTs asked her politely.

"Well, yes. Does it look like we're sunbathing on the Riviera here?" Mrs. Sharpe's voice trailed off into the freezing air as she was loaded into the ambulance.

They watched it drive away. "Poor thing. I guess we won't be having tea with her anytime soon," Petra said.

"I wonder who *this* letter is for." Calder reached into his backpack and pulled it out. It was addressed, in neat handwriting, to Ms. Isabel Hussey.

They held the letter up to a bright light in school. The envelope was impossible to see through. Giving it directly to Ms.

Hussey was tempting, but they had made a promise to Mrs. Sharpe. It was hard to know who to be loyal to, or what the consequences of either decision might be.

After school, they crunched through the snow to the post office on campus.

"Maybe we could steam it open," Calder suggested.

"Maybe she's just sympathizing. Maybe we're just suspicious," Petra said.

"Hey! What if we rip open the envelope and then put the letter in a fresh one? We'll just rewrite the address!"

In their excitement, they stopped and gave each other a high five.

Petra suddenly looked unhappy. "But aren't we getting pretty two-faced here? We go there for tea, we act like nice kids, and then we betray her. How would we like it if someone we trusted read our mail? This is probably how people turn into criminals. They just do something a little bit wrong, and then something a little bit worse —"

"It's not like we won't mail it afterward. We're keeping our promise. It's an emergency situation, remember? We're on a mission to rescue Ms. Hussey, the Lady, Mrs. Sharpe, and ourselves — we may be in danger, too, now that we've got the third letter."

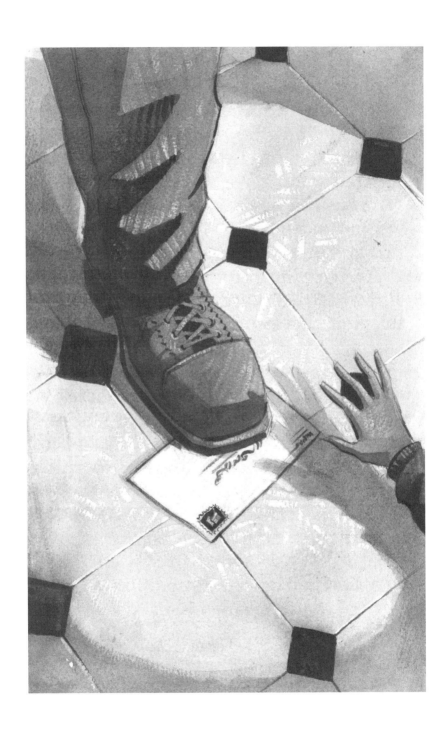

"So this is to protect everyone."

"Right. We're just doing a little much-needed detective work."

They were now inside, standing next to one of the slits in the wall that read: STAMPED MAIL.

"We could buy an envelope and re-address it here." Calder dug in his pockets for change.

Petra still looked worried. "What will Mrs. Sharpe do to us if she finds out? And what if Ms. Hussey recognizes our hand-writing?"

"This is foolproof. We're going to put the letter in the mail the minute we've read it. Mrs. Sharpe will never know, and I'm sure Ms. Hussey will throw away the enve-lope."

Just then someone jostled Calder's arm, and the letter fell. Calder reached for it, and his backpack swung off his shoulder, knocking both him and Petra sideways. The letter was now under a man's leather boot.

"Ach! So sorry! Zis is going in ze mail, too?" The man then swooped the letter up in a large red paw and stuffed it into the slit along with his mail.

"I don't believe it!" hissed Calder.

Petra gave Calder a weak smile. "I

guess we've been saved from a life of crime."

When they arrived at the hospital, Mrs. Sharpe was lying flat in bed. One leg was heavily bandaged.

"I can't give you tea, but you can have these. They're all I could get hold of." Mrs. Sharpe handed them each a large chocolate lollipop and pushed some buttons that made the head of her bed go up. "I wanted to thank you for mailing my letter."

The three of them sat for a moment in silence.

"I suppose you're wondering what that letter was about."

Calder looked down at his lollipop. Petra swallowed loudly.

Mrs. Sharpe's eyes narrowed. "Children! *Was* that letter mailed? There is something you're not telling me."

Calder decided to come clean. "Well, you see . . . we noticed the letter was to Ms. Hussey . . . and she's our teacher, you know . . . and we've been following the thief's letters and advertisements in the *Chicago Tribune* . . . and we're working together on trying to find the Lady . . . and Petra had a dream about the Lady . . . and so we wanted to read the letter . . . we were just curious to see if you were worried about Ms. Hussey, too —"

"STOP! Did you open my letter?" Mrs. Sharpe's voice was frightening.

"No," Petra whispered. "It was my fault, too. We thought that because you're smart and you like Vermeer, you might know something about the theft, and — that you might have some good ideas. We were curious about why you wrote to Ms. Hussey. We were going to read your letter and then put it in a new envelope and mail it for you, but we didn't end up opening it. That's the truth. I'm really sorry, Mrs. Sharpe, I don't know what got into us." Petra was almost in tears.

There was a long, unbearable silence. Neither Calder nor Petra dared look up. Then a strange creaking sound came from the bed. Mrs. Sharpe was laughing. It sounded as though she was a little out of practice.

The children looked at her in amazement. "You're not angry?" Calder asked.

"Oh, not really." Mrs. Sharpe was drying her eyes with a tissue. "I see myself in the two of you. I've done many things in my life out of curiosity, and have regretted very few of them. The important thing here is that you stopped yourselves before you did something wrong." Her face straightened. "Very wrong. The point is that you must *never* read someone else's correspondence." After allowing the children to feel uncomfortable for another few moments, she continued in a brusque tone, "My maiden name, Coffin, is from Nantucket Island, in Massachusetts, and when I read in the papers that Ms. Hussey was from there, I just thought I'd share the coincidence with her. Now. What is this about a dream?"

Grateful that Mrs. Sharpe didn't seem to be too furious about the letter, Petra started talking. She described in detail her dream about the painting, confiding that *no one* but Calder knew about it. She mentioned that Vermeer's Lady sometimes seemed to communicate with her. Mrs. Sharpe studied Petra intensely as she spoke. The old woman's eyes narrowed until they were almost slits in her face.

"Yes, she's speaking to you."

"Excuse me?" Petra's voice was almost a whisper.

"Well, there are many things about life, many experiences, that we don't have an explanation for, as Mr. Fort said. But what interests me is the idea that much of what we humans take to be a lie is true, and much of what we think is true is a lie."

Mrs. Sharpe was speaking slowly, looking at her hands. "Charles Fort would have said something to you like, 'Who's to say that art isn't alive, anyway? Who's to say what's real? If frogs can fall from the sky, why can't paintings communicate?' "

Calder had hopped up from his chair. "Petra! Remember the Picasso quote that Ms. Hussey told us about art being a lie that tells us the truth?"

"Sit down, boy. You're making my leg nervous." Mrs. Sharpe's frigid tone sent Calder back to his seat. Her face settled into an unreadable expression. "Truth . . . perhaps . . . you think you two could succeed where the FBI has failed?"

"Well, nothing happens in life unless you try. And we're pretty smart kids, you know." Calder had pulled out his pentominoes and was quietly making rectangles on the table next to Mrs. Sharpe's bed. "We haven't even told you about these."

"Smart, you think so?" Mrs. Sharpe watched Calder for a moment in silence. "What are those, boy? Some kind of new toy?"

"They're pentominoes," Calder responded with dignity. He told Mrs. Sharpe the letter name for each of the twelve pieces. Then he explained that you could make many, many rectangles out of them, but that it took practice.

"Push that table over here." Mrs. Sharpe tried putting the pieces together for a few minutes, mumbling "twelve pieces" under her breath again and again. Everyone was quiet. No rectangles appeared.

"It's hard at first. It takes time," said Calder kindly.

"Pah!" Mrs. Sharpe was looking frustrated. "I can think of something else you could do with these. How many, oh, five-letter words, say, could you make using at least three of these twelve letters in each word? Ever done that?"

"No." Both children were leaning toward the table now. Mrs. Sharpe was saying, "Let's see, the letters are F, I, L, N, P, T, U, V, W or M, X, Y, and Z. I love word challenges like these. Finds, flute, lines, filmy, tails . . ."

"Hey! That's thirteen letters. Who said the W could be an M?" asked Calder.

"I did." Mrs. Sharpe was busily pushing around the pieces.

"Wilts and tilts!" added Petra.

"Melts!" shouted Calder.

"Lower your voice, boy! We don't want

one of those policemen outside the door to start bothering us. Now if you could add another letter, you could have monkey, and then there's panel . . . and vines!" Mrs. Sharpe was looking very pleased with herself, muttering, "Finds . . . fruit . . ."

At that moment, a nurse bustled into the room. "Time for your medication, Mrs. Sharpe."

"Oh, go away!" she snapped.

The nurse refused, and Calder and Petra stood up to go. As Calder picked up his pentominoes, Mrs. Sharpe nodded at them. "Wonderful tools. Could be put to many uses."

"Yes, I even like to —" began Calder eagerly.

But Petra was pulling on his arm. "We've gotta go, Calder."

Mrs. Sharpe thanked them for visiting and waved one hand in dismissal. As they walked away, they could hear her arguing with the nurse.

That night Calder got a phone call from Tommy with the terrific news that he and his mom were moving back to Hyde Park. Tommy didn't know exactly when this would happen, but he said that the Dewey Avenue Rescue Fund, the money Calder and Petra had collected by selling brownies, was a definite help. Old Fred hadn't left much behind.

Then Tommy told Calder more news: Frog had been found. His parents had gone on a long trip and left him in Washington, D.C., with a relative. No one in Tommy's New York neighborhood had been willing to tell the "new kid," in Tommy's words, what was going on — either that, or they were all so unfriendly that they didn't know or care where Frog and his family were. Tommy said he'd just gotten a postcard from the National Gallery of Art, "one of those Vermeer pictures, the stolen one," from Frog. Calder couldn't wait to tell Tommy what was going on, but knew he and Petra had to keep quiet for the moment.

He called Petra immediately. She was thrilled to hear about Tommy.

Calder went on, "Remember the N for National Gallery, that day we were trying to get the pentominoes to say something about where Frog was? That day with the frog napkins and the rain?"

"Uh-huh."

Calder filled Petra in on the rest of the story. "Makes me think of a Charles Fort thing. Frog disappears to the National

Gallery, then a picture of the Lady travels back to Tommy. It's not teleportation, but some kind of strange symmetry —" Calder was quiet for a moment.

"Or some kind of weird joke," Petra finished. "Things going together that don't seem like they should."

"Things with a scary sense of humor," added Calder.

Chapter Nineteen

THE SHOCK ON THE STAIRS

After their visit with Mrs. Sharpe and the news about Frog, Petra and Calder couldn't wait to get back to the search.

The only remaining part of the University School compound that had paneling was King Hall. The middle school and the high school buildings were too new, and Poppyfield Hall had been carved up into studio and theater spaces.

Used only for college classes and offices, King Hall was practically empty after school. Starting on the first floor, Petra and Calder worked their way upstairs.

There seemed to be miles of dark wood. Leaving the lights out, they ran their hands along square wall panels in lecture rooms, tapping softly and looking for hidden compartments. They opened closets and cupboards, but all were empty. They leaned on grates and rattled bulletin boards. The building seemed discouragingly solid.

"This place is dead compared with Delia Dell," Calder said, looking out at the bright building across the street. Completed in 1916, Delia Dell Hall boasted countless gargoyles and faces half-hidden in decades of ivy. There were stone turrets, an assortment of chimneys, and casement windows. In addition to the original rooms, it had a pool, a pub, and a modern movie theater. Parties and performances were held there. The building cast a warm yellow glow on the snow, a glow that sent fingers of light into the dark classrooms of King.

"So much for my U for the U. School pentomino idea," Petra said, standing next to Calder at the window. "Guess she's not here. How about a quick look in Delia Dell before we go home?"

"Sure — plus, we can get M&M's there, and I'm starving."

Their voices faded into the early darkness as they headed across the street, leaving the quiet of King Hall to resettle behind them.

Calder and Petra sat on a long bench on the first floor in Delia Dell, sharing blue ones and a bag of potato chips. Snow was falling, magically softening and erasing the university world beneath it. They piled jackets and hats and gloves into a damp mound beside them.

Several college students on the other side of the room were talking about a Latin class. A man with heavy eyebrows sat reading a newspaper. A professor with a head like a pink bowling ball hurried in the direction of the pool, towel under his arm. A woman carrying a giant ring of keys passed their bench and headed up the stairs. Calder could hear the sharp *click* of a door opening, and the *thunk* of a lock sliding into place from inside.

Petra didn't seem to notice any of this. She was eating steadily, looking straight ahead of her with a sleepy expression.

Calder was feeling talkative. "Wow, this whole place is wood. Look at that staircase. I've never really noticed it before. It looks like something from an old movie — you know, like Bette Davis should be standing at the top."

"Right." Petra stood up and stretched. "Come on, it's getting late."

Away from the entrance hall, they wandered through room after empty room of paneled wood, stone fireplaces, tiled floors. They stayed in the older parts of the building.

Neither had realized how big the original part of Delia Dell Hall was. It twisted and turned gracefully, a rectangular dance with surprises in scale and mood. One moment it was grand, the next cozy. There was a huge ballroom space on the first floor, with a tai chi class going on in one corner. Across the way was a miniature reception room followed by what looked like a dining room. Plaster grapevines covered the heavy beams overhead, and the walls, paneled in rectangles of varying sizes, were interrupted here and there by almost-invisible doors. A small wooden knob and a keyhole were the only indications that something might be up. One door led to an old-fashioned kitchen, one to a back staircase, and three or four others were simply locked.

The dining area opened into a sunny library with a generous fireplace. Over the mantel, a wooden scroll read: DEDICATED TO THE LIFE OF WOMEN AT THE UNIVERSITY OF CHICAGO. Carved lions and horses flanked the dedication.

Petra stood in front of it, admiring the elaborate Gothic letters. "Cool. I wonder what that means?"

"My mom told me this was the first place at the university where women students could hang out. Anyway," Calder said, "let's keep going."

On the second floor there were some offices and three empty lecture rooms, all with rows of wooden chairs, old oil paintings on the walls, and elaborate leaded glass windows.

The third floor had a miniature theater. The walls of the room facing the theater were covered with a parade of young people in medieval costumes dancing, playing, and talking with one another in an idyllic country setting. The north wall had vaulted windows with French doors that opened onto a roof terrace. Petra and Calder stood, awed, at the entrance to the room. A red velvet curtain covered the stage, and on either side was a small wooden door.

Propelled by the same urge, they walked slowly toward the stage. There was no one in sight. Without a word, Calder tried the door on the right-hand side. It opened. Three short steps led up to a tiny backstage area.

They crept inside, stepping over frayed curtain ropes, a lute with no strings, a plastic pitcher, and an old broom.

"These look like props for a goofy Vermeer," Calder said.

He thought Petra would smile, but she didn't seem to be listening. "Not much place to hide," was all she said.

Petra suddenly felt as though she had forgotten something important, or as if she was supposed to be someplace but couldn't quite remember where. Or maybe it was that she didn't feel well. It was an effort to talk.

Back on the second floor, she wandered over to a window seat and sat down. Being next to the casement window felt oddly comforting.

Calder was down on all fours looking up into the fireplace. "I'm just checking for hidden shelves. This building could be filled with secrets we haven't even imagined, you know?"

Hearing no response, he peered around at her. "What's the matter? You look like you're half asleep."

"Calder. These windows."

Calder sat up. "Yeah," he said slowly. "Kind of like Vermeer windows."

Petra looked around the room. "And the paneled wood. I mean, millions of old buildings have paneled wood, but these rectangles . . ." Petra's voice trailed off, and she stared at her reflection in the darkening glass.

Calder came over and sat down quietly next to her. "Do you want to look around some more?" he asked, sounding like his parents when they were trying to get him to do something but didn't want to be too obvious.

Petra looked steadily at him. "Calder. What are you thinking?"

"That you sound like we might be getting warm."

Petra was suddenly feeling horribly warm. "I might just be getting sick. Come on, let's get out of here."

They headed back to the first floor. They passed the weasels that became brass door handles, the carved flute player overhead, the stone lions mounted high above the landing. Petra, resting her hand on the railing as they walked slowly down the sweeping staircase, stopped with a jolt. Calder kept going.

The railings were a delicate tangle of iron grapevines and creatures. There were birds, mice, and lizards. Instead of newel posts at the bottom of the staircase, an intricately carved oak monkey clung to either end of the railing. *Monkey, panel, vines, flute, finds* . . . She could feel the blood beating wildly in her temples: *monkey, vines . . . monkey, vines . . . panel, flute, finds . . . FINDS!* Mrs. Sharpe's words: Petra stood frozen, one hand gripping the railing.

She saw Calder pawing obliviously through their soggy clothing for his jacket. She hoped her face wasn't revealing her wild, screaming thoughts. Walk, just walk normally. . . . A man looked up at her as she passed, putting down his paper. Was the world able to feel her heart pounding, her thoughts on fire? She grabbed her things and burst out the door into the merciful dusk.

"Petra? What's up?"

"Come on!"

Calder could hardly keep up with his friend as she half-ran, half-stumbled through the new snow. She hurried a block east on Fifty-ninth Street and glanced back. Calder looked back, too, suddenly frightened.

"Let's go home through backyards. We need to disappear, okay?"

Calder walked quickly next to Petra, their shoulders touching. He thought of the P for *prey* — or was it *pray?* The blue shadows of late afternoon were menacing now. Bushes between houses seemed filled with pools of darkness, and people hunched against the cold looked dangerous.

When she was satisfied that they weren't being followed, Petra stopped. "Calder. This is it."

He looked around at the deserted alleyway and shivered. "This is *what?*"

"I think we've found her."

Chapter Twenty

A MANIAC

As Petra brushed her teeth that night, she went over what had happened in Delia Dell Hall. There had been a clear *zap* in her mind. It reminded her of the time she'd been plugging a frayed lamp cord into the wall and her finger had landed on bare wire.

Had Mrs. Sharpe let something slip? Was she hoping they'd pick up on her clues? Petra thought of what Ms. Hussey had once said about criminals wanting to be discovered. If Mrs. Sharpe and Ms. Hussey had been collaborating —

And then, as if someone had changed the prescription on her glasses, she suddenly saw how wild her ideas had gotten. Were she and Calder crazy to think those two women could be mixed up in the theft? Their suspicions about their neighbor and their teacher suddenly seemed overwrought and childish. How could this staircase experience be anything but a huge, strange coincidence?

First of all, she and Calder and Mrs. Sharpe had been playing a game with pentominoes. Mrs. Sharpe obviously had never seen a pentomino before. The words she had made up that afternoon were not something she had planned.

Second, she was an old lady. She was the widow of a murder victim. She had gotten a letter from the thief. After weeks of worrying, she had turned it in. She had asked for police protection. And Ms. Hussey was a young teacher, and a dedicated one. Why would she ever get mixed up in a major art theft?

Petra tapped her toothbrush on the sink in a businesslike way. Her imagination had run away with her in Delia Dell. Hoping to get the mystery solved, she had jumped to some ridiculous conclusions. All this looking was making her crazy. The zap was probably from not feeling well, and Mrs. Sharpe's pentomino words were nothing more than a magnificent Charles Fort incident. The stolen painting was probably in Switzerland or Brazil or Japan. She'd apologize to Calder in the morning for scaring him.

In two days it would be her twelfth birthday. Twelve-year-olds were old enough to sort out what made sense and what didn't.

Petra put down her toothbrush and, sitting on the edge of the bathtub, waited for the water to get hot. She suddenly thought about the Lady. Am I thinking clearly? she wanted to ask her. Did I just imagine what happened today? Are you in Delia Dell? She waited for a response. There wasn't one.

Doubt seeped back into her mind. Since when had she been so rational? Imagining: that was what she was best at. And hadn't she and Calder agreed that they needed to rescue Ms. Hussey? And how about that letter she had just found in Mrs. Sharpe's bushes?

She hopped into the tub and put a hot washcloth on her head. Letting her neck flop backward, she closed her eyes.

Suddenly she found herself picturing a rectangle inside a triangle. It was more a feeling than an image. She dunked her head, letting the water run into her ears. Couldn't she stop thinking?

It was a sparkling, whiter-than-white winter morning, a morning of brusque sky, inky black branches, and the blinding, two-dimensional look of new snow.

Glancing out her window as she dressed, Petra thought that the branches could be rivers on a map, or cracks on a blue plate. Maybe they were symbols in an unknown code — how do we know that trees don't talk deliberately with their branches, giving slow, intricate messages with an unnoticed vocabulary of shapes? Calder's thinking was infectious.

Whistling happily, Petra flew down the stairs to breakfast. The world felt rich with possibility. Her practical reasoning last night now seemed cowardly, unimaginative. What had gotten into her? She thought of the thief's phrase, *I congratulate you all on your pursuit of the truth.*

It was Saturday morning and her parents, still in pajamas, their heads almost touching, were absorbed in an article in the *Chicago Tribune*. They looked upset.

"The guy is a maniac! A self-absorbed lunatic!" Petra's father slammed his hand against the table. All the cereal bowls jumped.

"What's wrong?" Petra froze.

"More news on the Vermeer painting. We'll all have to pray that the FBI knows what they're doing." Frank Andalee stood up as he spoke, putting a hand on his daughter's shoulder. "Aren't you glad you aren't responsible for saving one of the world's masterpieces from a maniac?"

"Yeah, Dad." Her heart sinking, she began to read.

THE NATIONAL GALLERY OF ART RECEIVED THE FOLLOWING ANONYMOUS LETTER YESTERDAY. THE LAST COMMUNICATION FROM THE THIEF, AN ADVERTISEMENT SENT TO THE <u>CHICAGO TRIBUNE</u>, HAD BEEN MAILED FROM FLORENCE, ITALY. THE LETTER RECEIVED YESTERDAY WAS MAILED FROM A POST OFFICE IN WASHINGTON, D.C. BOTH THE FBI AND THE NATIONAL GALLERY OF ART FELT IT WAS IMPORTANT THAT THE PUBLIC KNOW IMMEDIATELY ABOUT THE THIEF'S LATEST INTENTIONS.

Dear National Gallery,
The recently released book, THE VERMEER DILEMMA: WHAT HAPPENS NOW? points to the public's overwhelming response to my letter and the three advertisements I took out in newspapers around the world. They have, indeed, come to agree with me. Now it is up to you and to your colleagues to agree, publicly, with us all.
I demand that you write letters to all other owners of Vermeer paintings. You are to state that my point of view is a valid one, and to request that the attributions

215

that I identified earlier be changed immediately.

If these attributions are not changed within one month, by January 11, I will, against my desires, destroy A LADY WRITING. *I will consider it a sacrifice in the interest of truth, a lesson for those too rigid, too dishonest, to do what is right.*

I am old and will not live long. I will, however, live to see this resolved on museum walls and in writing or, to the horror of us all, in ashes.

I beg of you to spare A LADY WRITING. *If you look into your hearts, I know that you will, as I predicted in November, come to agree with me.*

Do what is right.

Petra dropped the paper and rushed out of the kitchen.

Chapter Twenty-one

LOOKING AND SEEING

"This thief is way more ruthless than we thought." It was 9:00 a.m. and Calder and Petra were sitting in Calder's kitchen drinking hot chocolate. His parents were out grocery shopping.

"I'll bet if we called the police, Delia Dell would be searched today. And if the painting *is* there, they'd have a better chance of finding it than we would. The other thing we can do is tell our parents and leave it up to them." Petra didn't sound particularly happy about either idea.

Calder, absorbed in his own thoughts, grinned. "We can also tell no one. I can see the headlines now: 'Kids Locate Missing Vermeer' or 'Kids Brilliantly Track Down Vermeer Masterpiece' or 'Kids Lead Discouraged FBI Agents to —' "

"Calder! Come on! How can you even think about fame? What would be best for the Lady?" Petra closed her mouth in a tight, big-sister kind of line.

"To be found." Calder folded his arms across his chest and looked sulky. "You'd like to be on the news, too."

Petra paused to think about seeing herself on a talk show, or having her picture on the front of the *Chicago Tribune*. "Maybe," she said in a kinder voice.

"I vote we try to find it ourselves today, and if we don't, we talk to our parents and the police tonight."

"Fine. I think we should call Mrs. Sharpe first."

"Why?" Calder had pulled the I pentomino out of his pocket and was flipping it back and forth on the table. "Because the letter sounds like her talking? We know it's not. She's in the hospital and, besides, she would never harm a Vermeer."

"She might help us." Petra gave her mug a decisive tap with her spoon. "We'll tell her what happened in Delia Dell. That will make her curious. Then, if she knows something, maybe she'll just blurt it out."

Both were looking at the I. "What's it saying?" Petra asked.

"*Instant,*" Calder said. "Guess that means 'get going.' "

They called the hospital and asked for Mrs. Sharpe's room.

When she answered, Petra said, "Calder

and I were spending some time in Delia Dell yesterday —"

"And?" Mrs. Sharpe's voice could have cut steel.

"The letter in the paper . . . we're worried."

There was silence on the other end. "Mrs. Sharpe? We just didn't want you to worry. About us."

"Don't flatter yourselves. Why should I worry?"

Before Petra could tell her about the zap on the staircase, the old woman said, "Just be careful. Looking and seeing are two very different things."

The phone line went dead.

Calder left his parents a note. He and Petra put on their coats and headed for the campus. They hurried in through the side door of Delia Dell, and Petra skidded on the wet floor tiles. Her feet went out from under her, and she came to a painful stop in front of one of the benches.

Scrambling to her knees, she looked up into a man's face. He had eyebrows so thick that they hung precariously over his eyes, which seemed far too small for the size of his face.

"Slippery stuff, is it not?" The man's voice was low and pleasant; he had a foreign accent. "Zees old floors are terrible vhen zey are vet. But it's a vonderful building. Very vonderful." He smiled at Petra, his eyes almost vanishing beneath the outcroppings of hair. He offered her a large hand. "You two vere visiting ze ozzer day, no?" Something about this man was familiar.

Petra was on her feet. "I'm fine," she blurted, and shoved Calder back out the door in front of her.

"Great! That man noticed us, and you acted all nervous. *Now* what do we do?"

"What was I supposed to say, 'Which way to the Vermeer?' Did you recognize that voice? I think it was the man from the post office."

"What man?" Calder asked.

"The guy who stepped on Mrs. Sharpe's letter!"

"Well whoever he is, we could have just kept going. If we didn't stick out before, we sure do now."

This was the closest they had come to a fight. Petra's elbows were sore, and she was mad at herself. She knew Calder was right. After all, the man might be nobody.

"Wait," Calder said. "I have an idea. I

think I remember a basement entrance."

They walked quickly around to the east side of the rambling building. There, miraculously, was a small open door half a flight up behind a walled area. The door was propped open with a dented trash can.

"Wow! If anyone asks us what we're doing, we'll explain that we're making a plan of the building for school." Calder didn't sound as confident as he was trying to feel.

"Let's get out paper and pencils so it looks like we're really working on something," added Petra.

Armed with materials, they crept closer. It was hard to see into the darkened doorway. They paused outside, listening, then peered around the corner. There was no one in sight.

They tiptoed down a long corridor that curved to the left and then to the right. Swinging doors opened into a room with a single lightbulb overhead. Once inside, they were faced with three possible exits. They picked the one in the middle.

"*Ee-uw.*" Calder stepped over a nasty pile of garbage that smelled of sour milk and sneakers. Petra kept her mitten over her nose.

They were soon in a maze of small passageways.

"What direction do you suppose we're going in?" Calder asked, looking around at the peeling paint.

"No idea, but I want it to be up," Petra said.

They found themselves at a fork. To their relief, one direction led to an iron stairwell. They hurried toward it.

On the second floor, a diamond-shaped window looked into a hall.

"I can't see much. You try." Calder stepped aside. At that moment a blue sweater flashed by. Both kids ducked, and Petra hit Calder in the nose with her hair clip.

"Pet-*ra!* Watch what you're doing, will you?" Calder forgot to whisper, and the sweater reappeared, pausing for several long seconds on the other side of the door before going on.

"Calder, that looked just like my dad's sweater. I've got to peek out."

"What'll we say if it is him? He'll ask what we're doing here."

"I don't know, but I need to see if that's my dad."

They went as quietly as they could down the hall past several offices. When they

223

reached the corner, they saw the man in the blue sweater walking up the stairs to the third floor, carrying a smallish rectangular package.

The man was definitely Frank Andalee.

"Weird," Petra whispered. "What would he be doing here? He sometimes works Saturdays, but on the other side of campus."

Petra was remembering her dad's anger that morning, and the way he had pounded the table. She also remembered his words: *Aren't you glad you aren't responsible for saving one of the world's masterpieces from a maniac?* The word "maniac" echoed in a frightening way in her mind. Did he feel that *he* was responsible? Maybe he had stumbled onto something he shouldn't have and that was what had made him so grumpy lately.

She remembered him muttering the words "a loan," or had it been "alone"? Either one was spooky. And then there was the talk about two mysterious letters, and also what she'd overheard him saying that fall to her mom: *Everyone has something to hide.*

Seeing how miserable Petra looked, Calder patted her on the back. "I'm sure he has a good reason for being here."

Stashing backpacks and jackets in a

window seat, they began exploring the second floor of Delia Dell. During the next half hour they tapped, they studied, they pressed, they poked, they leaned, they tugged, they opened, they closed. Several closets appeared, walls creaked, but there was no sign of the painting.

Petra couldn't concentrate. "I just can't imagine what business he'd have in Delia Dell," she said.

"He'd be wondering the same thing if he saw you."

"And that package he was carrying was just the right size. . . ."

Petra suddenly felt very tired of suspecting people — first Mrs. Sharpe, then Ms. Hussey, then both of them, and now . . . her dad?

Calder seemed to pick up on her thoughts. "Sneaking around and trying to figure people out isn't as much fun as I thought it would be," he said.

Looking through one of the windows, she saw her dad and the man from the post office cross the parking lot.

"Calder! They're together!"

Petra noticed that her dad's shoulders were hunched and his hands were stuffed in his pockets. He was no longer carrying the package.

Chapter Twenty-two

TWELVES

By the time Calder and Petra stepped outside, both men were gone. There were no footsteps to follow. The snow was packed into an unreadable mass.

"Guess we should go," Petra said.

"Yup."

On the way back to Harper Avenue, Calder and Petra made a plan. They would return to Delia Dell that night. Each would tell their parents that they were over at the other's house.

"I guess we may be headed for a life of crime after all." Petra gave Calder a half-hearted grin. "But this is different — it'll be an early birthday adventure. I mean —" She stopped short.

Now Calder looked uncomfortable. "How did you know?"

"How did I know what?"

"My birthday."

"What? It's my birthday, too!"

To Petra's surprise, Calder seemed more

preoccupied than anything else.

He was looking at the T pentomino in his right hand. "T for twelve. . . . We're both twelve on 12–12. . . . Why didn't I see this before?"

"Wow," was all Petra said.

He went on, "It's a puzzle that hinges on twelves. There are the pentominoes, of course, and the fact that we're both turning twelve on the twelfth day of the twelfth month, and I'll bet there's more about the painting or about Vermeer that works with twelves."

"Calder, you're either totally nuts or absolutely brilliant. Maybe both."

"And we have just about twelve hours to figure this out — think we can do it?"

"I do."

That evening, the kids were crouched behind a bush just under the first-floor windows of Delia Dell. It was ten minutes to seven. The blue sky and white snow of the morning had deepened into an icy purple laced with black.

"It's the post office man!" whispered Calder. Sure enough, he was one of the last people to leave the building before the doors were locked. He walked slowly down the stairs to a parked car. Before he climbed in, he scanned Fifty-ninth Street as if checking for someone. Calder and Petra got a good look at his face.

As soon as his car was gone, Petra hopped out of the bush. "Quick!"

They hurried around the building to the garbage area. The back door they had entered that morning was still propped open.

They walked as fast as possible toward the dim opening and ducked inside. It felt like jumping into dark water.

They could hear footsteps several rooms away, and someone whistling.

Petra grabbed Calder's sleeve and pointed to a giant file cabinet. They crouched next to it, hardly daring to breathe.

The footsteps came closer, quick and heavy, and there was a grunt as someone put down a metal trash can. Both could see a man moving around in the shadows.

Another two steps and he was slamming the back door, locking it with a double bolt. He switched off the light from the next room, leaving them in darkness. The footsteps grew fainter. They waited until they heard another door shut.

Petra pulled the flashlight out of her backpack. It went on and then off. She shook it vigorously. Nothing happened.

She felt the darkness clamping down on them, and heard a noise like the ocean in her ears. The space around them started to shrink in an extremely unfriendly way.

"Oh, great!"

"Didn't you test it at home?"

"Of course I did!"

To their relief, the light came back on. Petra kept it pointed toward the ceiling.

Carrying the flashlight like a full glass of water, they walked carefully through the shadowy maze of halls and storage rooms. Nothing looked familiar. They must have taken a different turn. Calder was thinking to himself that "spooky" would be a mild word for this place. It made the basement in Gracie feel cozy.

Both tried not to think about anything but the next step.

The passageways felt endless. The flashlight went out once more, and this time stayed out. Holding on to each other, they groped their way around the next corner.

A red exit sign glowed in the distance.

"We did it!" They made their way down the corridor and finally through the door. They found themselves standing in the big entrance hall.

A high-backed choir bench in the center of the room towered above them. The moon had risen since they'd been outside, and light came through the casement windows on the second-floor landing. A path of broken rectangles and rhombi spilled crazily down the stairs, coming to rest on the heads of the wooden monkeys at the base.

"Maybe it's good the flashlight's out, in case someone is watching the building," Petra whispered.

"I was thinking the same thing." Calder glanced toward the banquet room and library.

Feeling small in the darkness, they walked through the entrance hall and up several steps to the next room. They headed under the arbor of plaster grapes and into the library.

The room was cavernous and lonely at night. Outside, students wandering back to their dormitories were talking and laughing. Petra and Calder felt separated from everyday life by a chasm of responsibility. What had ever made them think they could do this?

"Let's start over here, and stay together," Petra said. Looking for concealed closets or panels or knobs, they tapped along the south wall, straining their eyes against the shadows. It was slow-going.

They hesitated at the door to the dining room, peering into deeper darkness. There weren't as many windows here. Once in, they worked methodically, moving faster now. They pressed and knocked so hard on every panel that their arms were trembling and their knuckles raw.

Calder turned, moving so quickly that Petra jumped back. "What?"

No answer. Calder was running toward the stairs.

Petra raced after him. "Calder! Wait up!"

He stopped at the bottom of the stairs and walked up twelve steps, counting as he went. "What is it?" Petra's voice was a squeak.

"I think I've figured it out. Go back down."

"By *myself?*"

"Hurry! Stay right under the twelfth step." Calder was breathless but calm.

Petra thought she could see figures crouched in every corner. If she disappeared like Frog, it would be all Calder's fault.

"Here?" Petra's heart was pounding. It was painfully dark by the side of the staircase. Suddenly she remembered her thought in the bathtub: a rectangle inside a triangle. She was standing against a huge triangle.

"One step farther." Calder rushed down and crouched next to her. He ran his fingers over the surface of the wall. It was covered with small square panels, each about four inches wide.

"A series of twelves," Calder was muttering. ". . . six, seven, eight . . . here."

They tried rapping on the twelfth rectangle and then on the ones around it. There was clearly space behind this section of the wall.

They leaned with all their strength against the carved oak. Nothing happened.

"Let's press more slowly. Maybe there's a spring or a latch." Petra started on the upper right and Calder on the upper left. They worked their way carefully down for several inches.

They did this twice, each time trying to center the twelfth panel in a larger, imaginary rectangle. The third time, something gave.

There was a splintery groan and a loud thump. The panel slid back into the wall, revealing a shallow storage area.

Petra, trembling now, felt automatically for the flashlight and fumbled with the switch. Miraculously, it turned on.

"Oh my God, Petra!"

Leaning against the back wall, wrapped

in a cloth covering, was a smallish rectangular shape.

Calder took a shaky step backward. Handing the flashlight to him, Petra lifted out the object. The wrapping was velvet.

Side by side, they sank down onto the floor. Petra began to unwind the fabric, turning the object first one way and then the other, yards of deep red falling in folds around her knees. She touched the corner of a frame. The wood was cool and smooth. She stopped moving.

"You." The word was barely a sound.

Calder understood and carefully lifted the last layer of velvet.

It was a moment they would remember with perfect clarity for the rest of their lives. The flashlight picked up an answering glimmer from the pearls, from the satiny hair ribbons, from the woman's eyes: The image was finer and more delicate than either of them had imagined. Hot tears began running down Petra's cheeks, blurring her vision of the woman's familiar face.

Hearing a stifled sob, Calder felt his eyes suddenly fill. At that moment, there were just the three of them in the world: the Lady, who was almost 350 years old, and the two children, who were almost twelve.

"We'll get you out of here," Petra whispered, not trusting her voice.

Calder, wiping his cheeks on the sleeve of his jacket, pointed to the strand of pearls lying on the table. "Count."

Petra did. She looked shyly at Calder, aware that they'd both been crying. "Ten? Oh I don't believe it! The pearl earrings make twelve!"

They gave each other a wobbly smile.

"What made you see that?" Petra asked.

"I don't know. Maybe she did."

Petra, still looking at the painting, nodded in silent understanding.

There was a clearing of throats. They hadn't thought about what to do if they actually found her.

"Calder, it's so cold out. Do you suppose it will hurt her? I could wrap her in my jacket."

"We'll have to. It'd be worse to leave her. What if the thief decided to move her tomorrow? We'd never forgive ourselves."

As Calder held the flashlight, Petra rewrapped the painting carefully in the long strip of velvet, and then took off her sweater and tied it securely around the bundle. The wide frame made it an awkward size to carry.

They walked across the dark entrance

hall, both hardly feeling the tiles under their feet, and headed for one of the exits on the north side of the building.

Scanning the edges of the door, they spotted the telltale red light of an alarm.

"I'll bet all of these main doors are wired," Calder said. "We could try to get out through the basement, but that may be wired also. Or you could run from here and I could distract anyone who saw us."

"No. Let's stick together."

"Maybe I should be carrying something, too, just in case someone is watching the building. It doesn't matter if the police pick us up, right? In fact, that would be a relief."

Calder reached down and grabbed a DANGER: SLIPPERY WHEN WET sign that had been left by the door and padded it with a stack of university newspapers. He quickly pulled off his jacket, wrapped the papers and sign tightly in his sweatshirt, and put his jacket back on. He held the bundle in front of him as if it were fragile.

"Convincing? Wait." Calder reached into his pocket and pulled out a pentomino. "It's Y for *yes*. We're going to get her home." He tapped it gently on Petra's package.

"Absolutely." Petra was smiling now.

"Ready?" Both took a deep and shaky breath.

"On our marks —"

"Get set —"

"Go!"

They opened the door and started running into the cold night air, the alarm screaming behind them.

Chapter Twenty-three

HELP!

Petra and Calder raced toward the garden and playground behind the U. School. They looked back every few seconds. A man in a dark jacket appeared from around the Fifty-ninth Street side of the building. He was running in their direction.

"Can you see who it is?" Petra's voice was jagged.

"Are you the police?" yelled Calder.

There was no answer. Gasping for air, they paused for just a second, ready to hug a university policeman. At that moment the figure emerged from shadow and the moon caught the flat planes of his glasses, turning his eyes into pools of silver. He was moving directly toward them, and moving as if his life depended on it. He was not in uniform.

"Run!" Calder panted. Both kids took off, zigzagging around trees and bushes.

"HELP! HELP!" shrieked Petra. There was no one ahead of them. Where were the dog walkers, the students?

The man was gaining on them. They could now hear his breathing. Petra leaped over a sand box and headed out of the playground. She heard a *thud* just behind her, and out of the corner of her eye she saw Calder falling over the edge of the climbing equipment.

She stopped.

Calder shouted, "Go! GO!" He was up again, but the man was mere seconds behind him now.

Petra ran as she had never run before. She looked back to see Calder high on top of the slide, still clutching his bundle, the man standing below.

She could hear Calder's voice piercingly high with fright: "If you come any closer, I'll put my knee through it. I will. Then you'll be in big trouble." She couldn't understand the man's growly reply. Calder's voice drifted back: "You wouldn't dare hurt me!" She felt a sharp flash of fear for Calder, and at the same moment a flood of admiration for his quick thinking and bravery.

She was on Fifty-seventh Street now. She raced down the block to the Medici Restaurant, pulled open the heavy wooden door, and flung herself inside.

Luckily, a member of the university police was just leaving. Petra panted out her story about Calder and a man in the playground. She decided not to say anything about the Lady. She didn't want to waste time on questions. They hurried to the alleyway, and she jumped into the front seat of the policeman's car. Minutes later, they pulled up next to the playground.

The blue lights swept across a form on the ground. She heard the policeman grunt, then say, "Stay where you are, kid," as he reached for his door handle. Leaving the painting on the front seat, Petra leaped out anyway.

As they got closer to the slide, she saw that the lump was Calder's sweatshirt on top of a flurry of newpapers, the papers he'd carried when they'd run from Delia Dell. "Oh yes! Calder got away!" Petra hopped up and down.

The policeman knelt to look at the sweatshirt. "Looks like there's blood on it," he said.

Horrified, Petra knelt, too. She saw drips of dark liquid on the gray hood.

"Come on, kid — you shouldn't be over here." The policeman stood up. Then he shouted, "You! Stop right now! This is the police!"

Petra looked up to see the man who had chased them duck out of the patrol car. Her bundle was tucked under his arm. He ran east on Fifty-eighth Street, toward the yards and fences that Petra knew could hide him.

"That's him! That's the guy who was chasing us, and now he's stolen the painting!"

"He's got *what?*"

"Oh, please hurry!"

The policeman, one hand on his holster, ran to the patrol car. "Assault suspect heading east on Fifty-eighth Street — carrying stolen item. Immediate help requested."

"Say it's priceless, it's the Vermeer!"

Hesitating a moment, the policeman said gently, "Honey, they'll be right here."

"I'm telling you the TRUTH!"

Again, the policeman looked at her indulgently and shook his head. "What were you two doing out here alone at this hour, anyway?"

Petra whispered, "You wouldn't understand if I told you. Oh I hope Calder is all right!"

Petra, crying now, could hardly give her friend's address and telephone number. She had failed him and failed the Lady, and now Calder was hurt.

As they headed for the police station, she said in a still-shaky voice, "If you've ever believed in anything, please believe me now."

Calder was reported as missing. His parents and Petra's parents set off immediately to search the neighborhood with the police. The Pillays and Andalees were shocked and excited by Petra's news, but there was no time for explanations. Calder's disappearance was more than a little frightening.

A neighbor stayed in the Pillays' house in case Calder got back on his own. Down the street, Petra was left home with the younger kids, who were all asleep. Still dressed, she paced back and forth in her front hall. Where would Calder have gone? And how did he get away from that man who ran so fast?

She sat down on the front stairs. What if the man hurt Calder in the playground and then dragged him off someplace? She tried not to picture it. Stay positive, she said to herself. Calder would never let that happen.

She asked herself where she would leave the painting if she were the thief and were trying to escape from Hyde Park unnoticed. At least she could think about that.

She imagined the Lady, wrapped in velvet under her sweater. Show me where you are, Petra thought. Please help me find you. Suddenly she felt, she *knew*, the Lady was close by. Could the thief have stuck her underneath someone's porch? In a recycling bin, or a clump of bushes? No, he wouldn't be stupid enough to endanger her. She thought of a garage, but they were usually locked. Then she had another idea.

Petra grabbed a snow shovel from her front hall and headed out to the sidewalk. Her brothers and sisters wouldn't wake up, and besides, this would only take a couple of minutes. She'd be careful.

The Castiglione's tree house was right next door. Their kids were grown, and it was rarely used anymore. Petra thought she'd just take a look and see if anyone had left prints beneath it in the snow. If so, she'd go back in and call the police.

She shut the front door quietly behind her. There was a patrol car at the end of the block, moving in the opposite direction, the sound of the engine fading away. Silence. The moon was full and bright.

Stepping into the Castiglione's backyard, she held the snow shovel across her body like a weapon. And then she saw the boot prints ending in a trampled place under the tree. They were the size of a man's feet.

She stood for a moment, listening and looking up at the tree house. If those prints belonged to the thief, could he still be up there? It had been more than an hour since he'd grabbed the painting from the patrol car. Why would he sit up there in the cold, waiting for someone to find him?

There was only one set of prints, but Petra knew from experience that it was possible to leave the tree house by inching along a big branch and dropping down on the high bank near the train tracks. He could have hidden the Lady and gotten on a train or a bus unnoticed.

The tree house was a small structure with one glass window. It was more or less weatherproof, so it could work as a safe hiding place. She made a snowball and heaved it at the house. It thumped lightly on the side. She threw several more. If someone was in there, she hoped he'd look out and she could run.

Nothing.

"You up there!" she called in a shaky voice.

No response.

Petra had to do it. Propping the shovel against the tree, she began to climb.

One foot, one hand, next foot, other hand . . . Petra counted as she climbed. As she grabbed the twelfth board, she tried to steady the pounding in her throat. She was now just under the trapdoor. She paused, breathing deeply and listening. Her pulse seemed to be whispering, *twelve, twelve, twelve, twelve.*

She pushed gently on the trapdoor. No sound from inside. No big hand slammed it closed or jerked it open.

She pushed harder. The door fell back with a *thud.*

She stepped up onto the next rung and peered into the house.

"Calder!" she gasped.

He was lying on his side, curled into a U shape around the bundle. She shook him by the shoulder. She grabbed one hand and patted it and rubbed it. It was icy cold.

"Oh, Calder! What happened to you?"

His eyes opened and closed. "Knocked me off the slide . . . head hurts . . . but I followed him. . . ."

"That's okay, don't talk. We're almost safe now — you, me, and the Lady," Petra said soothingly. She took off her jacket, wrapped Calder in it, and started quickly down the ladder to get help.

"You'll never guess," Calder muttered.

Chapter Twenty-four

THE PIECES

Old Fred had been found dead on the train in the early hours of the morning, having suffered a massive heart attack. He was wearing boots that matched the prints around the base of the Castiglione's tree house.

Although Fred's beard was gone and his glasses were different, Calder had recognized his voice. Fred had knocked him off the slide, and Calder had hit his head in the fall. He then pretended to be unconscious. When it looked like Fred was gone, Calder got to his feet. His head was pounding, he was dizzy, and there was no sign of Petra. He hoped with all his heart that she had gotten help before Fred caught up with her.

Calder started for home, moving unsteadily through backyards. He was just resting in the bushes when Fred ran by carrying the Lady. Calder followed. Hiding behind bushes he watched Fred climb up to the Castiglione's tree house with the painting. When he heard the loud crack of a tree branch and saw Fred scramble up onto the tracks, he felt there was no time to go get official help. He had to get the Lady down. Fred might be sending someone back within minutes to retrieve her.

Calder staggered across the Castiglione's backyard, tried to step carefully in Fred's footprints so as not to leave a trail, and climbed the tree. When he reached the platform and saw that the painting was safe, he stopped to rest. That was when he passed out. Shortly after, Petra found him, possibly saving his life. He had a nasty concussion, but recovered enough to have birthday cake the next day with his friend. Petra reminded him that they were now even. He had probably saved her life by distracting Old Fred while she ran with the painting.

Fred Steadman's name, it turned out, was Xavier Glitts. He was the leader of an international crime ring. The FBI discovered that Glitts had advanced degrees from the Sorbonne in Paris and from Princeton University. His nickname, in the world of art theft, was "Glitter Man." He was famous for changing identities and for charming his way in and out of impossible situations.

In addition to his New York home, he had an apartment in London, and one in Rome. All of his files on the theft of *A Lady Writing* turned up in a bank vault in Switzerland.

Xavier Glitts had a customer who had wanted for many years to own this particular Vermeer masterpiece. The collector, a clever criminal himself, would pay Glitts sixty million dollars for her, but wanted a guarantee that the police would never trace the theft.

Glitter Man had come up with what he'd thought was a brilliant plan. He would pose as an idealistic thief. He picked Hyde Park as the perfect community in which to hide, and the role of Zelda Segovia's husband as a perfect disguise.

Shortly after he and Zelda were married, they attended a fund-raising dinner at the University School. There he chatted with a young teacher named Isabel Hussey who had just been hired to teach at the school in the fall. Discovering that she had been trained as an art historian, he drew her into a discussion about Vermeer, pretending to be ignorant himself about the painter's work. Ms. Hussey gave him all the ideas about attribution that went into the thief's letters.

At the University of Chicago's archives, Xavier Glitts gained the trust of one of the research librarians, who told him about a secret compartment in Delia Dell Hall, a compartment that was supposedly under the main staircase. Glitts had explained to the librarian that he was documenting "secret storage places" in the greatest universities in the world, and claimed that he had heard of several at Oxford, at Harvard, at McGill, and at the University of Salamanca. The librarian at the University of Chicago was happy to tell him all she knew.

While living on Harper Avenue, Glitts heard about his reclusive neighbor Louise Sharpe, and soon found out she was Leland Sharpe's widow. She, like Ms. Hussey, had passionate feelings about Vermeer's work. It was almost too good to be true.

And then Glitts met Vincent Watch at Powell's. They chatted, and Mr. Watch mentioned that his two great loves were art books and mysteries, and that he hoped one day to write an art mystery that focused on real issues in the art world. He had never gotten around to writing such a book, but had dreamed about it for years. Glitts had nodded sympathetically.

According to a journal found by the FBI in Glitts's bank vault, he came up with the idea of the three letters in order to confuse the authorities and to create three suspects. Then he had fun writing the letters that were published by newspapers, and watching the public's reaction. His theft had become a one-of-a-kind world event, and he was a hero to thousands of people. He was only sorry that no one would ever know he was responsible.

After writing the letter in which he threatened to burn the painting, and in which he said he was "old and would not live long" — hoping, obviously, to sound like Mrs. Sharpe — Glitts had planned to remove *A Lady Writing* from the secret compartment, deliver it for his sixty million dollars, and allow the world to believe it had been burned. He was quite sure that no museum would meet the demands in his last letter.

The FBI speculated that on the night he returned to Delia Dell Hall to get the painting, he had just parked his car when he heard the building alarm go off, and then saw Calder and Petra running. That was where things started to go wrong.

★ ★ ★

In their investigations, the FBI found that Mrs. Sharpe had a great deal of money and that she had made a very generous gift to the National Gallery *after* the theft had taken place. She explained in a steely tone that she had wanted to remain anonymous, disliking publicity after the circumstances of her husband's death. She had intended the money to pay for gatherings of Vermeer scholars to work on attribution and on the crime. When the money was used to pay for *The Vermeer Dilemma,* she was surprised but could hardly complain, given her request.

Ms. Hussey was horrified when she heard from Mrs. Sharpe about everything Calder and Petra had done to protect her. Never having lived in a big city, she had been lonely and homesick that fall. She had received a strange letter. When the painting was stolen and she realized that her ideas about Vermeer's work sounded like the thief's, she had been frightened. Trying to figure out what to do with the thief's letter had been the final straw. She had no one to talk to in Chicago — no one, that is, but her sixth-grade class.

★ ★ ★

Zelda Segovia was horrified that she'd been charmed into marrying a professional criminal. She knew nothing about Xavier Glitts or his shady business. When Tommy found out that his stepfather's real nickname was Glitter Man, he snorted. "More like Twitter Man. I never heard so much gabbing in my life. The way he promised stuff and then figured out how to take it away — what a sneak."

Frank Andalee felt terrible about having frightened Petra that day in Delia Dell Hall. He had been delivering an old print from one of the science labs to the guy with the big eyebrows, who was a publicity man working for the university. Petra's dad changed departments that winter and was much happier with his new job.

Vincent Watch had carried the letter around with him for weeks, getting a secret thrill from knowing it was in his pocket. He didn't want to contact the police before he was sure the thief wasn't going to contact him with an interesting proposal that he could then use in a book. The letter would be a good way to begin an art mystery. When the news came out about Mrs.

Sharpe and Ms. Hussey being the other two recipients, he decided to confide in Mrs. Sharpe. He knew she wouldn't talk and would give him sound advice about whether to call the police.

After Calder's last delivery to Mrs. Sharpe, Mr. Watch stopped by her house on the way home from work. When he reached into his pocket to show Mrs. Sharpe the letter, it was gone. He never understood how this had happened. He must have missed his pocket the last time he slid the letter back in, and it must have fallen out on his walk down Harper Avenue. He was extremely upset, but Mrs. Sharpe was sympathetic and practical. They agreed that it no longer made sense for him to tell the authorities about the third letter. Since he had no proof of having gotten it, he'd just look silly.

This, strangely, was the second time he'd lost the letter. He'd made a copy weeks earlier, in case he lost the original, and it had somehow gotten away from him between the copy store and Powell's. It was almost eerie.

This was the letter Petra saw blowing around, but as Mr. Watch hadn't told Mrs. Sharpe about it, Petra never knew where it came from. She told Mrs. Sharpe about finding the third letter tucked neatly into the bushes. They agreed it was a chain of events that would have intrigued Charles Fort.

As soon as the FBI had finished their questioning, Mrs. Sharpe, Calder, and Petra got together again for tea in Mrs. Sharpe's kitchen. This time, the tulips were yellow.

Mrs. Sharpe congratulated the children on their extraordinary bravery and intelligence. Coming from her, this was quite a compliment. After tea, Calder filled in Mrs. Sharpe on all the patterns of twelve he had identified. He told her about his pentominoes seeming to give him messages. He explained that he was quite sure there were more twelves involved.

Mrs. Sharpe's eyes became slits, as they had in the hospital when Petra had talked about her dream. The old woman was very quiet. They told her about the *"monkey-panel-vines-flute-finds"* moment on the stairs in Delia Dell. They asked her if she had done that on purpose.

"I wish," she said, giving them a smile that was almost wistful.

She thanked them both for sharing such fabulous secrets and promised she would never tell those secrets to another soul — not without their permission. Somehow, Calder and Petra knew they could trust her.

Then she offered a secret of her own, and

asked them to keep it until after her death. Both agreed immediately, and Petra reached out to pat Mrs. Sharpe's bony hand.

Mrs. Sharpe went over some of what Calder and Petra had already heard about her past. She said that just before her husband, Leland, had been murdered, she had received a letter from him saying he had made a stunning discovery about Vermeer's paintings, a discovery that would shake art historians all over the world. He couldn't wait to tell her about it, but wanted to save the news until he was "safe and sound in Hyde Park." And then, on the day he was due to fly back to Chicago, his body was found outside the Rijksmuseum in Amsterdam. He had been killed by a blow to the head. His date book had been in his suitcase, which was in the hotel lobby. When Mrs. Sharpe looked in the date book weeks later, she saw *1212* scribbled hurriedly, in his handwriting, on the day of his death. She pointed this out to the police, but no one knew what to make of it. Did it mean twelve minutes past noon, or past midnight? Did it represent the number 1,212? She wasn't able to figure it out, either. The police never brought anyone to trial, and the mystery had faded over time.

After telling the children this story, Mrs.

Sharpe sat quietly for a moment, looking down at the table. Then she blinked rapidly, sat up straight, and blew her nose.

She continued in her familiar business-like tone. "I became determined to pick up where Leland had left off, but I never could figure out exactly what it was he had uncovered or realized. In the years since, I've studied everything I could about Vermeer. I vowed that I would support any new research on his life or his paintings. And then, last fall, something very odd began to happen to me. And this is the part I want you to keep a secret."

Mrs. Sharpe said she had been "told" by the woman in *A Lady Writing* to clear the name of Vermeer, to make sure that the world knew that a number of his works had been done by followers. She had received pages and pages of messages, words she said she had merely written down. Calder and Petra looked at each other as Mrs. Sharpe disappeared to get a sheet of paper from the pile next to her computer. She settled back down at the kitchen table. This is what she read:

My lie is that I am only canvas and pigment. My truth is that I am alive. Some might call this your imagination, but it's not. Art, as you know, is about ideas. I am as real as your blue china or the boy with the box or the girl who dreamed about me. I am very much here.

Seeing how sober the children's faces had become, Mrs. Sharpe stopped to reassure them. "I am sharing this with you just to show you what I am beginning to see: Something much more powerful than any one of us has pulled us all together. Although Xavier Glitts thought he was in control, he was just a piece of the picture, if you'll pardon the pun. Something managed to communicate with each of us, including the thief, each in a way that we were willing to hear or see."

With the flicker of a smile, Mrs. Sharpe reached across the wooden table to straighten a tulip. Catching the afternoon sun, the petals filled with color, a clean cup of lemon in the winter light. Suddenly Petra remembered picking up a leaf on Harper Avenue that fall, and being struck by the thought that yellow was the color of surprise.

Calder did discover more twelves. First he made a list:

Petra Andalee
Frank Andalee

Norma Andalee
Calder Pillay
Walter Pillay
Yvette Pillay
Isabel Hussey
Louise Sharpe
Tommy Segovia
Zelda Segovia
Vincent Watch
Xavier Glitts (also known as Fred Steadman)

There were twelve names, and twelve letters in each name. Mrs. Sharpe got all pink-cheeked and pleased when Calder showed her the list, and after thinking for a moment, she said slowly, "Yes, how curious . . . the message '1212' also has twelve letters if you spell it out, and so does the name of the painting, *A Lady Writing*, at least in English." She reminded Calder and Petra that Charles Fort didn't believe in coincidence. He felt things were often connected in ways that no one could yet explain in scientific terms. But if none of this was coincidence, what was it?

Calder and Petra were more than a little spooked by it all. They were very glad that they had Mrs. Sharpe to talk to. They thought it was pretty extraordinary that she had, in the hospital, said just about the same thing as Picasso about art, lies, and the truth. Maybe the greatest ideas were quite simple. Or maybe certain experiences in life were made to fit together like pentominoes. Maybe the passage of time, even centuries, didn't matter when something really important needed to be said.

If there were twelve names involved, and if each name was a piece in a very big puzzle, did any of those twelve fit together in other ways? Over many cups of tea, Calder, Petra, and Mrs. Sharpe found a number of odd connections.

The most startling one was that the first letter of the first name of each person on Calder's list was a pentomino. "The U is my C," Calder explained. "It's just a matter of a simple turn, not even a flip. I never liked the U being a U, anyway."

Calder then realized that if you thought about those twelve people as pentominoes, you could see that certain ones fit into rectangles more easily than others. The X (Xavier), for instance, is the hardest pentomino to work with. The U or C (Calder) and the P (Petra), however, work easily into many solutions. The L (Louise) can fit easily with the I (Isabel), and the W (Walter) with the Y (Yvette), or the F (Frank) with the N (Norma). . . . Calder's thoughts were running wild. Then he and Petra remembered Ms. Hussey saying *The letter is dead* at the beginning of the school year. Well, one letter certainly was, they thought grimly: the X.

Although Leland Sharpe was not on the list, Calder noticed that the first letter of his first name began with the twelfth letter in the alphabet. Petra added that L was a very useful pentomino and worked easily into most rectangles. "Yes, he always did manage to fit into every new situation." Mrs. Sharpe sniffed and looked pleased. "He loved puzzles and codes, you know. He would have appreciated pentominoes."

Isabel Hussey and Louise Sharpe both turned out to be descendants of a member of the Coffin family on Nantucket Island. Both had lived there. Mrs. Sharpe *had* written the letter she'd told Calder and Petra about.

After the mystery was solved, Ms. Hussey and Mrs. Sharpe were often seen having dinner together in Hyde Park. They had lots to talk about and enjoyed each other's thinking. As the school year went on, Ms. Hussey became as much a friend as a teacher to Petra and Calder. The three often went to Fargo Hall after school for hot chocolate.

Petra did show Ms. Hussey her copy of *Lo!* The sixth-grade class tried to add to

Charles Fort's accounts and studied the idea of coincidence. Was it, as a number of interested scientists believed, just the human fascination with patterns? Or was it something more?

Frank and Norma Andalee and Walter and Yvette Pillay all turned out to be forty-three years old. They had all been twelve in the year of Leland Sharpe's death, which had been thirty-one years earlier. Mrs. Sharpe and the children wondered if there was any connection with the 1931 publication date of *Lo!* They also realized, with a shudder, that Vermeer had been forty-three when he died.

Petra's dad told Petra something else stunning: A part of his family had lived for centuries in the Netherlands, in an area not far from Delft. Family records were sketchy, but it was entirely possible that Petra was related to a member of Vermeer's family. Petra walked on air for days.

Calder, in his research, found that Johannes Vermeer had collapsed, quite suddenly, in December 1675. He had been buried in the Oude Kerk, in Delft, on December 16. It was thought that he died several days earlier, which would have made December 12 perhaps the last full day of his life. In addition to being Petra's and

Calder's birthday, it had also been the last conscious day of Xavier Glitts's life.

And then there was Frog. Once Petra remembered Fort's sentence *We shall pick up an existence by its frogs,* she pointed out to Calder that perhaps it had been some kind of strange clue. Maybe they should have picked up Glitter Man's existence from Frog.

Within weeks of the Lady's return to the National Gallery, the wall labels on a number of Vermeer paintings around the world were quietly changed to: ATTRIBUTED TO JOHANNES VERMEER. In celebration, Calder and Petra went to the Drake Hotel with Mrs. Sharpe for tea, and she told them both about deliveries that were soon to be made at each of their houses. She gave Calder an antique globe and a real Oriental carpet that looked just like the Geographer's. She gave her writing desk, an elegant seventeenth-century beauty, to Petra. She also gave her a string of real Dutch pearls.

Calder and Petra, in their interviews with the press, didn't share the entire story. They never mentioned Petra's dream, Calder's problem-solving, Charles Fort, the twelves, or the blue ones. They didn't know if the world was ready for it. And they still weren't entirely sure what had been real and what had not.

PRAISE FOR
THE GEOGRAPHY OF BLISS

"If you want to wag a politically correct finger in his direction, you'll have to stop laughing first...by the time the trip is over, you find yourself hoping that you'll hit the road together again someday. *The Geography of Bliss* is a journey too good to be rare."
—*Washington Post Book World*

"A wide, amusing, and ultimately quixotic quest for Shangri-La."
—*Chicago Tribune*

"This wise, witty ramble reads like Paul Theroux channeling David Sedaris on a particularly good day." —*Kirkus Reviews*

"Illuminating...a whirlwind tour of the world with an engaging and well-informed guide." —*National Geographic*

"Seductive...intriguing...charming and lovably grumpy... There's enlightenment in these pages." —*Los Angeles Times*

"Engaging...thought-provoking." —*Entertainment Weekly*

"Insightful...hilarious and poignant."
—*Denver Rocky Mountain News*

"Entertaining...head-spinning, ambitious." —Associated Press

"Weiner, equal parts philosopher, travel guide, and self-help expert—and wholly hilarious—has written a book you can delight in."
—*Vanity Fair*

ALSO BY ERIC WEINER

The Geography of Bliss

MAN SEEKS GOD

My Flirtations with the Divine

ERIC WEINER

TWELVE

New York Boston

Twelve
Hachette Book Group
237 Park Avenue
New York, NY 10017

www.HachetteBookGroup.com

Printed in the United States of America

RRD-C

Originally published in hardcover by Twelve.

First International Trade Edition: February 2012

Twelve is an imprint of Grand Central Publishing.
The Twelve name and logo are trademarks of Hachette Book Group, Inc.

The Hachette Speakers Bureau provides a wide range of authors for speaking events. To find out more, go to www.hachettespeakersbureau.com or call (866) 376-6591.

The publisher is not responsible for websites (or their content) that are not owned by the publisher.

10 9 8 7 6 5 4 3 2 1

ISBN 978-1-4555-0862-4

for Sharon

Faith is indeed quixotic. It is absurd. Let us admit it. Let us concede everything!

—Miguel de Unamuno

CONTENTS

MAN SEEKS GOD

INTRODUCTION

An Uncomfortable Question

Nobody likes hospitals, but I like them less than most. I think it's because my father was a doctor, an oncologist, and when I was young he'd drag me along while he did his rounds. He'd park me in the cafeteria, a fluorescent purgatory that reeked of burnt coffee and fear, then go see his patients. "Be back in twenty minutes," he'd say. An hour or two later he'd show up, apologetic. One of his patients had died. They always died. And they always died in hospitals. So, my eight-year-old brain concluded, if I just avoided hospitals I would never die. It was airtight logic. And aside from a broken leg at age seventeen, that's what I managed to do.

Until one warm August evening, not that long ago, when I found myself in the emergency room. My friend Michael had driven me there as I sat in the passenger seat, doubled over in pain. At first, I'd dismissed it as indigestion, but this was unlike any indigestion I had experienced before. They took some X-rays and CT scans, and a few long minutes later the ER doctor walked into the examination room, grim-faced. Something was wrong, though exactly what kind of wrong he couldn't say. The lines of worry

on his face sent a spike of panic through me. A surgeon was en
route. They had to interrupt his dinner party, he said, thus layer-
ing my terror with a film of guilt. Just wait here, he instructed, as
if I were going anywhere with an IV dangling from one arm and
a hospital gown wrapped around me, though "wrapped" was an
overstatement and, for that matter, so was "gown." Little separated me from the chilly, sterile air of the examination room.

I was shivering, partly from the cold, mostly from fear. Is it cancer? Something worse? What, I wondered, is worse than cancer?
There must be something worse than cancer. I was pondering what
this might be when a nurse walked in. She was about my age and,
judging from the accent, originally from the Caribbean, or maybe
West Africa. She leaned over to draw blood and must have smelled
my fear because she paused, maneuvered close to my ear, and said,
slowly and clearly, words I will never forget: "Have you found
your God yet?"

It was one of those moments when your mind takes a long
time, much longer than usual, to catch up with your ears. *Have I
found my God yet?* "Why?" I asked, once I could breathe again.
Will I be meeting Him soon? Have you seen my CT scan? Do
you know something? She didn't answer. Just gave me this wise,
knowing look, and left me there alone with my careening thoughts
and inadequate paper towel of a gown. I knew her question was
not exactly standard operating procedure, even at a hospital called
Holy Cross, but there was nothing malevolent or accusatory about
it. She said it matter-of-factly, not exactly like "Have you found
your car keys yet?" but close. Her words also conveyed a maternal
concern, and the quiet certainty of someone who has already
found *her* God.

The hours in the ER turned into a few days at the hospital. Tests
were performed, blood drawn. I did not have cancer or that thing
that is worse than cancer (I never could figure out what it is) but

rather an unusually severe and prolonged case of...gas. Yes, gas. Apparently, my colon did not take kindly to the stress inflicted on it as I met an insane deadline imposed by a tyrannical editor. I was, in hospital parlance, discharged.

Within a week or two, I had fully recovered physically, but the nurse's words stayed with me, like an image burned onto a TV screen that's been left on too long. *Have you found your God yet?* Those were her exact words. Not have you found *a* god or *the* god or just plain God, but *your* God, as if there were one out there just for me, waiting.

For a while, I tried to forget about the incident. There is nothing to know, I told myself, no God to find, or at least not one I am capable of finding. Just drop it. Go back to your books and your single malt. Go back to the "world of dust," as the Chinese call our everyday existence. This worked. For a while.

Then the nurse's words returned, burrowing into my brain like a groundhog in early winter. Who, or what, *is* my God? I was born Jewish. That's certainly my religious heritage, but not necessarily my God, which is another matter altogether. The truth is: I have many doubts about God's existence. Yet calling myself an atheist doesn't feel right either. Too coolly confident. I'm not certain about *anything*. I'm not certain about argyle socks. I'm not certain about soy milk. How can I be certain that God does not exist?

Agnostic? The word means literally "one without knowledge," and that certainly describes me when it comes to matters of faith. Agnostics, though, strike me as atheists without the conviction. Agnostics are covering their religious bases, just in case there *is* an all-powerful Creator capable of granting eternal bliss. ("See, Lord, it says right there: 'agnostic.' Can I have my eternal bliss now please?") Also, implicit in the agnostic's creed is not only "I don't know if God exists" but *I don't particularly care.* That steady drip,

drip, drip of doubt can pool into a kind of wish fulfillment. Doubt God's existence long enough and He doesn't.

Perhaps I fall into that most elastic of categories, the "spiritual-but-not-religious." These seekers align themselves with the world's wisdom traditions while distancing themselves from anything that smacks of doctrine or, God forbid, an actual belief system. The spiritual-but-not-religious like their yoga without Hinduism, their meditation sans Buddhism, and their Judaism God-free. This approach is tempting. It strikes me as easy, and who, after all, doesn't like easy? Alas, the problem with the spiritual-but-not-religious is that it is *too* easy, too convenient. Also, too herbal, and I am, if anything, a fully caffeinated being.

Since no off-the-shelf spiritual category seems to fit me, I find I must invent one: Confusionist. As the name implies, we Confusionists are confused—deeply and profoundly—when it comes to questions of God and religion. Wait a second, you're probably thinking, isn't "Confusionist" just another word for "agnostic"? No, we Confusionists lack the smug uncertainty of the agnostic; we are, in a way, pre-agnostic, or maybe meta-agnostic. We're not even clear exactly what it is we're not clear about. We Confusionists throw our arms skyward and shout: *We have absolutely no idea what our religious views are. We're not even sure we have any, but we're open to the unexpected, and believe—no, hope—there is more to life than meets the eye.* Beyond that we are simply and utterly confused.

I blame my confusion, as I do most things, on my parents. I was raised in a secular household where God's name was uttered only when someone stubbed their toe (*God damn it who put that chair there?*) or ate something especially delicious (*Oh my God this is to die for*). We were gastronomical Jews. Bagels and lox, of course, but also *rugelach*, whitefish salad, *challah*, *latkes*, *hamantaschen*. If we could eat it then it was Jewish and, by extension, had something to do with God. As far as I was concerned, God resided not in Heaven or the Great Void but in the Frigidaire, somewhere between the cream cheese and the salad dressing. We believed in an edible deity, and that was about the extent of our spiritual life.

Oh, once a week, I did attend Hebrew school (my parents enrolling me owing to that other Jewish tradition we maintained: guilt), but I found it much less relevant to my life than, say, breakfast. I couldn't understand what these ancient peoples, who weren't even smart enough to invent indoor plumbing, could possibly teach me about life. My family attended synagogue once a year, on Yom Kippur, the Day of Atonement. It wasn't a lot of fun. I had to wear this blue polyester suit and clip-on tie, and all the adults were crabby, owing to the fasting, no doubt. The fasting bit really confused me because, as I said, I equated God with food so I couldn't figure out why on this, the holiest day in the Jewish calendar, people weren't eating.

Later, my years as a foreign correspondent for National Public Radio did little to rehabilitate God in my mind. I saw firsthand what was done in His name, and it wasn't pretty. I lived for a while in Jerusalem, the city of peace, though it was anything but. Even a blind person, *especially* a blind person, could detect the tension that hung over the city like an L.A. smog. The thunderous kaboom of an Israeli fighter jet breaking the sound barrier alternated with the kaboom of a young Palestinian detonating a charge of explosives strapped to his chest. So similar were those sounds that we journalists developed our own auditory bomb-detection technique: A kaboom followed by the roar of a jet engine meant you could go back to your morning coffee; a kaboom followed by sirens meant a mad dash to a horrific scene.

I also lived in India, the overachiever of the religious world (over 330 million deities served!), and there found myself more perplexed than outraged. I once attended the *Kumbh Mela*, a Hindu

festival that attracts some eighteen million people to the banks
of the River Ganges. People traveled for days, weeks, in order
to dunk themselves in the filthy, brackish water. It supposedly
promoted good fortune and health. Yes, I thought, if the dysen-
tery doesn't kill you first. "It's faith, only faith," one of the holy
dunkers told me. "Isn't that enough?" I didn't know what to say.
Huck Finn's words sprang to mind: "You can't pray a lie." But
who was I, a foreign journalist with a microphone that I wielded
like an assault rifle, to say what was a lie? Shortly after, I remember
driving with an upper-class Indian playwright to an *Ashura* ritual.
That's when Shiite Muslims commemorate the death of Ali, cousin
and son-in-law of the prophet Muhammad. The playwright got
out of his SUV, removed his Ralph Lauren shirt (folding it neatly,
and placing it in the backseat), then, using a long metal prong of
some sort, began to flay his naked back, again and again, in order
to feel Ali's pain. I saw dozens of other men doing the same. Then
I felt a fine mist of red liquid spray my face. Blood. It was raining
blood. India made me long for the God of the Frigidaire.

I was—and still am—a rationalist. I believe that reason and its
offspring, science, are good. I question, though, whether reason
alone is sufficient for a happy, fulfilled life. Nobody, as far as I
know, has ever reasoned herself to a state of pure bliss. Reason
is an excellent tool for solving problems but offers little guidance
in identifying which problems we should solve and why. Reason
makes a wonderful servant but a poor master. Reason cannot account for those moments in life that "bewilder the intellect yet
utterly quiet the heart," as G. K. Chesterton observed.

I also believe in words, in the power of words, and for decades
my philosophy, such as it was, mirrored that of the great student of
myths, Joseph Campbell, who when asked what spiritual practice
he followed said, "I underline books." Me too. I'm a promiscuous underliner, also circler, highlighter, scribbler, margin-writer,

and dog-earer. I'm not sure why; maybe I'm like a cat marking its territory; maybe underlining a passage makes it real, makes the author's ideas my own. Then again, maybe they already were. The act of underlining always contains an element of self-recognition.

I read, and underline, anything I can get my hands on, but I have a particular weakness for self-help books. I love these books, though I dislike the term "self-help." For one thing, it's not accurate. You're not helping yourself. The person who wrote the book is helping you. The only book that can accurately be called self-help is the one you write yourself. The other problem, of course, with self-help books is that they broadcast weakness, and thus invite judgment. That's why my wife insists I keep my sizable collection hidden in the basement, lest dinner guests suspect she is married to a self in need of help.

Despite my compulsive underlining, or maybe because of it, I've never made much "spiritual progress." (A term that also strikes me as very wrong; isn't being spiritual about transcending self-defeating concepts like progress?) Reading these books, I'd experience moments of clarity. I would read, then underline, some wonderful passage by Meister Eckehart or Gandhi and think, Yes, of course, I've got it! We transcend our duality by uniting with the Godhead. Then I'd spend the next three hours obsessing over the best color—spruce green or desert khaki—for a shoulder bag I was ordering online, or endlessly staring at a mole on my neck wondering if it was just a mole or possibly Stage 12 melanoma. The books did little to relieve my outsize fear of death, or alleviate my chronic low-grade depression, and at some point I began to suspect that I was using these books, using concepts themselves, in order to avoid having an actual spiritual experience. It seemed like a plausible theory. In fact, I found an excellent book on the topic; in it, you will find many underlined passages.

To be clear: I don't live only in books. I do get out of the house sometimes, where I am prone to peek at other people's spiritual lives. I like to watch. Always from a safe distance, though. I'm the guy standing near the exit of the synagogue or the meditation hall, plotting his escape in case things get dull, or strange. Or real. I'm the guy mumbling the prayers just clearly enough so as not to call attention to himself but not clearly enough to absorb any meaning. Even in silent meditation, I've felt like a spiritual fraud, waiting to be exposed.

So that was me: mildly curious about God, but not curious enough to actually do anything about it. A spiritual voyeur, at best. A hypocrite, at worst. Someone who had, theoretically, entered Dante's "age of wisdom," a stage of life that begins at age forty-five. And that was okay, really. Until now. What has changed? Is it just my brush with gas, or perhaps something as pathetically clichéd as a midlife crisis? Maybe it's parenthood. Being a parent forces us to confront head-on those nagging existential questions that we long ago stowed in our mind's attic. How do I want to raise my daughter? As a gastronomical Jew like myself? Something more? Something less? Children are brutally honest and ask questions adults are too polite, or scared, to ask, and my daughter is definitely no exception.

"Dad?" she said not long after my hospital stay. We were riding one of those tag-along bicycles. I was in the front pedaling and steering and she was in the back pedaling, always pedaling.

"Yes, Sonya." I was expecting another butt question. She'd entered the butt age and had many questions about that particular body part. But, as she often does, my daughter surprised me.

"Is God responsible for us?"

I nearly swerved into oncoming traffic. Two thoughts sprang to mind. First, that's an awfully heavy theological question for a four-year-old. Second, this is one of those defining parental moments when we have a chance to impart lasting wisdom, to inspire and mold our child's worldview in ways that will bear fruit for decades to come. Either that or make total asses of ourselves.

"Well, Dad, is He?"

"Just a minute. I'm thinking."

Finally, I blurted out, "God gave us everything we need to be responsible for ourselves."

I'm not sure where I pulled that one from—probably from the same part of the anatomy that my daughter was obsessed about—but it wasn't bad, I thought. Sonya seemed satisfied, saying simply and sweetly, "He *sure* did." As I pedaled, I marveled at her big-heartedness and thought of a wonderful line in a poem by Stephen Dunn:

> *you can't teach disbelief*
> *to a child,*
> *only wonderful stories*

A few days later, when I was putting her to bed, she announced that she saw God.

"You did?"

"Yes. He was in the sky, like a big cloud," she said, holding her fist above her head in order to demonstrate.

"How did you know it was God and not just another cloud?"

"I could tell."

"Well, what did you do?"

"I waved and said, 'Hi, God,'" she said, as if it were the obvious thing to do and I was slow.

I am. The ER nurse had laid down the gauntlet, asking me a question that demanded a serious answer and not, as is my wont, a clever rejoinder, a joke. At the time, there was an urgency to her question—*Have you found your God yet?*—as I lay in that cold examination room, thinking I was dying. Is it any less urgent now?

The fact is I *am* dying (we all are), though not quite as quickly as I feared. The nurse, wittingly or not, issued a call, in the old mythological sense of the word, and I feel compelled to respond, lest I end up like one of T. S. Eliot's "hollow men," those wretched, pitiful souls who hear a call but refuse to heed it.

The seventeenth-century French philosopher Blaise Pascal coined the term "God-shaped hole" to describe that yawning void that is the human condition. I quite like the term. Every time I hear it I think of donuts, and of my life. Over the years, I've attempted to fill my God-shaped hole with all manner of stuff: food, sex, bags, success, more food, travel, drugs, books, more food, leatherbound notebooks, red Zinfandels, Cuban cigars, yet more food, pretentious foreign films, and once, briefly and ill-advisedly, a concoction of Guinness and Jack Daniel's imbibed through a plastic funnel. None of this has worked. Why not try filling my Godshaped hole with... God?

I recently came across a passage from the Hindu sage Ramana Maharshi. Speaking of the burdens we all bear, he asks: Would you carry your luggage on your head while on board a train? "You are not lessening the burden of the train by keeping it on your head but only straining yourself unnecessarily." Likewise, Ramana says, we unnecessarily strain ourselves by laboring under the belief that we, and we alone, bear this heavy load called life. Put down that bag, he advises. Nothing disastrous will happen, and you might feel lighter.

I find that passage irresistible. (I have, of course, underlined it.) My wish, greater than any I've ever had, is that I can somehow, in spite of myself, find a way to live it. But where to begin?

CWM (Confusionist White Male), young at heart,
open-minded, God-curious, seeks omniscient deity for
fun, maybe more. Me: Funny. Endearingly neurotic.

Loves books and bags. Likes to watch. Hoping for
more. You: All-powerful but kind and loving. Sense of
humor. Health-conscious. Good with kids. Talker.
Please, no smokers or smiters. Are you the answer to
my prayers? Serious replies only.

I look at the words I've just typed, flickering on the screen. Not bad, I think. They neatly capture what I'm looking for, and in a format that seems surprisingly apt. Romantic and divine courtship have much in common. Both demand courage, a high tolerance for disappointment, and an unflagging faith in the power of dumb luck. There is such a thing as spiritual compatibility. We do not find all Gods equally appealing any more than we find all potential mates equally appealing, and finding the right God, I suspect, is every bit as daunting as finding the right partner. I'll take all the help I can get. I'm not sure where I'd place such an ad, though, and worry I might attract some crazy deity, one who looks nothing like his profile photo and is concealing a dark past. You can't be too careful out there.

This is where flirtation comes into play. Flirtation is a safe way of taking a potential relationship for a test drive. The flirter signals the flirtee and waits for a response. If none arrives, no feelings are hurt, and both parties move on. If the signal is reciprocated, though, the flirtation accelerates and may lead to more—or not; flirtation, like cooking, possesses its own unconsummated pleasures.

Our divine flirtations have grown increasingly bold and, at times, frenetic. We are a spiritually promiscuous nation. Nearly one in three Americans will change their religious affiliation over the course of their lifetime, according to a recent survey. It makes sense. We are a people that worships choice. Choice is freedom. Choice is good. If we can choose our elected leaders, our calling plan, our toothpaste, why not our God?

Choosing is not one of my talents, though. In fact, I am a terrible chooser. I always feel as if there is one, and only one, "right" decision, and live in chronic fear of making any number of other "wrong" decisions. So I tend to get stuck a lot, paralyzed by the fear of choosing the less-than-perfect thing. I find it helps to narrow my choices. I've been a vegetarian for the past seventeen years—not out of any concern about the treatment of animals (I don't care that much) or health benefits (again, don't care) but simply because it makes it easier to decide what to order in a restaurant. Really. I envy those who make choices effortlessly, and wonder: How can I possibly choose a God? I decide to look at the menu. See what my options are. I mean, how many Gods can there be out there?

Nine thousand and nine hundred, it turns out, with two or three new religions formed every day. That's according to David B. Barrett, a former Anglican missionary who has been tracking world religions since the 1970s and knows of what he speaks. Nearly ten thousand religions! How can this be? I experience that same flash of panic I get at the supermarket cereal aisle. As the French say, *Trop de choix tue le choix.* Too much choice kills the choice. Excessive choice has another insidious effect: It creates the illusion of ease. A proliferation of health clubs, for instance, leads us to believe that it is easy to get into shape, and if we're not, then—well, what the hell is wrong with us? Likewise, a proliferation of religious and spiritual options creates the illusion that it is easier than ever to know God. It is not.

I stumble across something called "rational-choice theory," and I like the way that sounds. (The rational part, not the choice part.) Proponents of this theory believe we choose our religion in much the same way we choose a new car or a house or a breakfast cereal. We weigh the benefits of a given faith against the costs and then make a "rational" choice. I'm skeptical. Choosing a religion is fundamentally different from choosing a breakfast cereal. Yes, we want something out of it, but we also want something that we don't yet know we want. ("Behold my need which I know not myself!" cried Archbishop Fénelon.) How can we possibly choose something of which we're not aware? Choosing a faith is an act of faith, yet we don't have that faith yet, which is why we're looking for one in the first place. You see the problem.

Maybe my choice doesn't matter. Maybe I could just throw a dart at the list of religions and take my chances. Hard-core atheists like Christopher Hitchens say sure, throw the dart. Religion, Hitchens says, is all mush, so feel free to choose your mush—or even mix various kinds of mush. In the end, you'll just get more mush. On the other extreme lies the politically correct belief that all religions are equally valid. In one study, nearly half of those surveyed agreed that "all religions of the world are equally true and good." I find this extraordinary. Would we say that about anything else? Would we say that all forms of government, be it totalitarian or democracy, were equally true and good? Would we say that all corporations were equally true and good? Would we say that all toaster ovens were equally true and good? Yet when it comes to religion we jettison our powers of discernment. Saying all religions are equally true and good is like saying none are, and that brings us full circle back to the atheists.

Religion, at its best, helps us grapple with, if not answer, the three big questions: Where do we come from? What happens when we die? How should we live our lives? In this sense, religion is a kind of applied philosophy or, as Alfred North Whitehead put it, "What a man does with his solitariness." All of which, I figure, makes choosing the "right" religion that much more urgent. "Seek and you shall find," the Bible says, as if it were so easy. Seeking (the word derives from "sagacious") requires a robust dose of intuition, a sort of spiritual intelligence. Do I have that?

I print out a list of religions. Page after page materializes from my printer until I am holding a sheaf fifty-deep. I sigh. There must be a way to narrow this down. Some religions I can eliminate immediately. Zoroastrianism, for instance, is a very old and fascinating faith but one that does not accept converts. The Rastafarians intrigue but smell like an excuse to fly to Jamaica, listen to reggae, and smoke some weed. Sadly, I scratch the Rastas. At this point, my father's advice springs to mind. "Eric," he said, "never date a woman crazier than yourself." He was right about women (a lesson I learned the hard way), but I'm not so sure the same applies to gods. One man's crazy is another man's liturgy or, as author and mathematician Martin Gardner puts it: "Exotic doctrines and legends always seem funny, just as everybody else's big toe looks funny." Besides, I've always found much wisdom loitering in life's margins. So, no, I don't dismiss "crazy religions."

I do eliminate cults, though, which I define not by their oddness or newness but by their coercive tactics. I eliminate the "parody religions" such as the Church of the Flying Spaghetti Monster, a faith invented in order to mock faith. I eliminate religions that require the use of hallucinogens, owing to a bad experience I had in a New Jersey dorm room in the 1980s that I would rather not talk about. Some religions seem overly narrow, such as Hungarian Folk Religion; others, such as Unitarian Universalists, overly broad. Believing in everything looks a lot like believing in nothing.

In the end, I come up with a list of eight faiths, eight possible answers to the ER nurse's question. A smattering of monotheistic, polytheistic, and atheistic religions. Some, like Catholicism, solidly mainstream; others, like witchcraft, solidly not. I have chosen not entire faiths but, rather, slivers of belief. God slices. I figure it is easier to wrap my mind around, say, Sufism, than it is all of Islam. Likewise with Kabbalah and Judaism. I am naturally drawn to the mystical paths, which strike me as a necessary counterweight to my head-heavy existence.

Religions aim high but often fall short of their own lofty ideals, as even a cursory glance at the day's headlines reveals: Muslim suicide bombers, Catholic pedophile priests, various doomsday cults. These perversions explain why so many of my friends give religion, *all* religion, a very wide berth. For them, *nothing* is worthy of belief. Belief is for suckers. Mentioning God in anything other than a mocking, ironic tone is viewed as laughably atavistic, like an outbreak of acne at age forty. If I am going to find my God I will need to disarm this caustic cynicism, kill it, while leaving unharmed its necessary sibling, skepticism. This won't be easy.

Indeed, I'm not sure how to launch my search, so I resort to my default strategy: I read. Books, I reason, have steered many a person to faith. "Pick it up and read it" were the words, uttered by a child, that inspired Saint Augustine to read the Bible and thus transform his life from one of self-degradation to bliss. I read Tolstoy and Huxley and Merton and Heschel and Gandhi. I read a lot of William James. Brother of the novelist Henry James, William studied medicine but soon discovered he was more interested in matters of the mind, and the heart. He became a philosopher and, a new profession at the time, psychologist.

His masterpiece is a thick tome called *The Varieties of Religious Experience*. As the title suggests, James was not much interested in rituals or theology. He wanted to know how religion affected people personally, not what they believed but what they experienced. The book, published in 1902, is often cited as the first scientific approach to the study of religion. It is no mere taxonomy, though. On each page, I sense James's quiet yearning, how he envied those he wrote about, those for whom "religion exists not as a dull habit but as an acute fever." James never experienced that fever himself. He wrote like a world traveler confined to home, forced to rely on secondhand accounts of journeys he desperately wished to take himself.

Like me, James suffered. Throughout his life, he was prone to bouts of depression, and had recurring thoughts of suicide. Perhaps ashamed of his melancholy, as am I, he hid it from public view, writing about it only briefly under the guise of a "French correspondent," whom he quotes as saying, "I have always thought that this experience of melancholia of mine had a religious bearing."

Like me, James could not pray. (He felt "foolish and artificial.") Like me, he was obsessed with death, and like me William James was a case study in competing impulses. He complained about Americans' mindless worship of the "Bitch-goddess SUCCESS" yet tracked his book sales with greedy eyes. He was a hard-nosed scientist but also a "tender-minded" one, as he put it. Ultimately, as his biographer Linda Simon writes, "he was convinced of his own essential complexity." James was, in today's parlance, high-maintenance—something else we have in common, at least according to my wife. William James died in 1910. When doctors performed an autopsy, they found that the cause of death was "acute enlargement of the heart." Of course, I thought. How could it have been anything else?

As much as I admire William James, I do not seek to emulate him. He may have been brilliant, but his brilliance never extended beyond that of an interested observer, nose pressed against the window, peering into people's religious lives from a safe distance. I realize I'll never know that "acute fever" through books, even good ones. No, I need to try on these eight faiths, see if they fit. I need to *experience* the varieties of religion. I need to get *my* nose out of these books and onto an airplane. So I do. My nose and I fly to California, which seems like as good a place as any to launch a spiritual quest.

CWM seeks forbidden deity. Looking for a crazy love. Take me for a spin, and let's see where our hearts lead. Are you my hidden treasure?

I motor north toward Mendocino, venturing deep into California pot country, listening to the Doors and wondering what I've gotten myself into. I've signed up for a weeklong Sufi camp. It was a spontaneous decision based partly on the tantalizing juxtaposition of the words "Sufi" and "camp," and partly on the seductive nature of the brochure. "Come drink with the beloved," it teased, accompanied by colorful illustrations of chunky wine goblets that looked like something from an Elizabethan tavern. Not only is Sufism the mystical heart of Islam, the way of poets and ecstatics, Sufis are also known as "the drunkards of Islam." I'm hoping there will be wine.

Besides, I want to dive into Islam straightaway. More than any other faith on my dance card, Islam necessitates a reaction. That one word—meaning both "submission" and "peace"—elicits fear, admiration, puzzlement, full-body scans. Islam is a religion of either peace and beauty or war and intolerance, depending on whom you ask, and when. People may not know a lot about Islam, but everyone has an opinion about it, even if they keep it to themselves. Allah is the eight-hundred-pound God in the room. I can't ignore Him.

Overseas, reporting for NPR, I had witnessed firsthand the dark side of this faith. Not only terrorism committed in the name of Islam, but also a general harshness, an aridity, that left me cold. Islam seemed as severe and unforgiving as the Arabian desert from whence it sprang. There were exceptions. In India, I had caught whiff of another, softer Islam. I was living in a Muslim neighborhood in Delhi called Nizamuddin, named after a thirteenth-century Sufi saint. There was no harshness there; only light and joy. Nizamuddin was alive with colors and music and a welcoming vibe. People smiled. Moreover, they smiled at *me*, an infidel. Were the Muslims of Nizamuddin an aberration, or had I stumbled across the "real Islam"?

That question nests in my mind as I stalk the Pacific with my rented PT Cruiser and mangle Jim Morrison. *Don't you love me gladly, wanna be her badly.* Then I spot a hand-painted sign with a little red heart on it (Sufis are big on heart) and an arrow: Sufi camp this way. I turn down a dirt road and am enveloped in a cathedral of towering redwoods. Immediately my blood pressure drops. Then I notice that I've lost my cellphone signal and my blood pressure spikes again. No, I tell myself, this is good. Yes, this is very good. There is a long tradition of retreating into nature in order to find oneself: Thoreau, Gandhi, that South Carolina governor who hiked the Appalachian Trail. *They* didn't freak out over a few missing bars, and neither will I, no sirree. I am going to embrace the blessed isolation. Besides, maybe they have WiFi at the campsite.

I follow a few more heart-signs, the road grows rougher, the trees taller, and then I arrive. I park and walk to the check-in desk. The air is fresh and cool, much cooler than I expected or packed for. I look up and see the redwoods stretching toward the heavens

like spires, blighting the sun. These trees, which wear their height
so well, existed for centuries before I was born and will survive for
centuries after I am long gone.

"Welcome, campers," bellows Richard, the camp director, a
well-aged man dressed head to toe in black. I hear the word
"campers" and I am ten years old again. Sufi camp, though, is different. It's devoted to mysticism and spiritual exploration—and, I
hope, some fine California Merlot, or perhaps a nice Zinfandel.
First, though, explains Richard, there are a few earthly matters
that need to be addressed. Every morning we will meet in the main
hall for meditation at six thirty. Then the conch bell will sound
at precisely seven, indicating that breakfast is served. Afterward,
we'll all head to the redwood grove to receive "the sacred manuscript of nature," whatever that is. "There will be insect repellent,"
adds Richard helpfully.

I look around. Most of my fellow campers are aging hippies.
Some have aged better than others. The ponytails are still there,
but the hair is thin and gray, and the legs don't curl so easily
into the lotus position. Some have brought their children, who
seem to have followed in their parents' rebellious footsteps, though
their rebellion manifests itself mainly through hair color. I see one
teenager with purple hair and what looks like a dog collar around
his neck. Another has hair like a snow cone. All of the mainstream
religions are represented here, from disillusioned Jews to recovering Catholics. They're happy to have found a freestyle faith where,
as one woman puts it, "Nobody is telling me I'm doing it wrong."

Richard tells us to consult the menu of activities for the week.
It's all optional, we're told, we need not do anything, but I feel
that old adolescent peer pressure welling up inside me. I look at
the menu. It's a smorgasbord of spiritual offerings: Hindu yoga,
Buddhist meditation, Japanese tea ceremony, writing workshops,
Jungian dream analysis, astrology. There's a bit of Sufism thrown

in too, but not much. I feel like I've fallen down some New Age rabbit hole.

The next morning, at six thirty, I join the others in the large main hall, which looks something like a hippie ski lodge. Hanging from the rafters are nine flags representing nine religions. Over the fireplace is a photo of a bearded Indian man staring cross-eyed at something in the distance. It's Hazrat Inayat Khan, an Indian musician and mystic who brought Sufism to America in 1910. Americans have always been a nation of restless souls. The nineteenth-century transcendentalists, Whitman and Emerson and Thoreau, epitomized this spiritual yearning. Read their words and you'd be forgiven for thinking you're reading a translation from Sanskrit or ancient Chinese. Consciously or not, they borrowed heavily from the eastern traditions. And the east borrowed back; Gandhi was inspired by Thoreau.

"Good morning, holy beings," says our instructor, a man named Shabda (formerly Peter). But I am not holy, barely a being, frankly, at this hour, and without my morning coffee. We meditate. More precisely, others meditate while I watch from the sidelines, near an exit. A woman sidles up to me and says, "You won't get it unless you experience it," and I know she's right but now she's talking about smoky green tea from China that is good for digestion and something about antioxidants. "Take in the deliciousness of the air entering your lungs," says Shabda. "Fill your heart with lovingkindness." (Fine and good, but I'd rather fill my heart with loving caffeine, and stat.)

Finally, I hear the sound of the blessed conch bell and we are served a plentiful and delicious breakfast, accompanied by a robust dark roast. "He who tastes, knows," the Sufis say. They are speaking about a direct experience of the divine, but the same concept applies to breakfast.

Our stomachs full, caffeine coursing through our veins, we take off our shoes and form a circle, "a self-correcting circle," I'm told. We're circling and circling and within seconds, I'm holding hands. We dance to the goddess Tara, who has something to do with bliss and virtue, I think, but nothing to do with Islam. "We're doing a full-body prayer," says someone, and then the pace picks up. I can't get the dance moves right. I kick someone next to me. I'm tired and tell the person attached to the hand I happen to be holding at that moment that I'm going to take a break. "Good," he says. "You're in touch with your body."

They look like one giant organism, expanding and contracting, in constant flux. I admire their proficiency and am filled with spiritual envy. This is not good. I need to get back in there. Which I do and immediately regret because the next "dance" entails looking into one another's eyes and saying, "May God's presence illuminate your heart now and forevermore." This makes me uncomfortable. I don't know these people. How can I say this? Plus, I have a hang-up about eye contact and avoid it at all costs. My partner is a teenage girl with a nose ring. She looks me in the eye and says, "May God's presence illuminate your heart, now and forever." The strange thing, the thing that catches me completely off guard, is that she seems to genuinely mean it. I parrot the words back to her, but I don't mean it. I wish I did, but I don't. Does that make me a bad person?

And so it goes at Sufi camp. We begin the day with a Buddhist *sutra*, then some yoga and perhaps a Japanese tea ceremony. On Friday evening, we celebrate the Jewish Sabbath, and are told that the braids of the *challah* bread represent the five pillars of Islam. Someone says, "May Allah turn to face you and grant you shalom. *Shabbat shalom* [good Sabbath]." Sufism is the mystical heart of Islam, and has been for centuries, but these California Sufis have stripped it of its Islamic roots. Everyone here considers themselves Sufi but hardly anyone considers themselves Muslim.

Instead, there are so many Gods here, rubbing up against one another, that I'm suffering from spiritual whiplash. I ask someone about this and they say, "Sufism doesn't make me choose. I get to experience all of these wonderful things." It's the Mr. Potato Head approach to religion. A little bit of this, a little bit of that. Whatever works. I'm skeptical. It's one thing to experiment—Mahatma Gandhi was a huge experimenter and titled his autobiography *The Story of My Experiments with Truth*—but eventually you have to conclude the experiment, to choose or, to put it in the consumer vernacular of our age, head for the checkout line.

But we don't, which is why we're fast becoming a nation of "nones." A recent survey by Trinity College found that the fastest-growing religious affiliation is people with no affiliation at all. The "nones" believe in *something*; only 10 percent consider themselves atheists. The rest, presumably, can be found grazing at the divine buffet, going back for seconds. And why not? At no time in history have so many faiths been available to so many, and with relatively little risk. The odds of being burned at the stake have, thankfully, plummeted in recent centuries. We live in the age of no-fault conversion. "Whirl is King, having driven out Zeus," said Aristophanes two thousand years ago, and whirl we do, mixing and matching faiths like so many accessories. Churches offer yoga courses, synagogues meditation classes. We can have it all, or so we think.

Feeling adrift, I gravitate toward fellow outliers: a recently divorced pediatrician who is here for the dancing, an Afghan beauty queen—and an oil contractor named Hodi, aka Marlin, who, with his plaid lumberjack shirt and chunky, unstylish glasses, looks as out of place here as I do. Hodi, though, has been a practicing Sufi for decades. He invites me to tag along as he heads into town to pick up supplies. I eagerly agree.

What exactly *is* Sufism? I ask as we rumble along in his Dodge pickup. "An opening of the heart," he says. "A love of God." Sounds good, I think, but couldn't that define all religions? Sensing my doubt, he elaborates: "Sufism is wisdom school. All of reality is set up to prompt us to greater wisdom, like the house odds in Vegas." Sufis are in the world but not of the world, he continues, uttering a phrase I will hear many times over the next few months. Contrary to what we may think, he says, mystics have not checked out of the "real world" but are, rather, deeply engaged in it. "They throw themselves into reality with a big splash," he says, and I wonder what that would sound like.

"That's nice," I say. "But what about the dancing and the hand-holding and the staring into one another's eyes? You know, the goofy stuff."

"Yeah, we do all kinds of goofy stuff," he says unapologetically. "All religions do goofy stuff." He has a point, as anyone who has ever witnessed a Catholic mass or a Jewish wedding can attest.

"Rumi writes about the greater pleasures," Hodi says, invoking the name of the great Sufi poet who wrote in the thirteenth century but reads like yesterday. "You need to acquaint yourself with these greater pleasures. The problem is that Christianity took a left-hand turn," says Hodi just as we make a right turn onto the Pacific Coast Highway, which briefly confuses me, "and got into this guilt and shame thing. It turned people off."

I ask Hodi how I can get the most out of my time at Sufi camp. "I would challenge you to stop thinking for a while," he says, and I wish he hadn't. Better he had said, "I challenge you to complete an Ironman Triathlon," or "I challenge you to grow a new ap-pendage." Anything, *anything* but cessation of thought. For me, thinking is like breathing, only less productive. "Try dancing," sug-gests Hodi when I tell him about my thinking problem. "It's great for turning off the mind." I don't mention that I'm a terrible dancer and, given a choice, would rather stop thinking than start dancing.

While Hodi gets supplies, I dip into a café and check my e-mail. Nothing. Apparently the world is getting along just fine without me, which I find reassuring, and disappointing. Hodi picks me up and, driving back to the campsite, I mention how it's like two different worlds, there and here. "Only to the extent that you make it so," he says sanguinely, and I just sit there in his Dodge pickup truck, which reeks of Marlboro Lights, silently contemplating that one.

On day three of Sufi camp, Islam makes an unexpected appearance. It does so in the visage of a towering bear of a man named Bilal. He's a former California surfer dude, but you wouldn't know it looking at him now. He has a long, reddish beard and narrow eyes that make him look like he's always squinting even if he's not. He's wearing a Muslim skullcap and one of those long, flowing tunics favored by *imams* everywhere. In his hands, he's fingering a pair of cocoa-brown *misbaha*, worry beads. He looks like he just stepped out of a Cairo mosque, which isn't far off. He studied Sufism in Sudan, and it shows. His Arabic pronunciation is excellent. Even his hand gestures, the way he moves them like a conductor, seem authentically Arab. Now he lives in Berkeley where, despite his unusual appearance, no one notices him. Granted, it's extremely difficult to get noticed in Berkeley. One would have to be on fire. Or Republican.

Bilal tells us we will be doing *dhikr* (pronounced zikar). *Dhikr* means literally "remembrance" or "repetition." For Sufis, it is an essential practice. It is not mere rote repetition of words and phrases but an invocation that is done with one's entire being. "This remembrance travels from the tongue to the mind to the heart, where it has always resided," writes Seyyed Hossein Nasr, an Iranian-born scholar. *Dhikr* is similar to the prayer of Christ. *Thy will be done.* When one does *dhikr*, explains Nasr, "one must surrender all of the will and mind to God and place the whole of one's being in God's hands."

The Muslim God, of course, is *Allah*, which is often followed by *hu Akbar* (is great), which is sometimes—rarely but, still, too often—followed by a loud explosion. It's easier to approach a religion with an open heart than an open mind. My knowledge, imperfect, incomplete, trips me up. I know just enough about Islam to alarm me, not enough to inspire.

Bilal starts us off with the *shahada*, the most important Muslim prayer. Muslims say it every day. For them, it is like breathing. For me, it is like breathing under water. It does not come naturally. I suspect it's all that baggage weighing me down. *La ilaha illallah, Muhammad rasulu-llah.* "There is no God but God and Muhammad is His messenger," Bilal says, palms open, eyes half closed, and in impeccable Arabic; then we join in, with peccable Arabic. Arabic is a vibrational language. Sounds matter. It takes me awhile but then I get it. I have to admit: There is a musicality to the words that is soothing, almost hypnotic. Over and over we say those first few words: *La ilaha illallah.*

There is no God but God. What does that mean? I always thought it was intended to establish Allah's primacy. There is no God but *my* God. No, says Bilal, it means: There is *nothing* but God. Sufis see God everywhere. They are not pantheists—they don't believe that everything is God—but they do believe there are traces of divinity all around us, if only we look carefully enough. As the Koran says: *Wherever you look is the face of God.* Not God exactly, but God-in-disguise, the "hidden treasure that loved to be known."

That is what Sufis endeavor to remember, memory being a form of knowledge. Plato says true knowledge *is* recollection. In other words, we never learn anything that we didn't already know, even if we didn't know that we knew it. Sufis' knowledge is not book knowledge. They love reading but, I suspect, are not huge underliners. The knowledge they seek is that of direct insight, an intuitive knowing (or, as the mystics would put it, an unknowing). It is the way you know that the stove is hot or that you are going to marry that woman across the room whom you haven't met yet. Sufis are not anti-intellectual, but they aim to balance what they perceive as a head bias with a large dose of heart.

Bilal is all heart. He's gesturing with his hands, like a Muslim André Previn, stomping his foot and urging us on. *La ilaha illallah*, over and over again, varying the rhythm and intonation. "We need to be passionate and crazy and freak out," he says, his surfer-dude persona bursting forth. "This isn't just love. It's *crazy* love. It's the madness of infatuation. That's the kind of madness and passion we're talking about." *La ilaha illallah*. "Okay, breathe in the positive only God," he says, implicitly acknowledging that not all of God's ninety-nine names are equally appealing. Sufis don't focus on God The Destroyer but rather God The Exceedingly Merciful, and who can blame them? Now Bilal is really worked up, and the cultural dissonance is flying fast and furious. "Give it your all," he says, "give it your *oy vey* feeling," and I wonder which of Allah's ninety-nine names he might be invoking now, God The Mensch? *La ilaha illallah*. "Give it a little oomph at the end—*illallAH*—in order to get that rage out." I do and, sure enough, discover a surprisingly deep reservoir of rage to draw upon.

After we finish the *dhikr*, the room bathed in a plush silence, I sense movement coming from somewhere behind me. I pivot and see a woman. She is whirling like a...dervish. Which she is. I've heard about this but never seen it. It takes my breath away, what is left of my breath, that is. She is spinning and spinning, as if she could go on like that forever. Her dress is floating, like a disk, yet her feet remain pinned to the floor. Turning, as Sufis call this practice, is a form of *dhikr*, of remembrance. It is prayer in motion. I am smitten. At that moment, I decide I am going to do that. No matter what it takes, I am going to turn.

On my fifth day of Sufi camp I discover I've been holding hands wrong. Someone points out that my fingers are intertwined incorrectly. They're very nice about it but, still, it's embarrassing. Why didn't someone say something sooner? For some reason, this sends me over the edge. I need to get out of here. I can't take it anymore. I can't take the hand-holding and the hugging and the gluten-free food and the self-correcting circles and the made-up names and the snow-cone hair and the cultural relativism and the utter and complete lack of irony. I feel vaguely depressed, which is a ridiculous statement, actually. All depression is vague. If it were specific sadness, we would feel it, process it, and move on. Depression is sadness stuck. I don't know how to get unstuck, and could really use a drink, so I ask someone, Where's the wine? You know, drink with the beloved and all that?

"That was a metaphor, man," he says. Now, for the record, I am a big fan of metaphor, *huge*. I love metaphors like a seal loves fish, like a cat loves mice, like a...well, you get the idea. But you can't drink a metaphor. A metaphor doesn't swish around your palate, full-bodied and robust, with just a hint of fruitiness. And, ingested in moderate quantities, a metaphor won't make you feel all warm inside. Even the sober-minded William James saw the benefit of occasional intoxication: "Drunkenness expands, unites and says yes. It is in fact the great exciter of the *Yes* function in man." Yes! And only a real glass of wine, not a metaphor, can help us achieve that blessed state. Besides, Sufi camp has turned out to be considerably more camp than Sufi. These children of the '60s have imported Islamic Sufism, extracted the Sufi part, or some version thereof, and largely discarded the Islam part. The resulting concoction is musical and fun and harmless enough. But is it Sufism?

The New Age movement has a way of converting even the most

robust, ancient traditions into mush. Religions are like cuisines. They don't always travel well. They get watered down, diluted, and next thing you know you're ingesting the spiritual equivalent of chow mein. No, I need to go to the source. But where exactly? Sufis are active in dozens of countries. After some digging, I settle on Turkey. Turkey is where Rumi, Islam's poet laureate, penned his verse. Turkey is where the whirling dervishes took flight. And, I hear, Turkish wine isn't half bad. Yes, I will go to Turkey.

The next morning while everyone is busy checking in with their hearts, I check out. I slip in Jim Morrison, crank it way up, and this time get the lyrics right. *Don't you love her madly?* There is no God but God. *Don't you need her badly?* There is no God but God. Turning onto the Pacific Coast Highway, I fire up my iPhone. Reception, at last.

I arrive in Istanbul and it is raining. A substantial, moody rain that is different in quantity and quality from anything back home. The sheets are broad and weighty, each drop, it seems, straining under all that history. The rain bears this burden so that the city need not. Istanbul wears its history well. A Byzantine-era cathedral lounges unpretentiously between a four-star hotel and a McDonald's. Cobblestone streets nuzzle against four-lane highways. These juxtapositions materialize effortlessly.

The name "Istanbul," according to one explanation, derives from a misunderstanding. After capturing Constantinople in 1453, Turkish soldiers asked a group of Greeks where they were going. "*Istimbolin*," or "To the city," replied the Greeks. Thus, "Istanbul" was born. The city continues to operate on misunderstanding, and therein lies its genius. Outsiders can't figure out Istanbul. Is it European or Asian, religious or secular, ancient or modern? Istanbul, of course, doesn't care, and laughs off that lazy cliché about its being a "city of contrasts," an observation that, while true, is meaningless. Every large city, even seemingly monolithic Tokyo, is a city of contrasts. A city's greatness hinges on *how* it accommodates these contrasts. Istanbul does so by excluding nothing, and finding covert value in everything. No wonder poets love the city. Intersections make the best muse.

I check in to my hotel and chart a direct course for the bar. For me, no arrival is fully consummated without at least one drink at the hotel bar. On this evening I have two, maybe three, owing to my dry spell in California and the enormous task that lies ahead. I want to learn how to whirl, like a dervish. I want to find the "real" Sufism, not some tie-dyed version. Most of all, I want to find a way out of my thickening depression. No longer an intermittent presence, it has taken up full-time residence, like an uninvited houseguest who won't leave and yet stubbornly refuses to announce his intentions. This particular guest breaches the confines of metaphor; it possesses actual physical qualities, weight and mass.

The root of the problem, I think, is my fear of death. My friends say it is irrational. They are wrong. My fear of death is entirely rational. I will die. That is a fact. That I don't know precisely when or how affords small consolation. Simply put, the thought of not existing freaks me out. I don't know how people get out of bed in the morning knowing that each day brings us twenty-four hours closer to nonexistence. Theologian Paul Tillich defines neurosis as "a way of avoiding non-being by avoiding being." He's right. Neurosis is a psychic purgatory that leaves its victim suspended between pain and relief. It's also exhausting. The care and feeding of my pet neurosis increasingly leaves me with little energy for anything else. Like my family, for instance. Whatever success I've achieved has been in spite of myself, not because of myself. This has to change, and I don't mean change in the narrow, cynical sense that Freud suggests. I do not want to transform my neurosis into "ordinary unhappiness," as the good doctor prescribes, but something else. Something more.

The décor is all white and minimalist. My chair is hard plastic and swivels. Were it not for the view of the Bosporus, churning furiously outside the floor-to-ceiling windows, I could be in L.A. or New York. I crack open Leslie Wines's biography of Rumi. The bartender notices and nods his approval. "A great man," he says between shakes of an Absolut martini. Seven hundred years after his death, Rumi remains a rock star, and everyone wants a piece of him. The Turks claim Rumi as their own, since he lived most of his life here. The Afghans claim him too, since he was born there. The Iranian people (not the government) also claim Rumi, since he wrote in Persian. Fortunately, there is enough Rumi to go around. He was so prolific, and full of heart.

Sufis say every student needs a *murshid*, a guide. My guide to Rumi and the world of Turkish Sufism is a woman named Dilek, a friend of a friend. She strikes me as perfect for the job. She knows her way around the various *tariqahs*, paths, of Sufism, and has been following one particular path herself for years. She also happens to be an actual tour guide by profession, and this, I soon discover, is not only bursting with symbolic significance but comes in handy when attempting to decipher all this history, or haggle over the price of a carpet.

The next morning dawns dark and rainy, the winds whipping off the Bosporus with particular fury. Dilek and her boyfriend, Tan, a professional basketball player turned travel agent, pick me up from the hotel. "We're going to the other side," announces Dilek, as she does everything, with a theatrical thrust of her arms, palms aimed skyward. The other side. I like the way that sounds, and assume we are about to enter some mysterious parallel world, William James's "unseen order" perhaps. No, explains Dilek, we're going to the Asian side of the city. Istanbul bisects the European and Asian continents, and Turks think nothing of hopping to Asia for tea or lunch, or, in our case, a *sohbet*, a Turkish word with no direct translation but usually described as "mystical conversation."

We cross a bridge to the Other Side, Tan's little Fiat slicing through the sheets of rain, and before long we arrive at a ferry landing where we are met by a clutch of Dilek's friends, fellow Sufis, and then board a sturdy old boat. It's called the *Mirae*, which means "ascension to Heaven," and I like the way that sounds. Dilek says it's a sign. With the Sufis, everything is a sign. The boat is basic, not the least bit luxurious, but it feels solid and reassuring. We sit on hard wooden benches and wrap our scarves tight. A man—a boy, really, no older than fifteen—comes around with hot tea, which he pours expertly into small glasses. The sea is rough, and I struggle to drink my tea without spilling it. The others, I notice, have no such trouble.

I like the feel of the hot tea in my palms. I like the spray of the water, and even the rocking motion of the boat. We are embarking on an adventure. Shouting to make ourselves heard above the roar of the boat's engine, we talk. Inevitably, Ataturk's name comes up. His portrait is everywhere, including on this ferry. The beloved founder of modern Turkey, Ataturk forged a purely secular state. When he came to power, he banned all Sufi orders. That ban has since been lifted, for some orders, but Sufism still resides in the shadows of Turkish society.

Muslims everywhere tend to view Sufis as backward and something of an embarrassment, much in the way many mainstream Christians view the snake-handling Pentecostals. Sufis, with their music and dancing and juicy poetry, not to mention their veneration of saints and relatively liberal attitudes toward women, are not seen as "real" Muslims. Sufis counter that they are in fact upholding the tradition of the Prophet and the spirit of the Holy Koran. Indeed, their aim is to "reproduce within themselves that state of mind that made it possible for Mohammed to receive the revelations of the Koran," says the religious scholar Karen Armstrong.

William James would have agreed with that sentiment. Though he never had a mystical experience, he thought it wrongheaded to dismiss them out of hand. "One must have musical ears to know the value of a symphony; one must have been in love one's self to understand a lover's state of mind. Lacking the heart or ear, we cannot interpret the musician or the lover justly, and are even likely to consider him weak-minded or absurd." He also recognized that mystical experiences can be unsettling, for while they offer a glimpse of previously unknown terrain, they "fail to give a map."

But what exactly is mysticism? It's not a distinct religion but, rather, a way of relating to the divine. Mystics are less concerned with outer, exoteric aspects of religion and much more concerned with the inner, esoteric ones—with "personal first-hand knowledge," as Evelyn Underhill put it in her classic definition. The conventionally religious seek to know *about* God; mystics seek to know *of* God—and not in some theoretical hereafter, but *now*, in *this* lifetime. It's the difference between spending decades studying wine and taking one sip of an especially fine Pinot Noir.

I ask Dilek about her Sufi life. She wasn't born into a Sufi family, she says, but discovered it later in life. She hints at some personal crisis, but stops short of revealing more and I don't press. "I'm simply a seeker, a humble seeker," she says, asserting a basic Sufi tenet of humility, or maybe parroting it, I can't tell. "What is Sufism?" I ask, having never nailed that down in California. "For me, it is an all-embracing concept," says Dilek. "It is the instinctual search for truth." That sounds nice, but couldn't the same be said of any religion, and of science for that matter? And what exactly does she mean by "truth"?

Those questions will have to wait. We've arrived at our destination: one of the Prince Islands, so named, Dilek informs me in her best tour-guide voice, because in Byzantine times princes who fell out of favor with the king were blinded and dispatched to these islands. Today the islands serve as a summer getaway for harried Istanbulites and a year-round residence for a few hearty souls. Dilek has arranged for me to meet one of those souls, a Sufi *sheikh* named Mehtin. He's a pharmacist by profession. There is no such thing as a professional Sufi; they always have a secular vocation. In the world, but not of the world. Mehtin is special, I'm told. "If you're ready, he'll put you on a rocket," one of his students later told me. She didn't say where this rocket takes you, but I like the idea of catapulting clear of myself. Yes, a rocket would be nice.

We disembark and, after much negotiation conducted through wild gesticulations, board a couple of horse-drawn carriages. There are no cars permitted on the island, lending a quaint, timeless feel to the place. And then we're off, the horses clomping and me hanging on tight to the straps inside the carriage. A few minutes later, we arrive at a simple but pleasant house perched atop a hill. We take off our shoes—Sufis, like all Muslims, believe that shoes are anathema to spiritual progress—and join some fifteen others, sitting in chairs and overstuffed love seats, sipping tea. At the center of this informal circle is a middle-aged man wearing a striped sweater and wool vest. Eyeglasses dangle from a cord hanging around his neck. He has bright, intelligent eyes, expressive hands, and a soft smile. Mehtin. I like him immediately.

He announces that we are about to embark on a *sohbet*, a word that I have yet to fully grasp. "Heart talk" is how it is sometimes defined. Or, as Mehtin explains, deploying multiple metaphors, "A *sohbet* is not a restaurant, it's a picnic. Everybody shares something. It's like jazz improvisation; each time it is different, but the aim is always the same: a state of transcendence." I come to think of it as a spiritual bull session, which it is too. We talk for hours. Outside, the sky turns from gray to black, and still we talk, stopping only briefly to pile our plates with fresh cheese, bread, and figs. Mehtin does most of the talking, but he listens well too. Inevitably, the subject of heart arises. For Sufis there is nothing more important than heart. But what do they mean by it?

"The heart is not this pump," says Mehtin, pointing to his chest. But neither is it the sappy organ that westerners croon about. Heart is not raw emotion. It is possible to be dripping with emotion yet completely out of touch with your heart. The Arabic word for heart is *qalb*, whose root means "always changing, turning." For Sufis, the heart is an instrument of perception, and knowledge. "Seeing with the heart's eye" is a common Sufi expression.

The Turks have a word I like a lot: *gönül*, which means "knowing heart." Mehtin explains: "The gate to *gönül* can only be opened from the inside. *Gönül* is an intimate place, like the bedroom of the house. Only lovers can be invited into it." His choice of metaphor is no coincidence. Sufis often express themselves in the language of romantic love. These Sufis did not borrow from the romantics but, rather, the other way around. The very concept of modern romantic love stems, in part, from Sufi ideals.

On several occasions, when I suspect the conversation is getting a little too close to the bone, I resort to my old standby: humor. Others laugh, politely perhaps, but not Mehtin. "You like to make jokes," he says, "but we are serious men talking about serious matters." Oh no. He has my number.

At one point during the *sohbet*, I do something unexpected. I'm not sure why. Maybe it is all the heart talk, or the fact that I am on a carless island in the Sea of Marmara, out of my element, or that I am among strangers, or that we are serious men talking about serious matters. Whatever the reason, I decide to tell a story. It is a very personal story, the kind that is routinely mocked in certain circles, which is why, until now, I have shared it with only a few trusted friends.

My story unfolds on another island, this one much larger and definitely not car-free: the Japanese island of Honshu. I was living in Tokyo, working as a correspondent for NPR. Due to the time difference between Tokyo and Washington, DC, I often worked late into the night. This night was no exception. It was a pressing assignment, though now I can't recall about what. I pride myself on being the kind of journalist who is good in a crisis, a clutch player. I always deliver. But this night I couldn't. Try as I might, nothing worked. So I did something I've never done before: I gave up. Quit. I suppose you could say I surrendered, though I didn't think of it in those terms. I went to sleep knowing that I was about to disappoint my editors, and myself, and I simply didn't care.

A few hours later I was awakened, not by a dream but by a feeling, one so intense and unprecedented that I still struggle to name it. I have experienced moments of happiness in my life, flashes of joy even, but this was of an entirely different magnitude. Waves of bliss broke over me, inside me. Tears rolled down my cheeks. My body trembled, almost like a seizure, and on my lips came these words: "I didn't know, I didn't know." I didn't know such joy was possible. Slowly the waves subsided, and I drifted back to sleep.

The Tokyo Story, as I now think of it, was a one-off, and I soon forgot about it. Or nearly so. Every now and then I retrieve it, and wonder if I had briefly experienced the "acute fever" that William James observed among the mystically minded. I would have explored it further, were it not for the box problem. We need to store our experiences in a box. Without a box, an experience is easily lost, forgotten. Our culture provides us with many boxes: the family box, the career box, the consumer box. It does not, however, provide a box for experiences like the one I had in Tokyo, other

than the catchall "what-the-hell-was-*that*?" box. Which is exactly
where I stowed my Tokyo story.

Until now. I ask Mehtin what he makes of my Tokyo story.
There is a long pause, too long, I think, until finally he answers:
"Western people, rationalists, think analytically. They use their left
hemisphere and they always want methods. The left hemisphere
is male. The right is female. She is Sophia, which means wisdom.
The left side is male and has analytical logic but the right doesn't.
The right hemisphere is holistic perception. With the right hemisphere, we feel wholeness and inspiration. Right now, the entire
world is male-dominated. There is no motherhood, no affection,
no mercy. The world needs more right hemisphere. You felt this
yourself. This was an internal warning, a wake-up call for you.
Like a bell. Rumi said, 'Shut down the doors of your ears and eyes
and look inside.' Do not do anything. Just surrender, and this we
call *islam*, submission."

I have a problem with submission. It sounds defeatist, a close
cousin of resignation. Submission strikes me as a form of failure
and, frankly, un-American. We are taught to persevere at all costs.
Never give up, never submit to anyone. I suspect, though, that I am
misreading the word and ask Mehtin as much. To what, or whom,
are we submitting? God?

"Not to God. This is a lie. We are going to our inside, to a place
with no name, with no shame and with no images."

"That sounds...scary."

"Yes, yes, very. You're right. You become burdened, anxious,
when you are looking into this darkness. This is a very basic anxiety. And this is so good, perfect."

It doesn't seem perfect to me, quite the opposite, actually, and I
say so.

"When you encounter this fear, this anxiety, stick to it. The fear
of the Void is the beginning of wisdom. When you can stay in that

state, stay with the anxiety and the fear, then suddenly the darkness becomes lightness and the anxiety turns to joy. Suddenly. Like lightning. The whole body is electrified, purified. The goal of Sufism is this, and that's what you experienced briefly in Tokyo."

"So maybe I'm a Sufi and I didn't know it?"

"Everybody is a Sufi, but not everyone knows," Mehtin says, and flashes a toothy, slightly mischievous smile.

I ask about Rumi. How should I read him? I expect Mehtin to offer some sage advice about my *gönül*, or something like that. Not for the last time, he surprises me.

"Don't read Rumi. You should not read him."

What? This is like the pope suggesting I not bother with the Gospels. Why shouldn't I read Rumi, the greatest Sufi poet who ever lived?

Mehtin answers with a story, which is a very Sufi thing to do. When he was young he asked a similar question of his teacher: How should he read Rumi? Any way you want, his teacher said, nothing is forbidden, and he handed Mehtin a book of Rumi's poetry. It was all about burning and agony and separation. It made no sense, and certainly wasn't inspiring. Who wants to be burned by the Beloved? Mehtin tossed the book aside. There was nothing here, no wisdom. His teacher, not surprised by Mehtin's reaction, said, "The book of lovers can only be read by lovers." Only years later, when Mehtin's beloved teacher died and he was heartbroken, did he pick up Rumi again, and understand. "That," says Mehtin, "is why I say you should not read Rumi. To find Rumi you have to find yourself first."

I don't have that kind of time, I think, but decide not to say anything. Besides, the *sohbet* is over. We ride the ferry back to the Other Side, then drive to the European, left hemisphere of Istanbul. I crawl into bed and, jet-lagging, promptly disobey Mehtin. I read Rumi. Mehtin was right. Much of it is puzzling, and dark.

Take this line, for instance: "The man of God is distraught and astounded." I understand astounded, but distraught? Or this one: "I'm at once the feast and the disemboweled victim." What does *that* mean? And as Mehtin warned, there is much burning and annihilating in Rumi's world. It doesn't sound like a lot of fun. Which is precisely the point, of course. "The path of religion is full of trouble and disaster, because it is not a path suited to anyone with a cowardly nature," Rumi wrote. This does not bode well for me, I think, closing the book and trying, unsuccessfully, to fall asleep.

Rumi, the master poet, didn't care much for poetry. For him, it was just another idol. The finger pointing at the moon, not the moon, as the Buddha put it. I have no time for poetry, Rumi proclaimed, but my visitors demand it. "So like a good host I provide it." He did not want to be read, nor lionized in death. "Don't look for my grave in the ground," he famously said. "My grave is in the heart of lovers of God." The next morning, I disobey Rumi (clearly, I have an obedience issue) and, along with Dilek and her gaggle of Sufi friends, fly to Konya, the city where the reluctant poet lived, and died.

We arrive in Konya at daybreak. My first impression is that it seems awfully flat and barren. Tan confirms that this is indeed the case. In fact, there are so few trees in Konya that the Turks have an expression. When someone does something especially stupid, they say, "He hit a tree in Konya." A poster outside the airport shows a group of whirling dervishes, with their flowing white capes and serene expressions. I want that, I think again. I want to do that. I want to *be* that. I want to lose myself in God or ecstasy, or just silly dizziness—whatever it takes to shake my depression. I want to get out of my head, if only for a few seconds, and whirling at feverish speed just might do the trick. I express this desire to Dilek. The look on her face telegraphs the trouble that lies ahead. This won't be easy, she says. Secrecy surrounds the *semazens*, or "whirling dervishes." But she will try. Meanwhile, she suggests I look in my heart to see if this is something I really want to do. Dilek is always advising me to look in my heart, as if it were that easy, like checking the oil on my 2003 VW Passat, but maybe that isn't such a good example because I'm not very good at that either.

Konya is a city past its prime—seven hundred years past, to be precise. Back then, in the thirteenth century, it was a crossroads of cultures and religions. Saint Paul once preached here. Konya's favorite son, of course, is the Islamic scholar turned poet named Jalaluddin Rumi. He came here as a young man in his early twenties, his family on the run from the Mongols. It is here where Rumi wrote all of his fifty thousand verses. It is here where Rumi met his muse, a mysterious dervish named Shams (or "Sun") of Tabriz. And it is here where Rumi died and, it is said, people of all faiths attended his funeral.

One of our traveling companions is Dilek's friend Berrin. She is happy, quite possibly the happiest person I've ever met. Berrin warns me that during our stay in Konya, an auspicious time that coincides with Rumi's death anniversary, people, women *and* men, might suddenly cry for no apparent reason. "Sometimes it's so intense it's almost unbearable," she says. She suggests I don't fight the tears. Sufis consider crying a means of cleansing the heart, and for Sufis there is nothing more important than a clean heart. As our taxi traverses Konya's treeless streets, Berrin throws out this bit of Sufi folklore: If your tears are salty, your heart is not clean enough. If your tears are bitter, your heart is not clean enough. If your tears are sweet, then your heart is clean. What if your tears won't come at all, I wonder silently. I could use a good cry—salty, sweet, BBQ-flavored, whatever. My tears are calcified, backed up. Depression, contrary to what we normally believe, is not sadness but an inability to fully feel sadness. Depression is sorrow denied.

"Of course you're depressed, you're writing about God," my friend Jennifer told me, and she had a point. We have pathologized melancholy, transformed a complex human condition into a cut-and-dried disease, like diabetes or high blood pressure. The cure, by and large, is chemical. If Saint John of the Cross were alive today, doctors would no doubt prescribe Paxil for his dark night of the soul. I don't deny that for some a genuine chemical imbalance exists, and for them medication can help, but I can't help but wonder if my depression signals something else, a spiritual imbalance of sorts, one that no pill can cure. Or, as Rumi suggested, that no pill *should* cure.

> *Rejoice in grief; grief's the way to melt into Him*
> *Ascension, on this path, travels from heights to depths.*

In the distance, I can see Rumi's tomb: a green tower, rising above a dome. We pay a few Turkish lira then wander through an exhibit of dervish paraphernalia. There's a *ney*, the long reed instrument that is played during the whirling performance. The sound of the *ney*, Dilek tells me, represents "the cry of the suffering soul," and I do not doubt this. The *ney* is the most plaintive instrument ever invented. It is impossible to listen to it for more than thirty seconds without slipping into deep existential despair, assuming you're not there already. The *ney*, Rumi wrote, represents pain of separation, the separation of the reed from the reed bed and, by extension, our separation from the Beloved, from the divine. "Anyone separated from someone he loves understands what I say, anyone pulled from the source longs to go back," wrote Rumi.

So much of the dervishes' accoutrement is symbolic of spiritual death and rebirth: the cylindrical hats worn by dervishes, for instance, represent tombstones. Some Sufis carry axes, so that they can kill their *nafs*, ego attachments. (They don't actually use the axes, Dilek assures me. It's just another metaphor, like the wine.) Sufis believe we must "kill" our false self so that our true, divine nature can live. "O man of honor, die before you die," Rumi wrote, echoing Jesus's words. "Die unto thy self."

I notice a black square of wood with a nail in the middle. It's a practice board, Dilek explains. A dervish in training stands on the board and tries to turn while one foot remains pinned to the nail. Normally, the prospect of such pain would cause me to abandon a venture like this, but not this time. I still want to turn. Even if it hurts.

We enter the main hall, where Rumi's tomb is housed. Normally, at a religious site like this, people would remove their shoes, out of respect, but there are too many visitors and not enough room to store the shoes, so instead everyone dons these blue plastic booties. We look like nuclear-power-plant inspectors or those people who work in "clean rooms" making microchips, and the sound of plastic rubbing against itself competes with the plaintive music of the *ney*. Lamps hanging from the high ceilings represent the divine light. "Light upon light" is how the Koran describes Allah. Inscribed on one wall is perhaps Rumi's most famous, and to me, enigmatic, sayings: "Either appear as you be or be as you appear." I could spend a lifetime deciphering that one. Dilek has been here many times, always leading a tour group, until last year, when she came by herself, *for* herself, and was overwhelmed by the experience. She felt at peace for the first time in a long time.

I find a place to sit. I try to take notes but my pen—my brand-new pen—refuses to write. Berrin says this is a sign that I don't want to write. Perhaps. Or maybe my pen is broken. So instead of writing, I watch. There's everyone from Japanese tourists to Iranian pilgrims. Some people walk around with one hand over their hearts, while others sit quietly, reading Rumi. I notice Tan across the room, sitting on the floor, his long basketball legs folded up like one of those collapsible chairs. The woman next to me is wearing a black-and-white head scarf, eyes closed, hand on heart, lost in…what? Thought? No, that is a silly expression. We are never really lost in thought. Thought, even discursive thought, is the opposite of being lost. When we are thinking we are *not* lost, and that is the problem. That's why many spiritual paths demand a true loss of our thinking selves, our egos. No, she is lost in nonthought, some state so sublime I can't even fathom. We may be fellow travelers, she and I, but I suspect she is further along the road than me.

I try putting my hand on my heart, this dead thing, but nothing. It's like turning on a radio and hearing only silence. Why can't I tune in to whatever station this woman next to me is clearly receiving? I remember something a German woman, a follower of the obscure Jain religion, once told me: "When you are desperate enough you will find your God." How much more desperate might that be? I wonder.

I like this place. It is reverential and relaxed at the same time, a rare combination. So, unable to write, I sit. And sit. And then, right on cue, get antsy and wonder if they have a gift shop. They must have a gift shop. All sacred sites have gift shops. Where is the gift shop? (Later I would find it, tucked near the exit, selling little pamphlets of Rumi's poems and glass figurines of whirling dervishes. Dilek and friends bought me one, and it still sits, and whirls, on my desk.) I'm about to go investigate when I notice a young man next to me, in jeans and ski vest, reading Rumi in a language that I think is Persian, Rumi's mother tongue. The man introduces himself. His name is Nader and he is indeed from Iran. He tells me that in Iran, Rumi is frowned upon by the authorities. "They consider it against morality," he says, and indeed some of Rumi's poems might be construed as borderline pornographic, if one read them literally, which is not the way Rumi intended them to be read, of course.

I ask Nader what he finds so compelling in Rumi that he is willing to defy the Iranian government and embrace him. "I find happiness in Rumi," he says. "When I'm desperate, sometimes I find something in a poem that charms my heart. His poems are very pure. When my daughter and wife are asleep I read Rumi and cry, a happy kind of crying. I cannot find that in any of the other Sufi poets." He sees my copy of *The Essential Rumi*, a translation by Coleman Barks. This is good, he says, but it's much better in the original Persian. He reads a few lines to me, and I close my eyes and think, Yes, it is; even though I don't understand a word I can appreciate the musicality, the beauty, of the couplets.

I say goodbye to Nader and find Dilek and friends. We decamp to a nearby restaurant where Dilek orders platefuls of bread and cheese and unrecognizable dishes that are nonetheless delicious. I see out the window a sign for the "Dervish Driving School" and smile at the thought of learning how to drive from a whirling dervish. I imagine their students spend a lot of time going in circles, getting nowhere, but doing so beautifully. Plans are discussed. Dilek says we have to be *zuhurat*, which means roughly "open to anything." *Zuhurat* is not fate, not exactly, she says, but it does involve an unwavering belief in a friendly universe. This becomes a running theme during our time in Konya. If something good happens, it is *zuhurat*. Even something bad can be *zuhurat*, the implication being that there is some hidden good to be found if only one looks hard enough. When I nearly walk into oncoming traffic, that is declared *zuhurat*, because I wasn't killed.

"So I can do anything and it's *zuhurat*?" I ask Dilek. "No," she says, citing a Sufi saying: "Tie your donkey to a proper pole first then go about your business."

The heavy lunch and Turkish sweets conspire against the possibility of a spiritual breakthrough. Now I understand why fasting is an integral part of so many religions, including Islam. It's not easy finding God on a full stomach. Carl Jung believes one reason modern man is less spiritually developed than his medieval ancestors is overnutrition. Rumi, as always, put it musically: "There's a hidden sweetness in the stomach's emptiness."

Dilek takes me to an event. A highly respected Sufi *sheikha* is giving a lecture. We enter a simple concrete building and walk up several flights of stairs. People keep coming and coming until the room is packed. The *sheikha* is thin, with dark hair, a pleasant smile, and an awful lot of energy. "No ego consciousness," she says, "that is the key." And then she tells a story.

There was once a very important politician who rose to the rank of prime minister. During an official function, he meets with a dervish. "What will you be after you are prime minister?" asks the dervish.

"I'm not sure," replies the politician. "Perhaps I will be defense minister."

"And after that, what will you be?"

"Oh, I don't know. I'll probably retire and join a prestigious think tank."

"And after that?"

"I don't know," says the prime minister, increasingly exasperated. "I will be a roving ambassador, something like that."

"And then what will you be?

"Nothing!" screams the politician. "I will be nothing."

The dervish smiles.

"Why are you smiling?"

"Because, Your Excellency, I am already nothing."

Sufis aim for what Saint Teresa of Avila called "the clear perception of our proper nothingness." Many Sufis, in fact, describe mystical experiences where they feel like a speck of dust, which strikes me as rather depressing, but they don't see it that way. Thus, the paradox of the spiritual path: To become enlightened we must first become no one. Yet it is precisely this fear of nothingness, of nobody-ness, that terrifies me. Strip away my ego—my identity as father and husband and writer and, yes, as neurotic extraordinaire—and what is left? Nothing, the Sufis say. And isn't that wonderful?

The *sheikha* then asks us how coal turns into a diamond. The answer, of course, is through heat. Burn something ordinary, like coal, long enough, and hot enough, and it turns precious. "God occupies us with all sorts of trouble because He wants us to be transformed," she says.

Afterward, she agrees to meet with me one-on-one. For some reason, maybe it's her kind smile or gentle manner, I unload on her. I tell her about my hospitalization and The Question—have you found your God yet?—and my determination to find an answer and about how much I love books and the underlining of them and how this seems to be getting in the way of my search and how every Sufi I meet tells me that I need to get out of my head and into my heart and how they make it sound so simple but of course it's not so what am I to do?

Unfazed by my verbal onslaught, she answers. There are two types of mind, she says, and the way to reach the higher state of mind, a kind of heart-mind, is very simple: "You need to fall in love."

"With who?"

"With anything. Even with a stone. It doesn't matter. Just fall in love."

What a remarkable statement. Sufis are indeed lovers. That I knew. "For us, the whole business is a love affair," they like to say, but I always assume they mean love of God, not love of *anything*. But, in fact, that is exactly what they mean. Rumi took that notion a step further. He once said that the highest form of love is love with no object. Is such a thing possible? Or is that like saying the highest form of eating is when no food is involved?

On the drive back to the hotel, it's Dilek's turn to open up. She tells me how she was born Muslim but always wondered: If God is out there, why doesn't He show Himself? She dabbled in other practices. An Indian guru taught her silent meditation, and that helped, a bit. She had small hints that "there was more," as she puts it, but just couldn't get into *kundalini* meditation, couldn't do it. Then, a few years later, she became very interested in dreams. She read Jung, who had much to say on the subject. She started keeping a dream journal. "I found this fascinating world. I was so curious about myself. I wanted to decipher myself on a psychological level, and then spirituality followed." Then she read a book called *Catching the Thread*, by Llewellyn Vaughan-Lee, a British-born Sufi mystic. Something clicked. "It took me to my silent container," she says. (Dilek is big on containers. She's always talking about them.) In 2004 she met Llewellyn for the first time, in Germany, and that was it. Sure, she still had her doubts. Dilek describes herself as an "independent soul," raised in the east but with a skeptical, western mind. A head person, like me. "But I was also so desperate," she says.

"Desperate for what?"

"For my meaning of life. For the meaning of my suffering. My heart knew I was in the presence of a wonderful teacher."

I'm trying to understand this, really I am, but how do you give yourself over so entirely to a teacher? What if he turns out to be a fraud, or another Jim Jones, the cult leader who in the 1970s convinced some nine hundred people to take their own life in the jungles of Guyana?

"If you've ever been in love, then you know a little bit of what I'm talking about," says Dilek. "You just know. Besides, the teacher is not your god. The real God is in you. The teacher only puts a torch in front of your way so that you can acknowledge the God, which basically resides in each one of us. I know there is a hidden treasure in each one of us that some people like to call God. You have it. Tan has it. I have it. And before I die, I'd really like to discover as much of it as possible."

I ask her how Sufism has changed her, figuring that is the ultimate test of any religion: Does it make us better people? "Oh, I was a very different person. I had a lot of anger." I can't picture Dilek angry. Dilek hints at family problems but doesn't offer details and again I don't press. Ultimately, though, a persistent and admirable optimism defines her. "I want to believe that we are not as burdened as we think," she says, and I'm immediately reminded of what that Indian yogi, Ramana, said about how we're like passengers on a train carrying luggage on our head, unnecessarily. We are not as burdened as we think. I get that. Then Dilek says something that I don't get and must immediately add to my rapidly growing collection of metaphysical puzzles. "My problem," she says, "was actually my solution." That one I let just hang in the ripe Konya air.

We're heading to a *dergah*—a Sufi gathering. We drive to the outskirts of Konya. I didn't realize the city was so big and sprawling. It's dark now, and we're lost. We stop and ask directions. Twice. (Never a good sign.) This time Berrin jumps out of the taxi and engages in an extremely animated discussion with a passing family. Everyone, distant cousins, aunts, gets involved. Hands are flying in various, often opposite, directions. (Never a good sign.) I'm frustrated, but Berrin takes it all in stride. It's all *zuhurat*. "Everything is in His hands. You follow His will."

Finally, through God's good graces and some dumb luck, we find our destination. We are buzzed into a large courtyard. Shoes

off, then we're greeted by a young man in jeans, which contrasts
with his mannerisms, which I find almost regal. Inside, it's as if
we've time-traveled back to the Ottoman Empire. The floor is
covered with carpets: wine-red Bukharans, flowery Persians, no-
nonsense Turkmens. The walls are covered with framed works of
calligraphy, some done in classic black-and-white, others in bold,
primary colors.

We sit on cushions on the floor. On the other side of the room,
a world away it seems, are huge overstuffed Versailles chairs oc-
cupied by women with dyed-blond hair and generously applied
makeup. "Istanbul elite," Dilek whispers in my ear. There is much
shaking of hands and pecking of cheeks. One woman, her head
covered with a jet-black scarf, whips out a BlackBerry, a harsh
reminder of just which century we reside in. Plates of bread and
cheese and Turkish sweets are passed around, along with the ubiq-
uitous tea.

Then things start happening. Young men roll up the carpets.
A potbellied, middle-aged man removes a guitar-like instrument
from its case. I'm told he was in the Turkish army for decades—
that was his "real profession"—but he is a Sufi at heart. People
break out their worry beads. The room has been transformed.

Then a man, the same one, I realize, who had greeted us, enters
the room, also transformed. His jeans have been replaced by the
flowing white outfit worn by dervishes. The music starts, and he
begins to turn, slowly at first. His arms are tucked close to his
body, one hand on each shoulder, as if hugging himself, then grad-
ually he begins to open, like a flower. Now he is fully open, arms
spread wide, head tilted to one side. I am mesmerized. Then, suddenly, he stops and kisses the ground. No one applauds. What we
have just witnessed was not a dance but something much more.

According to Sufi legend, the practice of whirling, or turning,
began with Rumi himself. He was walking through Konya's mar-

ketplace one day when he heard the sound of a goldsmith's hammer. Rumi is said to have discerned in that sound the *dhikr—la ilaha illallah*, There is no God but God—and was so overwhelmed with joy he began to turn. I can imagine what the good people of Konya must have thought of him then, or later when he turned at the funeral of a friend, in a spontaneous celebration of his life. The *sema*, as the whirling ceremony is called, is loaded with symbolism. Individually, each dervish, or *semazen*, is turning toward the truth, opening to it. The head is tilted to one side, out of the way. One arm is held high, in another world, and the other low, in this world. With each turn, he or she says silently, *Allah, Allah*. In a group, the dervishes orbit one another, re-creating the movement of the heavens.

The way we in the west use the term "whirling dervish," colloquially, as in "He's running around like a whirling dervish," is all wrong. Whirling dervishes may be ecstatic and intoxicated, in the Sufi sense of the word, but they are not out of control; they are very much grounded, more so than most of us.

The next day we go to a large auditorium where an academic conference is being held on Shams, Rumi's muse. Shams would no doubt enjoy a good laugh at the thought of such a conference. He was one of the least academic people to walk this earth, and considered fame a disaster. But it is here, in the sterile cafeteria, with its god-awful Nescafé served in flimsy plastic cups, where I meet Pieter. He's from Holland, and he's a whirling dervish, has been for fifteen years. We grab some Nescafé and sit down to talk. I'm curious to know how a westerner like him has been able to conquer his *nafs*, not to mention his dizziness, and master the art of turning.

Posture is important, he says, and I can hear my mother saying: "*See*, I told you to stand up straight." Form matters, he says, but sometimes you have to break form. Form can be a prison. It's what is in your heart that matters. You turn in your heart. "When you are in it, really in it, you are—how to explain?—you have one foot in this world and one foot in another. It's beautiful, and you feel like you can do it forever."

"Don't you get dizzy?"

"No, never. You say *Allah, Allah, Allah* silently, with each turn. It comes from inside you; you rip open from the inside out. It can happen very slowly, or sometimes it feels like a fast fall."

Then he says—and this blows my mind—that you can turn without moving. What does he mean?

"The outer form is secondary. I can turn right here, sitting."

I take a good look at Pieter, who does not appear to be turning, but who am I to say? He is bald, with wire-rimmed glasses, and a slight paunch. In other words, he is not unlike me, and for the first time I think I just might be able to do this. I might be able to turn.

"Why did you decide to become a dervish?" I ask.

Pieter answers by pulling out a notebook that he carries with him everywhere. It belonged to his son. He died a few weeks before he was to graduate from high school. Overcome with grief, Pieter did what I probably would have done: He set himself in motion. He rode his bicycle from Holland to Konya, not knowing exactly what he would find there but knowing he had to go. For weeks, he pedaled and screamed—at the gods, at fate, at the Infinite Whatever. People, strangers, sensing this was a man in unimaginable pain, helped him, gave him water, a place to sleep. "It was beautiful," he says, a solitary teardrop forming in his left eye. "There is pain. There is beauty. There is help." This, I realize, is what Sufis mean by the "alchemy of agony." Suffering not blunted, but transformed.

When he got to Konya, he found a teacher and became a dervish. A teacher is necessary, Pieter says. "You can't do it on your own. You are alone, but you aren't doing it alone."

"But isn't that a cop-out? I mean, in a way, aren't you giving up?"

"Yes, surrendering. It's like I can love but I can also feel like I am loved. And the last piece is the will. The will is not 'What do I want?' but 'What is wanted and what can come through me?' The first step is to see where you are. That, and to find some acceptance, or to accept that you cannot accept it."

Accept that you cannot accept it. I like that a lot, and add it to my growing menagerie of impossible yet wise utterances. Then I decide to tell Pieter my Tokyo story, about that night of unexplained bliss. He listens intently then, once I've finished, says, "This is true. I feel it. I know it is true because my arms and neck shivered when you just told it. This is a real one."

"So it wasn't just my imagination?"

"No. This is the place where angels whisper. You never know where it comes from. All the great inventions came from thoughts where the inventor didn't know where they came from."

"You mean inspiration?"

"Yes, inspiration is like the breath of whatever. You should always ask yourself, 'To what am I true to myself?' "

"What do you mean?"

"What do you hold on to when everything else falls away?"

"You mean, what's left when you've lost everything?"

"Yes. What is your anchor? What keeps you going?"

"Well, I don't know. What's the answer?"

"Oh, you have to find that out yourself. For me, it is different than it is for you."

I was afraid of that. Just once, I'd like one of these remarkable people I meet to tell me precisely what to do and how to do it. Pieter's clearly not going to oblige, so as we crumple our plastic cups and stand to leave I ask if he has any advice for me. He takes my hand and places it on my chest. "Just trust your heart," he says.

It's one of those Hallmark gestures that, normally, I would dismiss, or mock. But the way Pieter says it, so sincerely, and knowing the pain he has endured and transformed, I'm inclined to believe him.

Something tells me that Pieter's happiness, his ability to transform pain, and his skill as a dervish are not unrelated. I want that. I want to turn and, as often happens when I want something very badly, I won't shut up about it. I keep pestering Dilek, who assures me she's on the case. In fact, she has a bead on an instructor she thinks will be perfect for me—a woman, which I'm told is highly unusual. Only very recently have women been allowed to participate in the *sema*, let alone teach it. She works at a Sufi center on the outskirts of Istanbul.

We leave Konya the next morning. I do so with no regrets, and as for disobeying Rumi by looking for him there, I'm sure he'd understand. He had obedience issues himself.

I'm excited about meeting my instructor, but try to keep my gusto in check, recalling Rumi's advice: "Don't analyze enthusiasm." I'm also nervous. It's one thing to fixate on the *idea* of turning and quite another to actually do it. My greatest fear, of course, is that I will be a complete failure, but I also worry that all that whirling will induce a sort of spiritual vertigo, or somehow worsen my depression rather than alleviate it. It's possible. Who knows what all of that centrifugal force might do to my fragile state of mind.

We cross to the Other Side and then we're driving for a very long time. The light is soft and golden. A good omen, I decide. Finally, we arrive at the place. A sign out front says, "Mind your manners for God's sake," and next to it is a small icon of a whirling dervish, along with likenesses of Rumi and Ataturk, now in death on friendly terms apparently. The one of Rumi is typical. I see it everywhere. He is rotund, cherubic, with a full gray beard and his head tilted slightly down, eyes doing something but I don't know what. It's an unfortunate illustration. He looks like a grumpy old man, which he wasn't.

I meet the man who runs the center, a well-known leader of the Mevlevi Order of Sufis named Hasan Dede. He is wearing a jacket and tie and looks more like a midlevel politician, or maybe a casino owner, than a Sufi *sheikh*. I remind myself that Sufis are hidden in plain sight; sometimes wisdom wears a suit.

"Welcome to the rose garden," says Dede, looking me squarely in the eye, and with that vaguely sly smile that I've come to expect from Sufis. Then a *sema* is held, one unlike any I've yet seen. This is no concert hall. The *semazen* are so near I can hear their leather shoes sliding against the wooden floor and feel the breeze that their outfits make as they spin round and round. I realize now what makes the *sema* so special: frenetic, ecstatic motion coupled with complete control. It is extremely active and passive *at the same time*. I notice one of the *semazen* in particular: a young woman whose face is aglow. She is lost in the moment, though not in thought. Something is going on there that I cannot begin to describe. How can I when even the great Rumi was rendered mute by the *sema:*

> *I have no name*
> *for what circles*
> *so perfectly*

The *sema* over, people file out of the hall, and I meet my instructor. Her name is Deden. She has fiery red hair and possesses the appearance and demeanor of an East German gymnastics coach. She scares me. We sit down with her and her husband, who, frankly, seems much softer. He offers some advice. First, he says, the *sema* is not a dance, which I find reassuring because, as I said,

I'm a terrible dancer. "It's a feeling of purity but it is very difficult to put into words. It's like tasting a fruit. It is indescribable, but delicious. It is when consciousness becomes pure. When you turn your heart is constantly in *dhikr*, remembrance of God."

I ask him how I should approach it, with what attitude. He laughs softly then says: "First, you should rid yourself of all negative thinking." I'm toast.

We walk to a corner of the main hall. Deden asks that I remove my shoes and, for some reason, my wedding ring. She hands me a pair of special whirling shoes, called *mes*. They're made of black leather and are soft, like slippers. This pair is a bit tight, though, and I worry that might defeat me from the get-go.

"Remember," says my instructor, "don't focus on anything. Empty your mind, get close to God, and then you will not experience any dizziness. You need to trust that the universe will carry you." Again, I have a bad feeling.

"Okay," she says, "watch me." She tucks her arms in tight, then swings one leg across her body and pivots. She makes it look easy. "Okay, now you try it."

I start off well enough. I've got the arm-tucking part down, but my pivot is all wrong, and I nearly fall over. "Relax," she says, and of course that makes me more tense. "Don't bend your left knee. Right hand over left. Stand up straight," she says. I feel like I'm trapped in some warped game of Twister. I'm hearing other voices. One of them is Pieter's. "Form doesn't matter. Turn from the inside." And I hear Rumi. "You can fall a thousand times but come, come again."

It's no use. I can't do it.

"Try to keep going," she says. "Just continue through the small missteps, just continue."

I try again, but by now I'm dizzy and nauseous and fear I might lose it right there on my *mes*. Then, for no apparent reason, I get it.

Beyond thought, I turn and turn. Propelled by some invisible force, I intuitively align myself with the laws of physics, like a planet spinning on its axis.

"I'm turning!" I shout, and immediately lose my balance. I had committed a cardinal sin. I had analyzed enthusiasm. Still, I turned. For about twenty seconds. But it was a blessed twenty seconds. And besides, as Rumi said: "The Sufi is the son of time present."

My lesson is over. "You did very well," says Dilek.

"Keep practicing," says my instructor.

And so I do. But two facts—a small hotel room and a little too much single malt—conspire against a successful practice session the next evening. Desk lamps and other items not nailed down go flying everywhere. A purple bruise blossoms on my thigh. A good carpenter, I believe, always blames his tools, so I decide the problem is my *mes*. They're too tight, and not firm enough. I express this concern to Dilek on the phone, and the next day I find a package waiting for me at the front desk. Inside is a pair of black leather slippers, perfect size and firmness, and a note from Dilek and Tan: "Bless your *mes*." I breathe deeply and think, yes, what mighty Sufi hearts these two have.

What about me? Do I have a Sufi heart? Or, put another way, have I found my God? I'm not sure. I like the turning and the "drunkenness" and the heart-first approach to life. But Sufism, with a few California exceptions, is very much tied to Islam, and *islam* means "submission." I'm still wrestling with that one. I asked a Sufi friend about this. Why would I want to submit to *anything*? "It depends on your motivation," she said. "Are you submitting out of fear, or love? It's a heck of a lot easier to submit out of love." When she said that, something clicked. This kind of submission is like surrendering to the pleasures of a fine meal or the company of an old friend you haven't seen in a long time. This sort of submission is not a relinquishing of personal autonomy but, rather, an acknowledgment of beauty. It's also just common sense. If your clothes were on fire, and there was a swimming pool nearby, wouldn't you submit to the water? That, I think, is what Sufis mean by submission. We are the person on fire. God is the swimming pool. It seems like a no-brainer. But so few of us jump because we've learned to live with our clothes on fire, or we don't believe the pool exists or, if we do, we fear the water is too deep and, while our flames might be extinguished, we would drown. The Sufis, so adept at not thinking, skirt these rationalizations and just jump.

On my last day in Turkey, Dilek and I go to see Mehtin again. This time we are meeting at his pharmacy, which is located, of course, on the Other Side. On the ground floor, it looks like any other pharmacy, but we are led upstairs to another world. There, we find Mehtin behind a large wooden desk, holding court as usual, dispensing wisdom rather than ibuprofen. My eyes are having trouble focusing. There are walls and walls of books, a scale of justice, family photos, an old black-and-white photo of Ataturk, a small bust of Socrates, the Egyptian "key of life," Taoist yin-yang balls. It's the sort of spiritual mishmash that, back in California, would put me off, but here, somehow, it works. The difference, I think, is that Mehtin is not merely collecting these various wisdom traditions, trying them on for size. He has fully absorbed them. When I ask Mehtin about the sundry stuff, he smiles, his usual sly smile, and says, "These are my idols you can see. The dangerous ones are the ones you can't see."

I spend five hours in that office above Mehtin's pharmacy. They are five of the most pleasant hours of my life. People come and go, visitors from next door, from Cairo, and beyond. We munch on fresh tangerines, cake, and a delicious soup called *ashure*, but mostly we talk. I recognize it as a genuine *sohbet*. We talk about the *sema* ("It is a kind of meditation, an active meditation"); we talk about the true meaning of a Sufi ("He is an artist, a divine artist"); we talk about the left hemisphere ("As cold as Satan"); and we talk about death ("The one who died already won't have any fear of death").

Mehtin suddenly dims the light and announces, "We're going to drop our brains and listen to some music." It's Bektashi music, he explains, and I like it. It is simultaneously plaintive and joyous, a lamentation of joy. Mehtin closes his eyes. His hands bob and weave, toward his chest then away, without even a hint of self-consciousness, like a child. Dilek's eyes are also closed, her head tilted slightly to one side, like a *semazen*, the tears sliding down her cheek. Rumi is there too, his words ranging across the centuries, plucking at my not-dead heart with the finesse and quiet passion of a classical guitarist.

"A great silence overwhelms me, and I wonder why I ever thought to use language," says the reluctant poet.

Outside, it is raining.

CWM, dizzy, tired of going in
circles. Needs to sit still for
a while. Craves sanity and
peace of mind. Looking for
a levelheaded partner and
noble truth teller who has
been here before. Please,
enlighten me.

When I arrive in Kathmandu one morning, I can't say I am terribly surprised to discover that my body has not. It's still back in Washington. Most people dislike this fugue state, this temporal whiplash. I enjoy it. Crave it, *need* it. A jet-lagged mind is a confused mind and a confused mind is one that is open to the possibility of change, and God knows I could use some change. My depression has blossomed, though there is nothing flowery about it. It is all thorns.

Dostoyevsky says there are two kinds of cities: intentional and unintentional. Kathmandu is definitely an unintentional city. Accidental urbanness. There is no logic to its layout or its traffic patterns ("patterns" being generous). The smog is so thick I don't know why anyone smokes; it's redundant. My driver maneuvers among the cows and bicyclists and beggars as if they were cones on a driving course rather than sentient beings. The streets narrow, and my latent claustrophobia flares up. Our little van is squeezing into impossibly constricted spaces. Finally, we arrive at my hotel. It's nice enough, with a pleasant patio and colorful Nepalese art in the lobby, but I immediately sense that I am in the wrong place. My suspicion is confirmed when I go for a walk and am accosted by hawkers who want to sell me Gurkha knives, shoe shines, Himalayan treks, Tiger Balm, Tibetan prayer wheels, striped juggler's pants, more Tiger Balm, a massage, marijuana, and yet more Tiger Balm.

This part of town, called Thamel, is a ghetto. Unlike most ghettos, the inhabitants of Thamel—backpackers from Israel, middle-aged tourists from Europe, and the like—sequester themselves voluntarily. Nobody acknowledges the absurdly self-referential nature of the place. The backpackers strut with their Teva sandals and North Face knockoffs, pretending they are having an authentic experience, coolly ignoring the other backpackers, in identical outfits, who are trying just as hard to ignore *them*. It's a closed loop, and about as Buddhist as Times Square.

Regret swells up inside me. What am I doing in Kathmandu anyway? I had chosen the city because of its deep Buddhist history. The Buddha was born not far from here. Thousands of Tibetan refugees live in Nepal. And truth be told, the country evokes a certain pathos. When Buddhism migrated from India to Tibet in the eighth century, it transited through Nepal. So, yes, Nepal makes sense. But now, lying on my bed, staring at the ceiling fan going round and round like the endless cycle of death and rebirth, *samsara*, and listening to Steppenwolf blaring from the Maya Bar next door ("Maya" means "illusion," but there is nothing illusory about the decibel level), I slide headlong toward a deeper despair.

Then I see it: a small flyer on the desk. "Want to know your mind better? Come meditate with us. Himalayan Buddhist Meditation Centre." I like the way that sounds, especially the prominent use of the words "Himalayan" and "mind." Anything involving the Himalayas sounds exotic and expansive and vaguely dangerous, even though, so far, the closest I've come to a genuine

Himalayan adventure is the bottle of Everest beer I had with lunch. And as for my mind, yes, I *would* like to get to know it better. We've been drifting apart lately.

I run downstairs to the lobby, I'm so excited. The Nepalese man working the front desk senses my eagerness and, perhaps, I imagine, my blossoming Buddha Mind as well. He suggests I take the hotel's complimentary rickshaw. It will be faster than walking, he says, and, though he doesn't say it, will enable me to avoid all of those hawkers assaulting me with Tiger Balm.

Alan Watts, the British philosopher, calls Buddhism the "religion of no-religion," and he has a point. Buddhists don't believe in God, or at least not in a single, almighty creator God. That's probably why Buddhism is the one religion my atheist friends grudgingly respect. Also, I know the Dalai Lama, know *of* him, and have been impressed the few times I've seen him in person. I love his explosive laugh and playful manner. He just seems to be having a good time up there onstage, like it was all a big game. He exhibits none of the stiffness and covert moralizing endemic among many religious leaders.

And then there is the first of the Buddha's Four Noble Truths: "All is suffering." When I read that I thought—Yes! Finally, here is a religion that gets it, that gets *me*. A religion that acknowledges my way of life, consecrates it. People who meet me, those with the slightest intuitive sense, pick up on my melancholia. I suffer. Mine, though, is not the kind of suffering that I witnessed as a foreign correspondent. That suffering, regrettable as it is, at least has the benefit of authenticity. It is earned suffering.

My suffering is not. It is synthetic, self-inflicted suffering, otherwise known as neurosis. I have no reason to suffer. I live comfortably, if not luxuriously, solidly American middle class, which means I'm better off than 99 percent of the inhabitants of the planet. Other than my brush with gas, and the occasional bout of hypochondria, I am healthy. I have not only a beautiful daughter but also a lovely and loving wife whose numerous attributes include a superhuman capacity to tolerate her neurotic husband. Knowing how fortunate I am, oddly, only compounds my suffering.

Suffering is not all bad, of course. Suffering motivates. On a basic level, it does this the way a throbbing pain in our thumb motivates us to realign our hammer. On a grander scale, suffering motivates us to look beyond this world of dust. No one, as far as I know, has embarked on a spiritual quest because their life was one uninterrupted party. We look for God, however we define Him, because we are suffering and don't know how to stop suffering. We cannot evade suffering, believes Aldous Huxley, only transcend it "by accepting it and passing beyond it." We can accomplish this only by "being converted from righteousness to total selflessness and God-centeredness..." That seems like a tall order. Where does that leave us mere mortals? I wonder.

On the face of it, Buddhism doesn't seem to offer much hope in that regard. It seems like a profoundly negative religion. We are born. We suffer. We die. We're born again, we suffer again, we die again, and so on for a very, very long time. It's the perfect religion for malcontents and cynics, or so it seems. But I wasn't sure. I needed, as the Buddhists say, to investigate.

My Buddhist experience thus far consists mainly of buying vast amounts of Buddhist stuff. I've amassed a sizable collection of laughing Buddhas, tiny statues of a jolly, rotund guy, which I've sprinkled throughout my study; in my living room is my favorite Buddhist acquisition, which I bought in Laos a few years ago. It's a simple bust of the Buddha's head, but it's an especially good one, with great detail. The Buddha's eyes are closed, his lips curled slightly in a pose of perfect serenity. But there's something else going on. One side of the Buddha's mouth is turned upward slightly more than the other, lending a hint, just a hint, of a mischievous, shit-eating quality to the serenity, as if the Buddha is relishing some delicious metaphysical insight about the nature of time and space, or maybe he just got lucky. Either way, every time I look at that statue, which is often, I think, Why, you sly Buddha. You really are blissed out, aren't you? And, being the creature of desire that I am, my next thought is: I want a piece of that bliss *and I want it now.*

I walk into the Himalayan Buddhist Meditation Centre and immediately like what I see: books. Lots of books. Which is odd, because Buddhists don't think much of words. Words are distracting, deceptive, a poor substitute for a genuine insight, or a hug. As William James said, "Knowledge about a thing is not the thing itself." A child doesn't know *about* wetness. He experiences it. Only later does he learn to associate that experience, that sensation, with the word, the symbol, called wetness. The problem, James argued, is that modern man too often substitutes symbols for reality. It's as if we walk into a fine restaurant, sit down—and promptly eat the menu. We live in a mediated world of words and concepts rather than direct experience.

I flip open a book by Lama Yeshe, one of the founders of this meditation center, and, by chance, open to a passage that speaks directly to this point: "The experience of an atom of honey on your tongue is much more powerful than years of listening to explanations of how sweet it is." I find this all fascinating, and true, and make a note to read more about it. No, not read, *experience.* God, I need help.

A smiley Tibetan woman directs me to a vestibule where I remove my shoes. As I discovered in Turkey, there's something about shoes that impedes spiritual progress; Muslims, Sikhs, and Hindus all remove their shoes before entering a house of worship. It is a sign of respect, of course, but also a way to reconnect with the earth, as anyone who has walked barefoot through a carpet of freshly mown grass can attest. I enter a small room and—whoa!—my senses are bombarded. It's like a blitzkrieg in my head. I'm having trouble focusing. The first thing that strikes me is the barrage of colors: rich reds, maroons, purples, and blues, clashing yet somehow soothing at the same time. Thick Tibetan carpets cover the floor. On one wall is a picture of a young Dalai Lama, and below it a *chokse*, a small Tibetan table. It's decorated with fiery dragons and swirls of aggressive colors. Several candles are burning, and there's a row of copper pots, each filled with water and flowers floating in them. Scattered around the room are several gold statues of the Buddha in various poses.

On the floor, about a dozen round, maroon cushions sit neatly on top of yellow rectangular ones. We are told to take a seat; that is, a cushion. I instinctively move toward one of the cushions located in the rear of the room, and begin to slip into observer status. But this time I stop myself. I'm tired of being a spectator, a spiritual voyeur. I plop down in the front of the room and immediately assume the lotus position, which for me is a significant assumption. My legs don't bend that way, so instead I twist myself into what I call a "modified lotus." It looks somewhat like the real thing but is considerably less painful.

Meanwhile, sitting in a genuine lotus position, a cup of tea resting at his arm, is a middle-aged man with grayish hair and stylish glasses. He is trim and fit and, I notice, has very good pores. He is wearing slacks and a crisply pressed dress shirt. He looks like he might work for an advertising agency. Only the beads looped around one wrist belie his Buddhism. The man arises, without saying a word, and then suddenly swan-dives onto the floor, with his arms outstretched over his head then back to his body then outstretched again. He looks like he is swimming on dry land.

Just as suddenly as he started he stops his land-swimming, effortlessly resumes the lotus position, and introduces himself. His name is Antonio, he says, with an indeterminate accent, possibly European. I shift on my cushion, trying to get comfortable.

"This room is a gym," Antonio says. "A mental gym. Here, you have all the equipment you need: your body and your mind. It is the same for everyone. Improvements of the mind are not that easy to see, unlike physically working out. You don't just sit down and close your eyes and then—bang!—you're concentrating. You have to first recognize that there is a problem with the mind; you are a product of your mind. And it's important to be clear why you want to meditate."

Why, I wonder, do I want to meditate? I'm not sure. It is a self-contained activity, just me and my mind, and as much as that thought terrifies me, I know it's exactly what I need. Meditation is, as the late Tibetan lama Chögyam Trungpa said, "a way of un-masking ourselves." I like the way that sounds. Masks are heavy, and they make it difficult to see clearly. For Buddhists, meditation isn't really a choice. "There is no other way of attaining basic sanity than the practice of meditation," concluded Trungpa.

Antonio is unusual, though I'm having trouble putting my finger on exactly how. There's an intensity about him, but unlike with most intense people, Antonio's intensity is free of any hint of aggression. When he speaks, he alternates between distracted flightiness and pure presentness. He's either here, really here, or he's not. Nothing in between.

Antonio continues talking, in his grounded, flighty way, but shifts metaphors. We need to take our minds for a test drive, he says. I like this image and wonder, If my mind were a car, what kind of car would it be? A finicky British one, I decide. A Jaguar, perhaps. Antonio talks for a good fifteen minutes before he even mentions Buddhism. When he does, though, he says something odd: "What you see is not." That line sticks with me, and later I would ask Antonio about it. What did he mean? What you see is not?

"I mean," he said, "if you put it the other way, 'What you see *is*,' then you're fucked."

I laughed, even though I wasn't sure exactly what Antonio meant. Buddhism, I'd soon learn, is often like that. Meanings are hidden, words deceive. What you hear is not.

Finally, it's time to meditate. Spines straight. Eyes three-quarters closed. Chin slightly down. Tongue against the roof of the mouth. Watch the breath. In. Out. In. Out. The breath is the only bodily function that is both involuntary and volitional. We can't control whether we breathe or not but we can control *how* we breathe. In several languages, "breath" and "spirit" share similar roots (like "inspire" in English). In the Upanishads, the ancient Hindu texts, they made absolutely no distinction between breath and spirit. They are one and the same. In. Out. Watch the breath.

The meditation goes very well—for about seven seconds. Then my "monkey mind" takes over or, to use another Buddhist metaphor, my unleashed elephant stampedes. It stampedes in one direction, toward nail clippers. I can't stop thinking about nail clippers. I did not bring any with me and, I fear, my nails will grow to grotesque, Howard Hughes proportions. I'm convinced there are no nail clippers in all of Nepal. I am doomed. This is not a fleeting thought, mind you, but a persistent, recurring one. Breath. Nail clippers. Breath. Nail clippers. Nail clippers. Nail clippers. Breath.

Finally, Antonio rings a little bell and puts me out of my misery. My God, how long was that? Twenty, thirty minutes?

"Five minutes," says Antonio.

Okay, so this enlightenment thing is going to take a little bit longer than I thought. The problem, I conclude, as usual, is not my mind but my location. I need to get out of the Thamel tourist ghetto and closer to the heart of Buddhism. I plot my escape. But first, I decide to buy some books. Yes, books are what I need. I find a great bookstore near my hotel. I love South Asian bookstores. They are cluttered and crowded and utterly without any sense of order. Unintentional places. This particular store has a great selection of Buddhist classics: *The Words of My Perfect Teacher*, *The Way of the Bodhisattva*, *The Tibetan Book of Living and Dying*. I hungrily gather them all up and go to the register to pay. There, I notice a small sign, a Nepali proverb, that reads, "Tell no one the way your mind travels." It strikes me as particularly good advice.

I load the books into my suitcase and check out of my hotel. I am heading across town to a place called Boudhanath. That's where the Buddhists are. I feel the wind at my back now. I have a destination. I have velocity.

My velocity is slowed considerably by the congealed Kathmandu traffic. The little taxi stops and starts, jerks and swerves, more than my mind during meditation. The driver is wearing one of those surgical masks, common in Kathmandu because of the pollution. I'm thinking how nice it is that people here are taking care of their health when he tugs at the mask, lowers one corner, inserts a cigarette, takes a few drags, then replaces the mask. We finally make it to Boudhanath and I instantly fall in love. Boudhanath, I can tell, is a "thin place." Thin places are those rare locales where the distance between Heaven and earth is compressed and you can sense the divine—the transcendent, Buddhists would say—more strongly. Despite the fact that it has been swallowed up by Kathmandu, Boudhanath (Boudha for short) retains the self-contained coziness of a village. Life here revolves, literally, around a giant marshmallow. Well, that's what it looks like to me, a giant white marshmallow, pinched at the top by a giant toddler, and with two giant eyes painted on it. In actuality, it's a stupa, a Buddhist shrine, and those eyes are the All-Seeing Eyes of Buddha. There is some elaborate myth surrounding the stupa's history, but I can't make heads or tails of it. All stupas, though, represent the Buddha Mind, and circling it is said to bring one closer to enlightenment.

At any time of the day, hundreds of people are walking around the Giant Marshmallow. They always walk clockwise—never counterclockwise. Why, I don't know—but they just keep going and going, chanting mantras, kneading their *mala*, prayer beads, and twirling prayer wheels. Tibetan prayer wheels are metal cylinders that contain passages from the *sutras*, the Buddha's teachings. Most prayer wheels are small, not much larger than a cellphone, but I see some here the size of small refrigerators—so large their owners have harnessed them to their waists.

With the flick of a wrist, the prayer wheels turn round and round, while the people walk round and round, a circularity that would make a dervish proud. Buddhists love round things: the mandala or "wheel of life," the prayer wheel, the bulbous stupa, the cycle of death and rebirth. Buddhists talk in circles, too. It's hard to get a straight answer. Maybe that's why, as one American convert told me, the lamas are notoriously tardy and prone to changing their plans at the last minute. If everything is circular, including time, punctuality becomes a matter of perspective. You might be very late, or very early. It all depends on how you look at it.

I roll my luggage (more blessed roundness) over the pavement and think, Yes, I like the circularity of Boudha. If anything, we in the west are too linear, too straight. We could use some more roundness. A few dozen monasteries have sprung up around the stupa, and at least as many shops selling "Happy Buddhist Things," as one store advertised. And then there are the restaurants where you can sip Pinot Noir while gazing into those Buddha eyes. Boudha is a rare and wonderful confluence of the sacred and the profane. I like it here.

I find a hotel directly across from the stupa. The lobby is a bit tired, and the rooms smell funny, but the location is perfect. All I have to do is career down three flights of stairs and then—wham!—I am face-to-face with the Giant Marshmallow. I am suddenly overwhelmed by this strong desire to stay in Boudha. Forever. For me, travel is, oddly, all about nesting. I traverse great distances, catapulting myself far from home, only to re-create home, or some version of it, on the road. I always unpack my bags immediately, filling up the drawers and closets of my hotel room and making sure everything is in its place. I don't know why. Maybe it's because as a child we moved so often—six times in the first six years of my life—that I feel this need to transform every place I encounter, no matter how fleetingly, into home.

Properly nested, I plop down on my hotel bed. I worry that I'm approaching this whole Buddhism thing in a half-assed manner. No, not half-assed. I don't do anything half-assed. Oh, how sweet life would be if that were the case. If I did things half-assed, I could sleep at night. No, I do things seven-eighths-assed. This is much worse, trust me. I line up my prey perfectly in my sights but can't pull the trigger. If I were a lawyer, I'd be terrible at closing arguments. Or take my tennis game. My footwork is excellent, as is my racket preparation. I line up nicely, hit the ball solidly, but no follow-through. That's the story of my life. Seven-eighths-assed. It's a curse, I tell you. I worry this is exactly what is happening now, spiritually speaking, in Kathmandu. I've traveled all this way, exhausted heaps of good karma, as a Buddhist friend put it, found a teacher, sat on a cushion—and then obsessed about nail clippers.

I decide I need a new teacher. Not a European with good pores but an actual Tibetan with wise, leathery skin. I dig out a scrap of paper with a phone number on it. James Hopkins is the friend of a friend of a friend, an investment banker turned Buddhist who now lives here in Kathmandu. I'll bet he knows some lamas. I call James and we agree to meet later that day. That gives me a few hours to rest and catch up on some twenty-five hundred years of Buddhist history. I sprawl out on the bed and crack open a book.

The Buddha was a spoiled child. Not a brat, exactly, but definitely spoiled. Born Siddhartha Gautama, the young prince had it all: gold, horses, women. His father spared no expense on his favorite son. If they had BMWs back then, he would have bought him a fleet on his sixteenth birthday. From the beginning, Siddhartha possessed a feisty self-confidence that bordered on arrogance. The name "Siddhartha" means something close to "mission accomplished," and legend has it that when Siddhartha was born he took seven steps and announced that he would achieve enlightenment in this lifetime. It was the spiritual equivalent of Babe Ruth pointing to the center-field bleachers before hammering a home run.

The Buddha wasn't always the Buddha, of course. "Buddha" is a title. It means, literally, "the Awakened One," or more colloquially, "the Guy Who Woke Up." Buddhists may refer to him as Lord Buddha, but they do not worship the Buddha as a god. He is simply the Guy Who Woke Up. In this sense, Buddhism is the ultimate aspirational religion. Anyone can become that Guy Who Woke Up. The people I see circling the stupa are all Buddhas in training, and they freely admit this. We are training to be Buddhas, they say. I can't imagine a Christian saying, I'm Jesus in training, or a Muslim saying he is a Muhammad wannabe.

Siddhartha's father may have spoiled his son but, like all such parents, he did so with the best of intentions. On his mind, no doubt, was a prophecy. When Siddhartha was born, the soothsayers warned the elder Gautama that his son faced one of two fates. If he stayed at home, he would become a great *Cakkavatti*, or "universal king." If he left home, though, he would become a wandering ascetic and, ultimately, an enlightened being. Siddhartha's father thought universal king sounded like the more promising career track, so he did everything possible to sequester his son. He built high walls around the palace and posted guards. He offered his son every worldly pleasure he could imagine, and a few he couldn't. Of course, Siddhartha, like all teenagers, rebelled. (When I read this, I think that Siddhartha's father should have commanded his son, "Whatever you do, do *not* stay home.") Siddhartha, curious and crafty, snuck out of the palace one day. He saw several sights that shook him to the core: an old man, a sick man, and a corpse. Until then, Siddhartha had no idea that people aged, got sick, and died. This realization hit him like a body blow. Life was one long exercise in decay, followed by death, he realized. There must be a way out of this trap, he thought. But what? He couldn't enjoy life's pleasures until he solved this riddle.

A fourth sight hinted at a solution. He saw a wandering monk, an ascetic wearing a yellow robe and carrying a begging bowl. Who was this man, and what did he know? It was, in fact, a common sight in those days. Siddhartha lived in a voluble, restless time called the Axial Age. People were moving to cities, experimenting with their newly found individualism, and feeling lost. "They were consumed by a sense of helplessness, were obsessed by their mortality and felt a profound terror and alienation from the world," writes Karen Armstrong in her biography of the Buddha. Hmmm. That sounds familiar, I think. I read on. "Much of their pain sprang from insecurity in a world of heightened individualism in the new market economy." This sounds *really* familiar.

The wandering seekers of Siddhartha's time were universally admired. Those who decided to "Go Forth," in the lingo of the time, were seen as pioneers, much like, say, astronauts are today. Siddhartha desperately wanted to join this movement and midwife "a wholly different kind of human being, one who was not dominated by craving, greed and egotism," writes Armstrong.

Family life did not fit into Siddhartha's plans. He called his young son Rahula, or "fetter." He described his house as "dusty" even though it was clean. The dust comprised his possessions and his family, which he saw as impediments to spiritual progress. It's a common condition among spiritual visionaries. Jesus, Confucius, Gandhi also eschewed family life. Late one night, Siddhartha crept upstairs, kissed his sleeping wife and son, and left the palace grounds, never to return.

James Hopkins is tan and fit and looks at least a decade younger than his forty-nine years. Exuding the soft glow of the genuinely happy, he is a man clearly comfortable in his own smooth skin. I like him anyway.

We meet at a café called Flavors. Adjacent to the stupa, it caters to various seekers: solo wanderers like myself; "karma bunnies," as the young westerners studying at the nearby monasteries are known, and the occasional German tour group. We make some small talk. I tell James about my unhappy experience in Thamel, the tourist ghetto. He shakes his head sympathetically, reassuring me that I'm in the right place now. Boudha is for me.

Then I decide to dive right in and ask James how he went from investment banking to Buddhism. James skewers a tomato from his Greek salad, examines it briefly, then unreels his story. He was working in Los Angeles. He was good at what he did, though never, in his mind, good enough. Every day in the brokerage firm they'd announce the rankings, from one to ninety, and when James found that he was, say, number fifteen, he'd think, That is not acceptable. That is simply not acceptable. And so he'd redouble his efforts. He was working thirteen-, fourteen-hour days. He had an apartment in Malibu. He was, as he puts it, an "arrogant asshole."

One day, he met a Japanese agent who was impressed by James's classic American looks. Would he come to Japan to work as a model? Next thing James knows he is in Tokyo, on a hiatus from investment banking, smiling for the camera and earning more money than he was back in L.A. It was in Tokyo that James first encountered Buddhism. He stumbled across a book written by a man named Christmas, an irony that still brings a smile to his face.

The Buddhist way was entirely new to James. He grew up Presbyterian in rural Virginia, went to church twice a week because, well, because that was what everyone did. But here was Buddhism, a religion that didn't believe in God, whose motto was not "Come and believe" but rather "Come and see." James was intrigued.

Back in California now, James was rocketing up the banking ladder, but something was different; *he* was different. His heart wasn't in it anymore. He began taking extended vacations, two or three months at a time. He traveled with his girlfriend to India, Nepal, and Tibet. He was a "*dharma* tourist," hitting all the pilgrimage sites: Lumbini, in Nepal, where the Buddha was born; Bodh Gaya, in India, where he attained enlightenment; and also in India, Dharamsala, home to the Dalai Lama and his government-in-exile. James was hooked on Tibetan Buddhism—at first only with his head but, increasingly, with the rest of him as well.

And so began a pattern—every year James would return to South Asia, with a different girlfriend but the same intention. He wanted to get to the heart of this thing called Buddhism. What was its essence, and was it for him? He read everything he could get his hands on, he meditated, he contemplated. For James, the faith's biggest selling point was the Tibetans themselves. They had lost everything—their homeland, family members in some cases—yet they seemed so happy, genuinely happy. James, a results-oriented money guy, a Master of the Universe, began to suspect that perhaps it was they, not him, who were the true Masters of the Universe.

Meanwhile, his banking career was really taking off and by age forty-three James had amassed enough money so that he never had to work another day in his life. At this point, most investment bankers continue to work anyway because for them it's never really about the money—it's about the sport, about finding an outlet for all of that "disposable libido," as Joseph Campbell puts it.

James, though, wanted to catapult himself clear of himself, someplace far away where he "had no story." People don't pick up and move halfway around the world for the adventure, not that only. They do so in order to un-story themselves. But where to go? He and his current girlfriend drew up a list of a dozen possible cities. They narrowed it down to two, Barcelona or Kathmandu. Barcelona to write poetry (another of James's passions) or Kathmandu to study Buddhism. Next, they drew up a list of pluses and minuses for each city and did the math. Kathmandu won—by one point.

"To convert" means literally "to turn." It is never a decision taken lightly, for every conversion is a betrayal. We betray our family, our God, and sometimes ourselves. Typically, we imagine a conversion begins with an Augustinian moment of despair followed by a sudden transformation "as startling as a thunderclap," as Martin Gardner puts it. That is not how it usually happens, though. It's more gradual. Carl Jung observes that those who, like James, find religion later in life are less likely to experience a thunderclap but, rather, "an intensification of nominally held beliefs." In other words, James Hopkins may have always been a Buddhist; it just took him forty-three years to realize it.

But why Buddhism? Was it merely a coincidence? Might James just as easily have become a Sufi or an evangelical Christian? I don't think so. James is an intellectual, a skeptic. He has what's known as a "quest" personality. That is, someone who seeks knowing full well he will never find definitive answers. Gandhi was a quester. For him, it was *all* trial and error. Gandhi, like all questers, could live with doubt and ambiguity. He believed that, as the late academic Peter Bertocci put it, "to flee from insecurity is to miss the whole point of being human, the whole point of religion." This outlook may run counter to how my atheist friends view the religious—as weak people looking to wrap themselves in a theological security blanket—but it may hew closer to the truth.

James pictured himself enjoying a leisurely life in Kathmandu, sipping tea and reading all those books he never had time to read back home. It didn't work out that way. Buddhism, it turns out, is hard work. He enrolled in the *shedra*—a Buddhist school attached to a monastery. The subjects were esoteric, sometimes mind-boggling, and the monk-teachers unforgiving. It was like a Buddhist version of *The Paper Chase*. "Mr. Hopkins," a monk would bark, pointing at James, "can you tell us the difference between lack of inherent existence and nonexistence?"

I wish I could devote myself so fully to one path the way James has, but I am always consumed with worry. What if I'm on the wrong path? Even as I'm circling the stupa, seemingly present, part of me is somewhere else. One-eighth of me, to be precise. That may not seem like much, but it makes all the difference in the world.

James persevered and was making progress in his Buddhist studies. He felt like he'd finally left his old self behind, had un-storied himself. The monastery, though, was expanding rapidly, and it needed someone who knew the world of finance. The chief lama, the Rinpoche, caught wind of the fact that one of the students fit the bill perfectly. He asked James to help, and of course James couldn't say no. So now James is, once again, a money man. He travels with the lama, meeting wealthy donors and, yes, bankers. His old competitive juices are flowing again, and so is the stress. At the end of the day, James finds himself needing not one but three glasses of wine in order to unwind. He is not happy about this. He came to Kathmandu to get away from the world of money, but it followed him.

For James, Buddhism remains a slippery beast. Some aspects make perfect sense. The law of karma, for instance. Karma means action. It's Newtonian physics applied more broadly to our lives. Every action has an equal reaction or, as James puts it, "You act like a dick, you get dick back." The question is: When? Maybe in five minutes, maybe in five years, or maybe in five lifetimes, and this is where James is not fully on board. Oh, he gets the idea of reincarnation intellectually, but that's it. He asked his teacher about his reservations, and the lama, displaying quintessential Buddhist flexibility, said, in effect, "Don't worry about it. It's not important."

Personally, I like the idea of reincarnation. It's like a free refill. Buddhists, though, see reincarnation entirely differently. For them, it is a mark of failure. ("Wretched birth," the Buddha once remarked.) It's like being kept behind in the seventh grade, over and over. Another life means you didn't get the last one right.

I tell James that the whole lama thing makes me uncomfortable. You are putting your mind—your soul, one might say, though Buddhists don't believe in a soul—in the hands of a stranger. That is not easy for me. I don't even like trusting any one person with my finances or my dental care. How can I trust someone with my spiritual well-being? There are a lot of good teachers out there but plenty of bad ones too. Maybe your teacher is an enlightened being, and maybe he's a homicidal cult leader. Why can't we be our own gurus?

James's eyes widen. It's clearly something he has thought long and hard about. He acknowledges it's tricky, this guru thing. Yes, there are bad gurus out there and, yes, some seekers are looking for a parental surrogate—the loving father they never had, for instance. (The latest research, by the way, backs this up; one study found that most converts had "weak, absent or cruel fathers.")

The problem with going the self-guru route, James says, is that you're investigating your mind, which means your mind is really *investigating itself*, and that is a dodgy situation. Besides, what's important, says James, "is not how you are on cushion but how you behave off cushion."

"Off cushion?"

Yes, he explains, "off cushion" refers to how a Buddhist behaves when he is not meditating. It's one thing to feel compassion for all sentient beings when you are sitting quietly in a meditation hall and another altogether to feel that same compassion when driving in rush-hour traffic and a sentient being cuts you off. I like this off-cushion concept. I ask James if he's a different person, off cushion, since he's discovered Buddhism.

Yes, he says, he is more patient and, crucially, "less of an asshole."

"How's that?" I can't quite picture James as an asshole.

"I used to be angry," James says. "The tiniest thing would set me off, but not anymore." I am struck by how many "spiritual people," for lack of a better term, tell me the same thing: They are less angry now.

I wonder: Is that a legitimate spiritual benchmark, being less angry, less of an asshole? Should churches put on their signs: "Come to Sunday services—be less of an asshole"? It's not a bad idea, actually. Ultimately, if our spiritual practice doesn't make us better people, less asshole-y, what is the point?

Okay, so you're less of an asshole, but are you happy? I ask. I mean, isn't Buddhism a bit of a bummer? All this talk about non-attachment. It strikes me as cold. I tell James about my cat, Mango, who died recently. Mango was a great cat, more than most. When she died, I cried. I suffered. My young daughter suffered too. We didn't enjoy suffering, of course, but it was far preferable to not having loved Mango.

"I think you've confused non-attachment and detachment," he says.

"What's the difference?"

"Detachment is not loving the cat at all. Non-attachment is not being attached to the emotion. You're going to love the cat and love it well, but you're not attached to the loving of the cat. There's a difference."

I take a sip of my wine and ponder that one for a good long while. Loving the cat but not being attached to the loving of the cat. Is such a thing humanly possible? James concedes it is not easy, even for practicing Buddhists. He tells me a story of an accomplished lama who lost a close friend. The lama cried for days. One of his students, seeing his teacher's distress, said, "But, lama, surely you know that your friend was just an illusion."

"Yes," replied the lama. "But he was such a beautiful illusion."

We've been talking for more than two hours. James suggests we circumambulate the stupa, and I like the way that sounds, so much more Buddhist than "walking around the Giant Marshmallow."

We step outside. It's a glorious day. The sky is a deep blue and, for a change, the air is actually breathable. We start to walk, to circumambulate, and it feels good. I tuck in behind James. This is his world. We join the stream of Buddhist pilgrims, tourists, and others circling the stupa, clockwise. I ask James about that. Why clockwise? I brace myself for a deep metaphysical answer. Instead, James explains that in ancient times, when there was no indoor plumbing, people used their left hand to perform their ablutions. They didn't want to expose that hand to the sacred stupa, so they walked clockwise. Sometimes, the simplest explanation is the correct one.

I make some comment about the proliferation of shops selling prayer wheels, Tibetan singing bowls, and other happy Buddhist things. Yes, James observes, "there is a long tradition of selling religious crap near sacred sites." I nod in agreement.

There are plenty of beggars at Boudha. It's a good place to be a beggar, since so many people here are eager to earn karmic merit. James knows all of them. This one is an alcoholic, he says, that one's a sad case, pointing out a man who is literally doubled over, permanently stuck at a ninety-degree angle so that he is forced to stare at the ground all day. James stops in front of a woman who is crouched on the ground. She looks seventy but is probably only fifty. She's gabbing nonstop in Nepali, hands together, imploring James for money. Then I notice her teeth. No, "teeth" is an exaggeration. Her mouth is populated by random chunks of enamel clinging tenuously to her gums. James bends down and hands her a few rupees. He does this gracefully, with dignity, without even a hint of condescension. She seems pleased and smiles.

"It's good practice," says James.

"Practice at what?"

"At being compassionate."

James has a policy of giving only to people who are missing limbs, or a significant number of teeth or, in a recent amendment to his policy, certain mental faculties. This covers much of the population of Boudha's beggars, but not all. He won't give money to alcoholics or troublemakers.

James shows me the temple where his guru, or "heart teacher" as he calls him, worked and lived. He died recently. James says that it's not easy finding a guru; the Tibetan ones play hard to get, testing you, in a way, to see if you are serious.

"Do you want to hear a story about my teacher?" asks James. "Something a bit out there."

Yes, I do.

One night, James says, his teacher appeared to him in a dream.

"You mean, you dreamed about your teacher?"

"No," says James. "This was different. My teacher appeared in my dream, just as real as I'm standing in front of you now and—I can remember it clearly—he said a Tibetan syllable: *phet*."

James woke up with a start. What the hell was *that*? Later that day, when he saw his teacher, he said, "You came to me in my dream and you said *phet*. What did you mean by that?"

Without missing a beat, the lama shot back, "I did not say *phet*. I said *phaim*."

I'm not sure what to make of this story. It seems impossible. I wonder: Is Buddhism just a bunch of mumbo-jumbo? Is James a sucker?

James, sensing my incredulity, says, "I know, I know it sounds crazy. I mean, I'm a fucking investment banker. I don't believe this kind of shit. But it happened."

Buddhists don't fixate on the supernatural. True, the Buddha is said to have performed certain miracles, including a very Jesus-like walk on water. But these miracles are not central to the faith, and many Buddhists pooh-pooh them. There is a quotidian, workman-like quality to Buddhist practice. It's a faith that values regular attendance. Show up every day and examine your own mind. "Fake it until you make it" is their motto. Pretend you're enlightened, visualize it, and one day it will happen. It's like Michael Jordan visualizing a three-pointer and then—swoosh—he makes it. Reports of spiritual fireworks are greeted with suspicion. The religious scholar Huston Smith relays the comments of a western student of Zen that I think capture the Buddhist view: "No paranormal experiences that I can detect. But you wake up in the morning and the world seems so beautiful you can hardly stand it."

When *I* wake up in the morning, the world seems so foreboding I can hardly stand it. I need a change of perspective, and maybe Buddhism can provide that. James promises to help, and perhaps arrange a meeting with his monastery's lama, not because I'm special, but out of simple compassion.

I retreat to my hotel room and stare at the whirling ceiling fan, trying to process James's story. Is he on a genuine spiritual path, or is he merely caught up in the romance of Kathmandu, in the adventure of it all? Is he really "less of an asshole," as he claims, or has he simply transferred his competitive impulse from one venue, investment banking, to another, Buddhism?

Maybe it doesn't matter. James is clearly content. I envy his equanimity. I covet his quiet compassion. Yes, I'm liking Buddhism—and not only for the good skin it apparently produces. (The Buddha himself was said to have "exceptionally clear and bright skin.") I'm liking its do-it-yourself ethos, its emphasis on direct insight rather than blind faith. When most religions assess the validity of a certain spiritual practice or ritual, they ask: Is it God's will? Is it theologically sound? Buddhists ask simply: Does it work? If nothing else, Buddhism is a deeply practical path. Buddhists don't look "out there" for answers but, rather, inside themselves. "Be a lamp unto yourself," the Buddha famously said. I find this liberating—and terrifying. What if my wattage is insufficient?

There's one thing in particular James said that stuck with me. Buddhism, he told me, teaches that "ultimately, there is nothing to do." Nothing to do? Really? If true, what a relief! If there is nothing to do then there's nothing to do wrong. If there's nothing to do then I can stop this chronic striving. If there's nothing to do then I can stop, well, doing. Which would be nice. Because I'm tired. But how to jibe this nothing-to-do claim with the fact that James does so much? So do the Tibetans. They're constantly in motion, prostrating, chanting, circumambulating. It's exhausting just to watch. When I asked James about this frenzied ritual, he dismissed it as, ultimately, unimportant. The rituals, he says, are reminders, "Post-it notes on the brain." Perhaps, but Post-it notes can quickly pile up and overwhelm. Some religions are little more than giant, sticky piles of Post-it notes. Reminders of reminders of reminders of... of what exactly? Nobody can remember.

So, yes, Buddhism appeals to me. It also scares me. It's all about the mind investigating itself, which is like trying to bite your own teeth.

Enough. My head aches. I reach for that great soother of metaphysically strained minds: the remote. Click. A newscaster speaking Nepali. Click. Buxom women in wet saris thrusting their hips comically and singing like chipmunks on speed. Click. The BBC. Ah, nothing like the old, reliable British Broadcasting Corporation to relieve metaphysical angst. The announcers are always so earnest, so detached, not in a Buddhist way but more in a look-at-that-dreadful-thing-happening-so-far-away sort of way. On the BBC, everything is always dreadful, simply dreadful. Even when they don't say it they say it. On this particular day, the dreadfulness is centered somewhere in Colorado. Something about a "balloon boy." Judging by the way the announcer says "balloon boy," as if it were part of some shared vocabulary, I take it this story has been unfolding for a while. Facts are streaming in but they are disjointed, jumbled. A boy is missing, that much is clear. He may or may not be in a balloon gondola that is at this very moment hurtling across the state of Colorado. Balloon Boy's parents look worried. The police look worried. And of course the BBC announcer looks worried.

What, I wonder, would the Buddha make of Balloon Boy? Nothing is real, everything is impermanent, he taught, so he'd probably say we shouldn't take it all too seriously. Then again, the Buddha urged compassion for all sentient beings, so I suppose he'd say we should help Balloon Boy. My head is spinning again. I switch back to the singing chipmunks in wet saris but soon tire of that and decide to read more about the Buddha.

Siddhartha wandered the cities and villages of the Indus Valley.

He quickly plugged into the spiritual circuit and joined a group of fellow ascetics. He was a quick study. He achieved trance-like states that, while pleasurable, were always temporary and, therefore, Siddhartha concluded, of little value. He, along with several other ascetics, engaged in self-mortification, believing this was the path to liberation. Siddhartha survived on a single cup of pea soup each day, slept on mattresses made of nails, and held his breath for long periods of time. He became emaciated. He reached for his side and actually felt his spine. When he touched his head, clumps of hair fell into his hand. His head ached from all that breath-holding.

He was near death when a young woman offered him some lentils. Siddhartha accepted, and slowly nursed himself back to health. His fellow ascetics did not approve of Siddhartha's decision. "Oh, look at Siddhartha eating lentils and sleeping on an actual floor," they must have said. "He's gone soft."

On his own now, Siddhartha forged a new path, which he called the Middle Way. Neither too indulgent nor too depriving. He sat under a Bodhi tree, in what is now the Indian state of Bihar, and vowed not to leave until he "attained the supreme and final wisdom." He meditated. He fended off Mara, the demon of delusion, and early one morning Siddhartha announced that "It" had been liberated. Not "I" but "It." That word choice is significant. Siddhartha, now a Buddha, had thoroughly demolished his ego and attained Nirvana.

What do we know about Nirvana? Very little, actually. The Buddha was reluctant to talk about something that was beyond words. When he did, he often spoke of it in negatives. Nirvana is not a feeling. It is not a thought. It just is. Nirvana—literally "to put out," like snuffing out a candle—is a pleasant or even blissful state but beyond that we know precious little.

I close my books and ponder this. Buddhists spend their life, several lives actually, striving to attain enlightenment, Nirvana, yet nowhere are they told exactly what this Nirvana is. Christian scripture offers detailed descriptions of Heaven, as does the Koran, right down to the precise number of virgins (seventy-two) that await us in the afterlife. But Buddhism, this faith that supposedly takes nothing on faith, says when it comes to Nirvana, "Trust us." Buddhism, in other words, asks us to take a journey to an unknown destination. No wonder I'm drawn to it.

I pursue my enlightenment the way I pursue everything—frenetically, urgently, and in a way designed to maximize annoyance of others. As usual, fear plays a starring role; I feel as if I have no margin of error. I don't need just any guru or lama, I need *the best* guru. But where to find this perfect teacher? I hear about a meditation school in Pokhara, a short flight from Kathmandu, but when I call the place no one answers, and later I'd catch wind of "shady Belgians" running the school. I have successfully steered clear of shady Belgians thus far in life and I'm not about to ruin that perfect track record now.

I meet with a hip young Indian named Dinesh, who tells me about a wise monk who lives in a remote part of Nepal. I'm intrigued, assuming reflexively that the more remote the monk, the wiser. How do I find this wise monk? I ask.

"You take two flights," explains Dinesh, "then a seven-hour drive through winding mountain roads, and finally a two-day trek through remote terrain."

I'm thinking, Well, this must be one very wise monk indeed, when Dinesh, sensing my burgeoning excitement, says tantalizingly, "You might have an experience."

Yes, exactly! An experience! An unmediated, non-intellectual experience, the kind that William James could only fantasize about. I'm ready to sign up, to make this three-day journey, this expedition, to see the wise monk, when Dinesh adds that, by the way, the monk might not be home; he might be off on pilgrimage somewhere. Nobody knows for sure because the monk, of course, doesn't have a phone. Suddenly the wise monk seems like a long shot, a chance I can't afford to take.

I'm back to square one. The problem, I discover, is that all the good lamas are in America. It's not the law of karma that's at work but, rather, the law of supply and demand. The lamas have followed the money. More than one person tells me to hop on the next flight to California or Colorado. "That's where you'll find the lamas," they say. "You flew in the wrong direction, man." No, I've already tried that. It didn't go so well. There is value, I believe, in going to the source. "Have you considered Wayne?" suggests Manju, a well-known Nepalese writer. "Wayne is very wise."

"Wayne? Which part of Tibet is Wayne from?"

"The Staten Island part."

I see. This is not what I had in mind, of course, but Wayne has been living in Kathmandu for the past thirty years, which practically makes him a local. Besides, I'm getting desperate. I agree to meet this Wayne of Staten Island. Four of us—me, Wayne, his wife, Sally, and Manju—convene at a Japanese restaurant known for its "recognizable dishes" and pleasant garden, a respite from the noise and pollution of Kathmandu's unintentionally insane streets.

Wayne is wearing a white tank top, his graying hair pulled back tight in a ponytail. He greets me with a soul handshake, which I haven't seen since 1975, which makes sense since that was the last time Wayne lived in the United States. He and Sally were in Berkeley, studying and searching for the Infinite Whatever, when they stumbled onto a talk given by a visiting lama. It was held in a giant aircraft hangar. "We were different when we left that hangar than when we entered," says Wayne.

Some sort of irreversible force was set in motion that day. Wayne drove all the way to Staten Island, said goodbye to his parents, and hopped on a flight for India. Wayne and Sally spent their first year at an ashram; Sally meditated, while Wayne spent most of the year crouched over a toilet. Eventually, his intestines acclimated. Somehow—the details are a bit fuzzy—they landed in Kathmandu, and haven't left since.

I want to say that I instantly like Wayne of Staten Island, but that's not true. In fact, I dislike him. (Later, I'd be told this is a good sign; the less you like your teacher at first, the more likely he's the one for you; it's sort of like dating.) I detect a standoffish vibe, a reluctance to share his hard-earned cosmic insights with a spiritual upstart like myself. I act deferential, though, asking about my meditation practice. What first steps would he recommend?

"First steps are often last steps," he says. I nod knowingly, but in fact I don't know—have no idea, really—what he means. A lot of things Wayne says are like that; at first they sound vaguely profound but upon closer inspection turn out to be simply vague. Like when he tells me, "You need to be thrown back against your own experience." That one strikes me not only as obtuse but also painful. I tell Wayne that I have only a few weeks in Kathmandu and I'm eager to make some serious spiritual headway.

"Meditation is like a mortgage," he says.

"You mean I'm likely to default?"

"No, you have to give yourself a thirty-year trajectory."

"But I don't have that kind of time."

"Look," says Wayne, reaching for a napkin. "Can you draw a stick figure?"

"Not very well, but yes." And I do, I draw this pathetic little kindergarten stick figure on the napkin.

"Good. That's all you need. You are a stick figure."

I am a stick figure? I don't get it and, after slurping my *udon* noodles, decide to steer the conversation in a more philosophical direction.

Isn't Buddhism a profoundly negative religion, I ask, given all that talk of suffering and emptiness?

No, says Wayne of Staten Island, Buddhism is the most positive religion in the world. There's no original sin, and therefore no guilt either. I wonder: Can Buddhism really be classified as a religion if there's no guilt involved? I keep this thought to myself and instead ask about the Buddhist emphasis on suffering. Isn't that defeatist?

No, says Wayne, it's realistic. The Buddha acknowledged that life is suffering, but he also offered a way out. Just the way a doctor might diagnose a disease then provide a cure. The Buddha was an optimist.

I ask Wayne if he believes in God. It seems like a reasonable question of a man who has spent the better part of half a century on a spiritual journey, but I immediately sense I have committed some terrible Buddhist faux pas.

"God's been done," Wayne replies tersely. "You need new questions."

"Okay," I say, trying to recover. "What does God mean to you?"

"It means nothing to me," he snaps back.

After some gentle prodding, Wayne does acknowledge the existence of the "unfathomable." I consider that a small victory and return to my noodles.

After lunch, we continue our conversation on the street, as Wayne and Sally steer me toward my hotel. We have to shout over the traffic, and I have an especially hard time hearing Sally through her mask, a colorful, elaborate affair, with air filters poking out on all sides. It looks like something a clown might wear if asked to perform at an asbestos site. "Be careful," says Wayne, speaking of the traffic, I think, or maybe my spiritual quest, or perhaps life in general. I'm not sure. We say goodbye, and when I turn around a few seconds later, they are gone, subsumed in the thick smog.

That evening, back at my hotel, sipping Johnnie Walker Black Label and smoking little cigars, I wonder: Is Wayne the right teacher for me? He's not exactly what I had in mind, guru-wise. I had envisioned a wizened lama with twinkly eyes who promised secret wisdom, not a ponytailed Jewish guy who speaks in riddles. Then again, maybe what I see is not. Maybe I should give Wayne a chance.

Robert Thurman, the Buddhist scholar and practitioner, writes of "patterns of meaningfulness." He's describing religion but could just as easily be referring to travel. Travel is often misconstrued for escapism, but that is not right, or rather it is only half right. We fling ourselves halfway around the globe not to fall apart but to come together, to create new patterns of meaningfulness. Every traveler has a routine. Mine at Boudha is this: I wake at 5:30 a.m., splash some water on my face then stumble downstairs, past the guard pretending he wasn't just sleeping, out the front door, and join the already significant number of people circling the Giant Marshmallow. I've grown to appreciate mornings. At dawn, anything seems possible; disappointment rarely shows its face before noon.

At this hour, too, there are no tourists. It's just me and a few hundred Tibetans, going round and round, always clockwise. It feels good to walk, to sense the ground beneath my feet, to take in the "Suchness" of the place, as a Buddhist would put it. The light is milky and soft, the sun only beginning to peek above the horizon. I hear the clickety-clack of prayer wheels, the murmur of mantras, the flutter of pigeons flapping their wings, the clanking of store shutters yanked open, the chortle of spoken Tibetan. And always, that soundtrack to Boudha, seeping out of every trinket shop and *chai* stand, or hummed aloud by the circumambulators: *Om Mani Padme Hung*. It is the best-known of the Tibetan mantras. It means literally "Hail to the Jewel in the Lotus." The lotus flower grows in muck and mud yet blossoms clean and beautiful. It's a nice, Buddhist sentiment—the world, I suppose, being the muck and we being the flower—but what I like most about it is simply the way it sounds in Tibetan, the vibrations. The mantra worms itself into my mind, and I find myself chanting it without realizing I'm doing so.

Sound is more primal than visuals. Our ears wander less than our eyes. That is why so many religions contain auditory components: Christian hymns, shamanic drumming, Koranic recitations, and, of course, Buddhist mantras. Tibetan, along with Sanskrit and Arabic, is a vibrational language. The words convey meaning on a primal, intuitive level. A mantra is, as Lama Yeshe puts it, "inner sound." Or as James said of his own mantra, assigned to him by his heart teacher, "I feel every syllable in my body."

I'm hearing voices. James's in particular. I recall his advice to visualize enlightenment, like Michael Jordan making a free throw. The truth is, during my short-lived basketball days, I was always much better at rebounding than shooting. In football, I was always a receiver, never a quarterback. I'm very good at responding to objects, reacting to phenomena already in motion. I'm much less good at initiating. Spiritually speaking, I see how this is a problem. I'm waiting for a push, when maybe I need to push myself, to create my own momentum. I decide to start with a prayer wheel, one of the many that line the perimeter of the stupa. I curl my fingers around its metal base and jerk my wrist. It moves. A start, I think.

I continue to walk, round and round, until my legs tire and my mind settles. That's what I like about this circumambulating. It's open-ended, freestyle. There's no priest or rabbi dictating the prescribed number of circuits. You walk until you no longer desire to do so.

On my eighth lap, or maybe my ninth, I pull over like I'm exiting a freeway and dip into my breakfast spot, an unassuming place called the Saturday Café. It has a nice patio with a spot-on view of the Giant Marshmallow. I take my seat—always the same seat, close to the stupa but not too close—order the banana pancakes, and crack open a book. Today it's one by Lama Yeshe. At one point he says, "Basically, your mind is weak." I'm wondering how he knows that. Have we met? Now he is talking about the ego, that thing that schools and parents try to fortify in the name of "self-esteem." Only Lama Yeshe, like all Buddhists, believes that the ego is the enemy. "We dedicate all our energy to our ego and what do we get in return? What does our ego offer us? Mental pollution. It brings us a foul suffocating smell in our minds [so] that there's hardly room to breathe."

He has a point. We strive to meet our goals, exceed our objectives, and yet we're miserable. There is another way, he continues, a way that leads to—and this bit I love—"the inner nightclub of everlasting joy." That is one club I would definitely frequent. And then I wonder: Is there a cover charge at the Inner Nightclub of Everlasting Joy? Bouncers? Buddhists, I suppose, would say yes, there is a cover charge: diligent meditative practice. That is the price you must pay in order to enter. And yes, there is a bouncer. Your ego. It's a particularly treacherous bouncer, one that pretends to be your friend but then beats you silly.

I put the book down, sip my American coffee, and take in the scene below. Several older women are prostrating. Arms stretched outward, diving to the ground in a sweeping motion. Then up again. Over and over. Buddhist calisthenics. One woman's been at it for a good hour now. To an unknowing observer, it looks like they are worshipping the Giant Marshmallow. They are not. The gesture is another Post-it note on the brain, an exercise in humility, a reminder that we do nothing, *are* nothing, by ourselves. I very much like the idea of prostrating. That's the problem. I like the idea of things more than I like the things themselves.

Later that day, James and I meet for coffee. I ask him how

I should circumambulate the stupa. Is there a proper technique, other than visualizing enlightenment, which frankly is too nebulous for me?

"You don't need to do anything," he says. "There is an energy at the stupa."

Ah, the E-word. I was waiting for this. Followers of eastern religions, not to mention the New Age movement, are fond of this word and use it promiscuously. "But there is energy everywhere," I politely counter. "What's special about stupa energy?"

"It's special in the way that Jimi Hendrix's guitar is special. It does something to the way you see the world."

I'm pondering this when James, a twinkle in his eye, adds, "Of course you could come to the stupa and just check out the ass."

The next day I decide to send Wayne an e-mail expressing my humble eagerness to work with him on my meditative practice. Wayne replies in verse as, I learn, he always does:

> if you want to learn to meditate
> I can teach you
> a more than basic technique
> in 3 to 5 sittings
> early mornings
> or late afternoons work best

The next morning, I stumble down the stairs and flag a taxi. I'm excited about my first session with Wayne but also apprehensive. I keep thinking about what he said when I first met him: *You need to be thrown back against your own experience.* It sounds so...uncomfortable. I'll be placing my soul—no, not my soul, of course, I don't have one, the Buddhists believe—my spiritual fate in his hands. What do I really know about Wayne? What if he's a fraud?

The taxi stops. We've arrived at the temple, the landmark near Wayne's house, where he suggested we meet. It's a Hindu temple and a particularly ghoulish one. On one wall is an inlaid statue of a skeleton; it looks like something straight out of one of those haunted-house rides at amusement parks. I'm sure there is an interesting story behind the skeleton, Hinduism being replete with interesting stories, but how, I wonder, will it quiet my mind? Buddhism, Alan Watts once said, is "Hinduism stripped for export," and he had a point. Buddhism is a streamlined faith.

I spot Wayne, loping up the hill, a baseball cap on. We shake hands—the conventional way this time—and I follow him down a winding road, past a little barbershop and a tiny vegetable stand, the eggplants and cauliflower sunning themselves in plastic bowls while flies hover overhead. We arrive at a gate that leads to a garden that leads to a house. Inside, it's cozy and nicely decorated. It looks like they've been living here a long time. Wayne grabs two ratty cushions and a wine bottle filled with water. Wayne is a Buddhist but no monk. He clearly enjoys wine and, he tells me, one and a half cups of French-press coffee each morning.

We head up to the roof. I like roofs. There's something vaguely delinquent about being up on a roof, as if you're trespassing, even if you're not. This particular roof looks out, sort of, on the Himalayan foothills. When Wayne and his wife moved here many years ago, the vista was clearer, but new construction and smog have conspired to obscure the view.

We sit on a ledge. The sun feels good. Off in the distance, I hear the bleep of car horns. Wayne explains that he takes a "secular approach" to meditation. He's not going to teach me Buddhism. He's going to teach me meditation, though, he adds tantalizingly, if I meditate properly the odds are good I will reach many of the same insights that the Buddha did. I need not have any Buddhist predilections, he says. Except for one. "You are undertaking this practice not just for yourself but for all sentient beings."

"Wayne, I have to be honest. I'm doing this for myself."

"I know, but that's only because you're the first person you met. The circle will expand." That bit of business dispensed with, Wayne continues. "Many people bring a grasping to meditation when it's about not grasping. You are working on the distinction between thought and mind. You are weaning yourself off your thoughts."

"So I want to get rid of thoughts?"

"Not get rid of," snaps Wayne, karate-chopping the thick Nepali air for emphasis. "That 'get rid of' is a thought. Just be with the body. Check in with the body. Rely on the body. The body knows."

"The body knows?"

"Yes. The body is not stupid. Everybody says the body is stupid and the mind is smart, but it's not that way. The body is simple and wise already. It's taking care of itself. It's your final teacher."

He asks me to draw another stick figure, which I do.

"Think of your body as a stick figure. Legs, arms, torso. That's what we're going to work with. Keep coming back to that. You're a bag of bones. And the great thing about your body is that you carry it with you wherever you go."

It seems odd to me that Wayne is focusing so much on the body. I never thought of Buddhism as an especially physical religion. In fact, I've always considered it very much a religion of the mind, monks sitting perfectly still and that sort of thing. But this is faulty Cartesian thinking, separating mind and body, as if they were two strangers who happened to be living in the same house, rather than two aspects of the same person. Every religion, in fact, uses the body: the whirling dervishes of Sufism, of course; the *tai-ji* of Taoism; the ecstatic singing of Christian revival; the rhythmic dav-

ening of Jewish prayer. The body is what we have to work with. It
is not inferior to our minds. In a way, it *is* our minds.

Wayne is a font of useful information, like when he tells me that
I can get a free massage anytime; my mind can massage my body,
he says. I'm skeptical and say as much.

"Move your sensation to your fingers. What do you feel?"

"Tingling."

"Yes, now move the sensation from your fingers to your butt."

I do and, sure enough, I now have a tingly butt. I have a few
more questions about this free massage and how it works but
Wayne asks me to hold off. He has something important to say.

"You're not training for a performance where you have to give
100 percent every time. You're not observing, you're experiencing. Don't judge the experience, and don't judge the judging. Now,
what was your question?"

"I forgot."

"Good," says Wayne, "you've got it," and smacks me on the
back with surprising force. "Okay, shall we meditate?"

"Why not," I say, deciding it's better not to mention how my
first attempt at meditation went.

Wayne asks me to choose a cushion, and I freeze. My meditation
career, my path to enlightenment, nearly ends right there, on
Wayne's roof. I can't choose a cushion. In my mind, this is a crucial
decision—which cushion is best? Finally, I decide on the more tattered of the two.

"Okay, your eyes are slightly open, your awareness is in your
heart. And then you just let it go and sit there for five minutes."

And so we sit on our tattered cushions, side by side, and meditate. I'm incredibly self-conscious. I'm convinced that Wayne is
inside my head, observing my churning mind. Then I imagine myself in a helicopter above the roof. I wonder what we look like, two
middle-aged Jewish guys, wearing baseball caps, sitting on a roof

in Kathmandu, with our eyes closed, or nearly closed, doing nothing. Of course Wayne would say we are not doing nothing. We are doing everything, the only thing, and nothing, too. Wayne would also say that I'm into my story again, and I need to return to my body. It's funny. I thought, I've spent all of my life in my body and here is Wayne telling me that, no, I haven't. My mind spends very little time in my body. Where exactly it hangs out, I couldn't tell you. But I suspect it's been up to no good.

"How is it going?" Wayne asks.

"Good," I lie.

"Any distracting thoughts?"

"Maybe a few."

"Don't judge it, sense it. Just notice what happens."

"Just experience."

"That's right. Just be in your body."

"But my body isn't doing anything."

"It's doing a lot. It's breathing. Sense your accomplishment."

"Accomplishment?" I ask, nonplussed.

"Yes, you've accomplished a lot by sitting here for five minutes."

"So, we...meditated?"

"Some core of meditation has been touched."

I take that for a yes.

I confess to Wayne that I'm having difficulty stilling my mind. "If you could get inside my head then you would see what is going on."

"I don't need to get inside your head. I have enough in my own head. Look, meditation is so ridiculously simple. That's why people trip over it and never learn it."

But it doesn't seem simple to me. It seems very complicated.

"The point is, when you take up a practice let it go," says Wayne.

"Let what go?"

"The practice."

"I thought the whole point *is* the practice. Why would I let it go?"

"You're letting go of the form that you projected into the practice."

"I don't understand."

"You're doing something."

"Yes, I'm meditating."

"But the key goal is not to meditate. You have to meditate for twenty years in order not to meditate."

The contradictions are infinite. Beyond beyond. I take a deep breath. "So I'm trying to meditate but I don't want to meditate because I'm not really meditating because meditating is not doing anything?"

"No, you're doing something."

"What am I doing?"

"Non-doing."

"How can I do non-doing?"

"By doing."

At this point, I suggest we take a vodka break. Wayne offers me water instead, and I suppose that will do. I notice one of Wayne's cats sitting a few yards away. He looks so serene that I swear he is engaged in some sort of feline meditation. I point this out to Wayne, who concedes, "Yeah, there's something going on there." Cats make great Buddhists. They practice mindfulness, and are certainly aware that, ultimately, there is nothing to do. Cats do not, as far as I can tell, suffer. Yet, by dying before we do, they teach us painful yet valuable lessons about the nature of attachment and impermanence. Maybe the Buddhists have it wrong; maybe, if you accumulate enough good karma in this lifetime, you come back as a cat.

We agree to meet in a few days. In the meantime, Wayne wants me to practice meditating twice a day. I agree to do that, and feel surprisingly buoyed by that simple commitment. I'm going to do it, going to get reacquainted with my mind, even if it kills me.

Which it might. All of this thinking about not thinking. It's exhausting. I return to my hotel room, plop on the bed, and click on the one device guaranteed to ensure that no thinking takes place: the television. Balloon Boy is back and, judging by the somber tone of the BBC announcer's voice, the situation has grown even more dreadful. Balloon Boy is fine, unharmed, but doubt is swirling around the story. The officials look less worried and more angry. The boy's parents look defensive. The story has entered a sort of *bardo* stage, a nether land between incarnations. We had believed one narrative. We were, as a Buddhist would say, attached to that narrative. Now we're not sure what to believe.

My phone rings. It's James, with good news. The Rinpoche at his school has agreed to meet me. I'll have only a few minutes with him, but James assures me this is a rare opportunity, a sign that I must have accrued a mother lode of good karma in a previous lifetime.

The Rinpoche's name is Chokyi Nyima. He has a loyal following and a formidable reputation. He once met Cher, who supposedly asked, "Don't I look beautiful?" The Rinpoche replied, "You look like a pile of decaying bones." I met one of his students, an earnest American named Gerry, who told me that the first time he met the Rinpoche the lama handed him a piece of chicken. I don't eat meat, Gerry said. Well, you do now, the lama said. I guess I do, said Gerry, and promptly tucked into the chicken, thus ending a decade of vegetarianism. Oh, and the Rinpoche may be clairvoyant.

So on the morning of my scheduled appointment, I am both excited and nervous. James and I meet for breakfast at a café beforehand, where he briefs me on what to expect.

"Do you have the offering?" he asks.

Yes, I say, pulling out of my bag an envelope containing a thousand rupees (about fifteen dollars). I slip the envelope back into my bag, feeling a bit like I'm about to embark on some dangerous espionage mission. We finish our breakfast and walk through winding side streets to the monastery. Out front, people are milling about. Then suddenly James perks up, his eyes brighten, and his spine stiffens. There he is, the Rinpoche. He is wearing ordinary monk's robes, nothing special. He is quite short, and when he turns I notice that he is wearing a pair of Gore-Tex Ecco boots under his robes. This makes sense, given the muddy streets of Boudha, and, not for the last time, I admire the Tibetans' deeply practical streak.

I'm ushered upstairs, told to take off my shoes, then led into a room. The walls are covered with *thankas*, Tibetan art that depicts the wheel of life and other Buddhist concepts. There are statues and trinkets and paintings everywhere; my eyes don't know where to focus. The Rinpoche is seated on a slightly raised platform, so that he is a few inches higher than anyone else in the room. In front of him is a small table covered with offerings: apples, milk, envelopes of cash. I am maybe twenty yards away, waiting in a line of people who are also here to see him. A young Dutch woman approaches the Rinpoche, lowering her head as she does. Clearly nervous, she mumbles something about the world needing more love. It's the kind of generic statement that is hard to argue with, but the Rinpoche shoots back, "Wisdom first, then love." Frazzled, she says something else I can't make out then steps away.

I wait as more people—westerners, Tibetans, Nepalese—plop down their offerings and engage in a brief conversation with the Rinpoche. Some people, like me, are seeking spiritual guidance; others have more earthly concerns. Is it safe to fly next Friday? Is next Tuesday an auspicious day to start a new business? Sometimes he answers right away; other times he throws some dice, then consults white scrolls before giving his answer. He is guru, therapist, and soothsayer, all rolled into one small package.

I notice that the offerings circulate. The Rinpoche gratefully takes, say, an envelope, from one person but then hands it to the next person, so that the offerings are constantly recycled. It's quite ingenious. The people making the offerings accrue karmic merit, and also get something tangible.

As my turn approaches, I grow increasingly nervous. This is a rare opportunity to acquire spiritual insight from a possibly enlightened being, someone so fearless he has stared down both Mara, the demon of delusion, *and* Cher. It's a chance to hop on the express lane to enlightenment, gain entry to that Inner Nightclub of Everlasting Joy. I'm afraid I might blow it.

My anxiety is heightened by the fact that I can't get a fix on the Rinpoche. At times, he has an explosive, gruff manner. He doesn't talk to people so much as bark at them. But he also displays a more nurturing side; sometimes he sounds like a Jewish mother. "You need to walk more," he says to one person. "You look tired. Are you getting enough sleep?" he says to another. He also reveals a self-effacing quality. "People believe we lamas have some kind of energy or power or special vibration, but believe me, we don't. I'm jittery," he says, holding up his trembling hand to the sound of giggles. These lamas are no cardboard saints. They are quirky, funny, rude. Real.

Finally, it is my turn. I approach the Rinpoche. James introduces me, and the lama greets me by looping a white scarf, a *kata*, around my neck. I hand him the envelope of cash, which he adroitly places on the table alongside the apples, oranges, and biscuits. He then places a white powdery substance in my palm. I just stand there, staring at it, not sure what to do. James nudges me and whispers, "You're supposed to eat it." I do. It tastes like nothing. (Later, James would explain that it was a *dutsi*, or "precious pill," and supposedly promotes long life.)

James explains to the Rinpoche that I am traveling the world, "shopping for God," a shorthand I've used to describe my search. The Rinpoche shoots me a sharp look of disapproval. I instinctively recoil, taking a half step backward.

"What is this? Shopping for God?" he says. His expression is that of someone who has just eaten something extremely bitter and can't decide whether to swallow it or spit it out.

"Well, Rinpoche," I say, trying to save face, "shopping is just a metaphor. I am searching, seeking God." The Rinpoche still looks displeased, and I'm vaguely aware of a murmur of nervous laughter in the room.

"It's a bit limited, don't you think?" he says.

"Oh no, Rinpoche, I am searching for God *everywhere*. All over the world."

Then it dawns on me. It's not the shopping part of my expedition that he objects to but the God part. That is what he finds "a bit limited." I am stunned. Leave it to a Tibetan lama to call God a bit limited.

Tibetan Buddhists do believe in gods; they just don't think too highly of them. These are lowercase gods. While they do enjoy certain supernatural powers and live much longer than we humans, they are still subject to *samsara*, the perennial cycle of death and rebirth. Better to be an enlightened human than an imperfect god. Such an enlightened human, the Buddha said, "even the gods envy." It is a counterintuitive, seemingly blasphemous concept, this notion of Man residing in a higher place than the gods, but one that intrigues me.

I have time for one question. I blurt out something about my doubts. With so many religions out there, how do I know if Buddhism is the one for me?

"You need to do three things," the Rinpoche says. "Investigate, contemplate, meditate."

Then that's it. My time is up. I'm ushered to a cushion and *chokse*, where I'm served tea while the Rinpoche attends to his other guests. "You managed to maintain your dignity," someone whispers to me reassuringly. I'm not so sure. Meeting a revered lama is like having sex with a woman whom you've fantasized about for a long time. There's the rush of excitement, the I-can't-believe-this-is-actually-happening feeling, the heightened sensory perception, much fumbling of opening moves, a desire to prolong the moment, and, inevitably, disappointment. As I peel myself off the floor and out of the lama room, I'm thinking: Is that all there is? Where's the flash of insight? Where's my Inner Nightclub of Everlasting Joy?

It turns out, though, the Rinpoche is not done with me yet. Perhaps sensing my disappointment, he's invited me to his regular lecture afterward, hinting that he will answer my question more fully there.

We move to a large hall, which is decorated in Early Tibetan Garish. There are maybe a hundred people here, most of them longtime students, as well as a few scraggly backpackers here for the first time. I take a seat—a cushion, that is—alongside James and listen.

"We don't practice Buddhism as a normal religion," the Rinpoche says, speaking through an interpreter. My mind wanders. I'm getting only fragments. "Our mind is like a feather in the wind." Yes, a feather. "We have to drop constructs but dropping constructs is itself a construct."

I shift my weight but can't get comfortable. Why do we have to sit on the floor, I wonder. Why can't we absorb this ancient wisdom in something more comfortable? I look over at James. He is bolt upright, locked in a perfect lotus position, clearly rapt and absorbing every word of the Rinpoche's wisdom into his perfect, Buddhist pores.

What the Rinpoche says next, though, gets my attention. He says—and I swear he is looking right at me—that nothing is real. "Everything you are experiencing is a delusion. All of these sense impressions of things we've thought about or what we have experienced is something that appears real but isn't really there. Just like when we're under the influence of a drug or like what you see in a dream, as real and as insubstantial as what you see in a dream. Your whole life is just a dream! What do you say to that?"

I know this is supposed to broaden my mind, to expand my perspective, but instead it just terrifies me. My mind races back to the events of April 1994. I was living in India at the time and working on a story about a flying eye hospital. These doctors fly on an old DC-8 to developing nations like India, performing eye surgery. It was what we in the news business call a "feel-good" story. But I wasn't feeling good. Something was wrong, very wrong. I couldn't sleep, and the left side of my face was numb, or maybe that was just my imagination, I wasn't sure. I wasn't sure of anything. The ground beneath my feet was sliding, melting. This is it, I thought, I'm finally going insane. It's in my genes. Every family has a few loose screws; mine has a hardware store's worth.

All of this was swirling around in my mind, like a Kansas tornado, when I hopped into a shared taxi. My fellow passenger was an Indian woman who intuitively sensed that something was not right with the American sitting next to her. It's easy to confess to strangers, so that's what I did. I told her about my sleeplessness, about the melting earth, about how nothing seemed real.

"You might be having a waking dream," she said matter-of-factly.

"A waking dream? What's that?"

"It's when you think you're awake but you're not. You're dreaming. In fact, you might be dreaming right now."

Well, that did it. That sent me over the edge. Right over. I honestly didn't know if I was awake or dreaming. Maybe I was dreaming that I was awake or awake but thinking that I was dreaming. I couldn't catch my breath, then suddenly my hands and feet went numb. I couldn't feel a thing. The numbness crept up my legs and arms, and then I couldn't move. I was paralyzed. The Indian woman took me to my hotel, where the ophthalmologists from the flying eye hospital carried me to my room and then shot me up with something. I slept for two days. When I finally woke up, the doctors asked me what medicine I had been taking. Only these antimalarial pills, I said. That was it. I'd had a psychotic reaction to the medicine. I wasn't dreaming after all. I was real. But now here is this Rinpoche telling me that I am not real, and that my whole life is a dream.

After the lecture, I'm feeling disoriented. I need to get back on solid, familiar ground, so I walk to the Hyatt Hotel that has sprouted incongruously in Boudha. It sits behind a wall, fortress-like, hinting at earthly comforts inside. Yes, this is what I need, the familiar artifice of a five-star hotel. I rap on the metal gate and the guard, once ascertaining that I possess the requisite degree of whiteness, lets me in. I use the gym, running and running on the treadmill as if I were being chased by hungry ghosts, hoping to clear my head of all this unreality and impermanence. It feels good to sweat, to be, as Wayne would put it, in the body.

Afterward, I'm sitting in the steam room when a Tibetan man introduces himself. I explain what I'm up to, searching—not for God, I don't make that mistake again—for the Great Something, the Infinite Whatever. Sonam—that's his name—takes this in stride. I imagine the Hyatt steam room sees a lot of western spiritual seekers taking a break from all that heavy karmic lifting. I ask Sonam if he meditates. No, he says, he's too busy. The lamas meditate but they don't have a family or a business to look after. Sonam, though, does circle the stupa each morning. It's good exercise, he says, patting his not-unsubstantial belly and smiling as if to say, "I still have work to do."

The next morning, sure enough, I see Sonam at the stupa. He's wearing a black tracksuit and smiles at me as he practically runs by. I'm starting to recognize other people too, like the guy swinging the steaming cauldron of incense, the young woman in Nikes, the old lady helped around the stupa by relatives, the man feeding pigeons, the woman selling garlands of bright yellow marigolds, and a monk with amazing eyes. I've never seen anything like them. Deep brown pools of calmness. What does he know? I wonder. On the third lap, I become aware of how my mind constantly judges. Nothing is neutral. I never knew I had so many opinions. I have opinions about everything, from Ethiopian cuisine (too squishy) to postmodernism (also too squishy). I have opinions about my opinions, and opinions about those too.

On the fifth lap, I try to imagine, as Buddhists do, that everyone here was once my mother in a previous lifetime. Some people are easy, like the nice old lady lugging the huge prayer wheel. Others, such as the guy who nearly runs me over with his motorcycle, require more work. That's the point. Everyone was once our mother. If we believe that, *really* believe that, it completely changes the way we interact with other people. We might still lose our temper with people, as we do with our real mother, and we might still get exasperated, as we do with our real mother, but we'd approach these situations from a standpoint of love. We'd find a way to work things out, and as compassionately as possible.

I'm a full participant in the scene here, but part of me still feels like a fraud, an impostor. I start to think of myself, as I am wont to do, in the third person. *Eric is walking around a large white monument. Eric is having a spiritual experience. Eric is...* This is not good. I know what Wayne would say: I need to get out of my thoughts and return to the body. I do that, and discover that my body is hungry. I drop by the Saturday Café and take my usual seat.

Today I'm reading *The Way of the Bodhisattva*. Written by Shantideva, an eighth-century Indian scholar, it is considered the definitive guide to Mahayana Buddhism, the populist sect of Buddhism that includes the Tibetan and Zen schools. A Bodhisattva is an enlightened being, or, rather, a nearly enlightened being, who voluntarily forgoes his own salvation in order to help other sentient beings. The Bodhisattva is like someone in a war zone who has a plane ticket out, could board the next flight but, inexplicably, remains behind in order to help others get their tickets too.

The book is filled with all sorts of advice. Practical stuff like, "It is shameful to urinate in water or land used by others." Can't argue with that one. Advice for dealing with other people: "One should flee far from childish people." Again, solid. What I like most about it, however, is its emphasis on compassion:

> *When both myself and other*
> *Are similar in that we wish to be happy*
> *What is so special about me?*
> *Why do I strive for my happiness alone?*

A good question, I think as I take a sip of my good coffee. If we have compassion for our own limbs, by reflexively grabbing an injured arm, for instance, then why "are embodied creatures not regarded as limbs of life"? I'm contemplating this when one embodied creature, a young American woman, catches my ear. She catches it because she is shouting, I mean SHOUTING, into her laptop. Why is she angry at her laptop, I wonder, when I realize that she is angry at the person at the other end of her Skype call. She's one of the karma bunnies, I suspect, judging by the way she is trying, and failing miserably, to modulate her anger. It's her poor boyfriend she's yelling at. He's probably back in the States, and he has committed the apparently unforgivable sin of not calling her on her birthday, not that she *expects* to be called on her birthday, mind you, but it would have been nice, would have been the *respectful* thing to do, and on and on. This is not what the Buddha meant by "right speech," one of the Five Precepts. It is wrong speech, very wrong, and, worst of all, it is messing with my experience.

I'm ready to reprimand her, to really lay into her about public decorum, when I hear a voice in my head. The voice, which has a slightly nasal, Staten Island accent, is telling me to be in the body, not to judge, to separate sensation from experience. I listen to the voice. I breathe. I can still hear the woman's passive-aggressive rant, and it still annoys me, but less than before. It's now a minor annoyance, like static on the radio dial. I just might be making progress.

I decide to drop by James's apartment and share my minor breakthrough. I find him kneeling on the living room floor, half a dozen watches sprawled in front of him.

"Going into the watch business?" I quip.

No, it turns out he had promised some people in the village watches from the United States but forgot to buy them last time he was there so he's buying them here in Kathmandu. A small, white lie—technically in violation of right speech, but overall a minor infraction, a spiritual misdemeanor.

The village, as James calls it, is a settlement of beggars, migrants from India. James explains how he became involved, became their business consultant and benefactor. Several years ago, James was having a "Vajrayana crisis," Vajrayana being the sect of Buddhism that places great emphasis on compassion. Whenever his Buddhist teachers cited an example of such a compassionate person, however, they invariably invoked Mother Teresa. Where, James wondered, was the Buddhist Mother Teresa?

So James decided to become one, though he probably wouldn't put it that way. He'd seen these beggars hanging around the stupa, scrawny young boys and girls who were as cunning as they were filthy. They had all kinds of scams, their favorite being the milk scam. A young girl holds a baby (not her own but a relative's) and pleads with passing tourists to buy her milk. She doesn't want any money, just milk for her baby. A tourist buys the milk, at an inflated price, then the beggar turns around and sells it back to the shopkeeper, who is in on the scam. It's quite clever.

One of the beggars, a bright light named Bimla, began talking to James, and they soon struck up a friendship. You will come to my village for tea, Bimla said. It was not a question. Bimla never asked questions. So James went. He was struck by the "chaotic joy" of the village. At first, the villagers treated James the way they treat all foreigners, like an ATM. Push the right buttons and money comes out. Soon, though, they realized that James was not dispensing cash, no matter how they pushed his buttons.

James wanted to help change their lives in a more profound way. Medical care at the village was nonexistent. James had taken one year of pre-med at Duke, which he figured qualified him to play doctor. "Advil and the power of suggestion will cure anything," he tells me, with only slight exaggeration.

So James becomes the village doctor and one day he notices that the women make colorful quilts. They sleep under them, bundle their children in them. James, ever the capitalist, sniffs an opportunity. Tourists, he bets, would pay good money for these quilts, money that could be used to send kids to school. James is right.

The quilt business takes off, and a few dozen kids now attend school who didn't before.

Take me to the village, James, I say. I want to go. Why? I'm not sure. Maybe it's just more voyeurism. Maybe I want to see the poor people so I feel better about myself. No, that's not it. I want to witness a genuine act of compassion. James agrees to take me. I follow as we cross an insanely busy street, then head downhill to the village.

The village, it turns out, is really a slum. The "houses" are tents, and not very sturdy ones at that, flimsy tarps strung between two bamboo poles. Mangy dogs with open scabs scurry about. James, the quintessential neat freak, had a fear of feces, a real phobia, which he had to overcome in order to help the village. There is no running water or indoor plumbing, though I notice they have satellite TV and cellphones. It's a very twenty-first-century slum.

James shows me his hut. The beggars built it for him, decorating it with catalog photos of Caucasian babies and cruise ships, figuring that would make him feel at home. James plops down on the bed, a makeshift cot, the sun streaming in from all sides. Bimla walks into the hut. She is not well. Kidney stones. James reaches into his bag and pulls out a bottle, imploring her to take the medicine.

I am impressed with James's natural compassion. He doesn't make a big deal of helping, he just helps. Could James have done all of these good deeds without Buddhism? Yes, I suppose so, but he didn't. Compassion spontaneously arises from wisdom, the Buddha taught. When your knee hurts, your hand reaches for it automatically because it's all the same body. Likewise, Buddhists believe, when you realize that we are all one body you help without thinking, without even considering it "helping." As James explains: "I feel that, wow, I really just want to help these people calm down and just fucking relax and stop smacking their kids. I really want them to be happy. It isn't because I've been told to do that. It's a natural result of being a Buddhist. It's part of the path." Buddhists believe that compassion is not some slobbery emotion but, rather, a skill, like playing the piano or crocheting. Love without wisdom is ineffective and, to a degree, self-indulgent. That's why the Rinpoche upbraided the Dutch girl who said the world needs more love. Love, yes, but wisdom first.

That evening, I meet an American Buddhist named Matteo at Flavors. If James is Buddhist as Intellectual and Wayne is Buddhist as Sphinx, then Matteo is Buddhist as Action Hero. He is the James Bond of Tibetan Buddhism, slashing his ego, head-butting illusion, and—Pow!—karate-chopping negative karma. His life reads like a spy thriller, albeit a mellow Buddhist one. There's Matteo hiding flash drives in his shoe and sleeping with Chinese policewomen, enjoying the experience, in a non-attached way of course, but also picking up valuable morsels of information about China's treatment of Tibetan prisoners. There's Matteo meditating. There he is having lunch with Richard Gere. No doubt about it: Matteo is one cool Buddhist.

When I meet him, he's wearing a *kurta*, an Indian-style shirt that hangs low and comfortable, and multiple pairs of *mala*, Tibetan beads. I tell Matteo about my meditation lessons with Wayne and about my disappointing meeting with the Rinpoche.

I'm trying too hard, he says. "Enlightenment is as close as your face."

"What exactly does that mean?"

"Look at your face right now."

I sit there, staring blankly at Matteo.

"It's a little hard, isn't it? The guru holds a mirror to your mind. Similarly, when the guru does something"—Matteo snaps his fingers—"he teaches that method so that we can see who we really are. Ultimately there is nothing to fucking do but look at your mind."

But all the rituals and superstition of Tibetan Buddhism—the compulsive soothsaying, for instance—make me uneasy. "It turns me off," I say.

"That's okay," says Matteo. "Big, fat women turn me off. They turn other people on."

I nod, not sure where he's going with this. I decide to switch gears and ask about impermanence. This is something I've been wrestling with, this Buddhist notion that nothing, absolutely nothing, remains the same from one moment to the next. Isn't it depressing?

"No," he says. "It makes me feel more alive, more aware of the fragility of everything. Impermanence isn't negative. It's the way things are. It's real. You can taste it and touch it with everything we encounter. How much more real can you get than that?"

"Okay, I'll give you that. But what about emptiness? Frankly, I've had my fill of Buddhist emptiness. It's so negative, a real bummer."

No it isn't, says Matteo. I've been reading some "bad translations," he continues, as if bad translations were some sort of bug that's been going around. A better translation of *shunyata*, the Sanskrit word, is not emptiness but "pregnant with possibility."

That does sound more appealing, I have to admit. Emptiness as pure potential. I look at a blank canvas and see a void. Picasso saw possibilities. But, I ask, what about this idea that nothing really exists? That seems like insanity. Of course things exist.

"Do you see that bicycle over there?" says Matteo.

"Yes."

"Go over and touch the bicycle."

I walk over and touch the bike.

"No, you touched the tire. That's not the bicycle is it? Touch the bicycle, please."

I touch the seat.

"No, that's the seat. Touch the bicycle."

I touch the frame.

"No, that's a metal tube. Touch the bicycle."

I give up.

"You see, there is no bicycle to touch," says Matteo. "It doesn't exist. Yet it does, as a mental construct. The bicycle is like an illusion, real and yet not."

I'm pondering this when suddenly the power goes out and the café is thrust into darkness. No, not thrust. It just sort of coasts into darkness, with a complete absence of drama. Nobody is the least bit flustered. Matteo doesn't even comment on the fact that we are now sitting in darkness and can no longer see each other's faces, let alone our own. He just keeps talking while the waiters come by and light candles at each table.

I tell Matteo what I've been doing, meditating with Wayne, watching my breath, placing my mind in my body.

"That's fine," he says. "But he has you on a very graduated path. It will take you four incalculable eons to perfect."

I'm not sure just how long four incalculable eons is, but I'm pretty sure it's later than next Tuesday, when I'm due to leave Kathmandu.

"Look, you're already past fifty, right?"

"Only forty-six," I protest.

Matteo shrugs, as if to say, "Same difference." "You're on the downward slope. You don't have time to waste." What I need, declares Matteo, is the Diamond Vehicle. Tantra.

"Tantra? As in crazy sex?"

Tantra, explains Matteo, is another misunderstood term, another bad translation. Tantra is not about mindless crazy sex. It is about *mindful* crazy sex, and that makes all the difference. It is also about mindful sipping of green tea, mindful eating, mindful anything, really. While most schools of Buddhism view desires as distractions, bumps on the path to enlightenment, Tantra views those same desires as fuel for enlightenment. It's never easy, sometimes dangerous, and often abused, but, Matteo assures me, with Tantra it is possible—and this is the part that hooks me—to achieve enlightenment *in a single lifetime.*

I am fascinated by Tantra. I need to find out more. I buy several books on the subject and dive in. I don't get very far. Everything about Tantra is shrouded in mystery and danger. The original texts were written in the "twilight language," decipherable by only a few. Tantric masters warn that theirs is a slippery path, ripe for abuse. When it is discussed, it is always in hushed tones.

Tantra is a sort of alchemy of the mind. It enables us to transform our base desires into something sublime. "Tantra seeks to transform every experience—no matter how 'unreligious' it may appear—into the path of fulfillment," says Lama Yeshe. "All of our actions—walking, eating, and even urinating!—can be brought into our spiritual path." I pause and try to picture how this would actually work, and the confusion it might sow among the uninformed. "Excuse me, honey. I have to go to the bathroom and get spiritual."

Tantra is suspect because ordinarily we don't think of pleasure and religion as compatible. If it feels good, it must not be spiritual. Which, if you think about it, is quite absurd. Pleasure is not the problem, says Lama Yeshe. "It is our grasping, exaggerating, distorting attitude toward pleasure that must be abandoned." This sounds good, but how exactly does it work? I'm not sure.

The next morning I decide to try Wayne's mind-massage technique. It strikes me as a Tantric thing to do. Lying on my bed, I place my mind in different parts of my body, as Wayne suggested. After several minutes of this, I've managed to give myself a splitting headache and that's about it. So I walk to a nearby massage parlor, where another sentient being massages my body with her hands. There are no minds involved. This proves much more effective.

Another session with Wayne. I almost canceled this one. I had woken that morning and discovered that my large intestine was having its own Vajrayana crisis. I spent an inordinate amount of time in the bathroom that morning and was ready to call Wayne, but I thought, No, the Buddha wouldn't cancel because of some intestinal trouble and neither will I. So here I am, back on Wayne's roof.

"Remember," says Wayne, "you've withdrawn a little bit from the world. You've settled."

"I have?"

"Yes, so the basic movement is simply being here."

"Be here now," I say, reflexively uttering that 1970s refrain.

"Yes, but be here now *in a certain way*," says Wayne.

Of course. That last bit is crucial. It's less catchy than simply Be Here Now, and does not fit so easily on a bumper sticker, but it makes all the difference. There's all this talk about living in the moment, which sounds nice, but what does it really mean? We are, by definition, always in the present moment; it's the only way we can experience time. Even if we're brooding about the past or worrying about the future we are doing so now. And here. The crucial distinction Wayne seems to be making is *how* we are here now. Fully or partially? Mindfully or mindlessly?

"You're giving your body a preponderance of weight," says Wayne. "You *are* the body. Put the mind in the body."

"Ah, and the body is observing," I say, feeling like I'm really getting it now.

"No," says Wayne, "not observing. You are experiencing. There is a difference. If you are observing you are a spectator, sitting in the stands. If you are experiencing, you are the one shooting the ball into the basket."

I'm tempted to mention to Wayne that I've never been good at basketball, but he would probably tell me I'm caught up in my narrative, so I stay mum about that and instead ask Wayne about the ultimate goal, achieving Nirvana.

"You are starting to use language," says Wayne, as if that were some sort of crime. "You have to make it clear what you mean by that. Achieve. Nirvana."

At this point, I am ready to throttle Wayne, or maybe pick him up and throw him back against his own experience. Everything with him is contingent. Nothing ever just *is*. If I said, "It sure is cold today," he'd probably reply, "Yes, you may be experiencing coldness." If I said to Wayne, "Help! My clothes are on fire," he'd probably say, in an annoyingly measured tone: "You are using words. Clothes. Fire. Words have meanings. You need to investigate these meanings, examine them."

I ask him what he has against words. Nothing, he insists, "but words hurry us." In one sense, he's right. Words can rush us into feelings and sensations that we haven't genuinely felt or sensed yet. But words can also propel us. Sometimes we don't recognize truths until we say them aloud.

So I persist with Wayne, using different words this time. "Where does enlightenment fit into all of this?"

"You can go straight to enlightenment if you want."

"That would be great, preferably by 5:00 p.m."

"Sure. By 5:00 p.m. is no problem. But the first thing you need to do is jump off the roof."

That's the last time I mention enlightenment to Wayne.

We sit and meditate, side by side, but I'm having an especially hard time today. My large intestine is doing somersaults, and the mosquitoes are biting with a vengeance. I tell this to Wayne, hoping for sympathy. Silly me.

"Congratulations," he says. "That is a basic Buddhist teaching. You are suffering."

"Yes! I am suffering."

"Because you own a body."

"So you're saying it's a good thing—these mosquito bites, the pain in my stomach?"

"No, I'm asking you to experience, not observe."

"I *am* experiencing. That's the problem. I'm experiencing tremendous discomfort."

"It's okay. It means you're alive. If you didn't suffer, you'd miss it."

Then, suddenly and inexplicably, I get it. Our experiences are constantly being mediated by our thoughts. We're not aware of it, because it happens nearly simultaneously. A mosquito bites us, we itch, we suffer. We perceive it as an unbroken chain of cause and effect, but it's not. There is a moment—a nano moment but a moment nonetheless—when we have a choice, when we can interpret that sensation on our skin as either discomfort or something else—or, better yet, nothing at all. This phenomenon applies not only to relatively minor irritants like mosquito bites but also to backaches, headaches, annoying people. I share my insight with Wayne, who smiles.

"There is a pause between thoughts," he says. "And that pause is the basis for the meditative experience." Noticing the pauses first, he explains, then elongating them, which is accomplished simply by acknowledging them.

I know of religions based on grace, or submission, or learning. Buddhism is based on the pause, a tiny barely perceptible pause between our thoughts, a pause that, while we normally are not even aware of its existence, contains the entire universe. We know this intuitively. We say that something "gives us pause" when it makes us stop and think, or rethink. A good artist or interior designer knows that the gaps are crucial. A musician or public speaker uses silence to great effect. It is this pause, the space between things, that imbues those things themselves with meaning and beauty.

I no longer want to throttle Wayne. I want to beatify him. Saint Wayne. In fact, I'm tempted to start a new religion, Waynism. Waynists would all wear their hair in tight ponytails and drink precisely one and a half cups of French-press coffee every morning. The Waynists would, in a markedly nasal intonation, utter statements at once profound and impenetrable. They would be freethinkers, these followers of Wayne. They would write e-mails exclusively in verse and scoff at the mention of all gods, except of course the Great Wayne of Staten Island, to whom they would bow three times a day—four times on Tuesdays, the Waynist Sabbath. I'm about to tell Wayne all this but I suspect Wayne would not approve of Waynism. Which of course makes the idea of Waynism all the more appealing. There is no more-irresistible guru than the one who insists he is not a guru.

It's been a good session, but I sense it's time to leave. For me, spiritual insights are about as sturdy as soap bubbles. One second everything is blazingly clear and the next second I'm obsessing about nail clippers. I tell Wayne I'm going back to my hotel to lie down.

"Okay," he says, "but when you lie down do so like this, with your knees up against your chest."

"Is that better for energy flow?"

"No, it makes it easier to pass wind."

Yes, I think, climbing down from the roof, Waynism is a pragmatic path.

The next morning, I'm doing my daily circumambulation. The air is brisk, the sky the color of cappuccino, as the darkness yields reluctantly to daylight. During one lap, I spot a crowd gathered around a bench. Perhaps it's a musician, I wonder, or maybe some street theater. I edge closer. I am shocked by what I see: a woman with a young boy, perhaps eight years old, presumably her son. The boy is badly burned, the skin on his chest a cluster of red-dish bubbles. His left hand has been fused into a club, individual fingers no longer identifiable. The woman is speaking Tibetan, au-dibly distraught, but the boy is remarkably calm. He is eating an apple, holding it expertly in his club-hand.

It is this calmness, almost contentment, that gets me. Something about the incongruity between the boy's physical disfigurement and his emotional equilibrium hits me like a body blow. I reach into my pocket and pull out fifteen rupees—about forty cents—and plop it into a cardboard box the woman had set up as a col-lection bin. I return to my circumambulation, walking faster and faster, trying to dislodge that image from my mind. Why did I give so little money? I should have dropped a thousand rupees into that cardboard box. Yes, that's what I'll do, I decide. But when I return to the bench, the boy and his mother are gone. It's as if they were never there. I circle the stupa, replaying what James had told me: Compassion arises spontaneously from wisdom. How, I wonder, can I be more wise?

I decide to ponder this question over coffee at the Saturday Café. I find my morning ritual especially comforting today and crack open my daily reading. This time, I've decided to go right to the source: the Buddha himself. Actually, the Buddha never wrote a single word. His disciple and attendant, Ananda, loyally recorded his master's words. I feel for Ananda, who was so busy attending to the Buddha's needs that he never had time to seriously pursue his own enlightenment.

I'm struck by how some passages sound like they could have come from the Bible, even though the Buddha lived some five hundred years before Jesus. For instance, the Buddha said, "Hurt not others in ways that you yourself would find hurtful." That sounds an awful lot like the Golden Rule: Do unto others as you would have them do unto you. Both Christianity and Buddhism teach nonviolence, compassion, and abstinence from worldly pleasures. Some academics believe these similarities are no coincidence and that, in fact, Jesus was influenced by Buddhist ideas. It is not as far-fetched as it seems. During Jesus's lifetime, Buddhist missionaries had sprouted as far west as Alexandria, Egypt.

But while Jesus suffered for our sins, the Buddha dismisses the notion of original sin and states simply that *all* is suffering. The Buddha was not speaking merely of the kind of suffering we experience when we lose our job, or fail an exam, or find a parking ticket on our car, though he meant that too. He was speaking of a deeper, existential suffering, what the Tibetan lama and bon vivant Chögyam Trungpa aptly called "a basic fuckedupness that is all-pervasive."

I can vouch for this basic fuckedupness, confirm its pervasiveness. It's always there, even when my life is going well, *especially* when my life is going well. For most religions, their bread and butter, so to speak, is the comfort they provide during life's rough patches. That is why die-hard secularists sometimes discover religion when tragedy strikes. Buddhism, though, seems more concerned with our frame of mind during the good times. Every moment, even the pleasurable ones, *especially* the pleasurable ones, contains the seeds of despair. Suffering is an empty wineglass, and a full one, too. Indeed, when life is going swimmingly, that is precisely when we need to pay attention, the Buddha taught. "Even as a solid rock is unshaken by the wind, so are the wise unshaken by praise or blame." Shaken by praise? Isn't praise a good thing? The Buddha would say it is not, for praise, like everything in life, is transitory and therefore contains the seeds of suffering. In fact,

this is the worst kind of suffering, because it is disguised as pleasure.

Back in my hotel room, I click on the TV. The Balloon Boy
mystery has been solved. It was all a hoax, a scam, cooked up by
Balloon Boy's ambitious parents, who were hoping to parlay the
stunt into a spot on a reality TV show. What you see is not. It
strikes me as a very Buddhist tale indeed. People worried about the
sweet little boy, they cried tears, they suffered. The emotions were
genuine but the situation was not; it was an illusion. Balloon Boy
was never in danger. Is life like that, I wonder—an elaborate hoax?
Are we all Balloon Boy?

Buddhists will tell you that theirs is a "scientific religion," one
based on experiment and direct experience, not belief and faith.
That is not entirely true. Buddhists, in fact, have a tremendous
amount of faith. Only it is not faith in a God but, rather, faith
in themselves and in their own Wisdom Mind. That is not easy.
Buddhism is like that exercise designed to engender trust—the
one where you fall backward, confident that your partner will
catch you. Only this time you are catching *yourself*, which sounds
impossible, of course, so we never try. The lamas, with their paraphernalia and their koans and their mantras, are all about one
thing: tricking us into falling backward. We will discover, as Alan
Watts put it, that "we think we're going to crash but we bounce."
Like a rubber ball. Or a balloon.

I like the idea of bouncing but still can't shake my nagging doubts
about Buddhism. There's something cold, almost clinical, about it.
Buddhists often compare the Noble Eightfold Path to a doctor's prescription. Just take this medicine and call us in a couple of lifetimes.
It's a good analogy, and therein lies the problem. Buddhism is about
as warm and comforting as a doctor's examination room.

Carl Jung sees religion as something that gives us "assurance
and strength so that [we] may not be overwhelmed by the mon-

sters of the universe." Buddhism offers little sanctuary from those monsters. Theologically speaking, it offers no shoulder to cry on. "Religion" comes from the Latin *religio,* which means "to bind," but Buddhism promotes a kind of unbinding. It is a religion about letting go—of concepts of the soul, of God, and, ultimately, of yourself. I don't know if I can do that.

In this regard, I'm with Martin Gardner. Gardner was a fideist. Fideists can't prove the existence of God, don't even try, but they believe in God anyway. They believe because it makes them feel good. I find this refreshingly honest. Gardner was no fan of Buddhism, or any religion that defines God in fuzzy terms, like "the universe" or "the unfathomable." We need an anthropomorphic God, he argued, because, "you can worship, love, thank, confess to, seek forgiveness from, make requests of, a person. You cannot do any of these things with a potato or a galaxy or a God who is a 6,000-foot-tall jelly bean." With Buddhism, all you get is a Giant Marshmallow and your own mind. Is that enough? I wonder.

My last session with Wayne. I've grown to like him. I don't always understand him, but I like him. I feel like I'm making progress, though I don't say so. Once, when I told Wayne that my morning's meditation felt good, he said, "Don't be too attached to the good feeling because when you don't feel good it will feel worse." Not only does that make sense, it neatly sums up Buddhism in eighteen words. All hail Lord Wayne.

Today Wayne suggests we descend from the roof and go for a walk. He knows a Hindu temple nearby. There, we find that families have set up blankets and are picnicking right inside the temple walls. We find a shaded spot to sit, and we talk. I tell him that I still feel frustrated during meditation. I keep getting it wrong, even though I know that my use of the word "wrong" is itself wrong. What should I do?

"Just start over."

Of course. You can always start over. Or as Rumi said, "Come, come again." It's so simple. When Mango our cat died, I struggled to explain the concept of death to my then five-year-old daughter. I had unintentionally appropriated Buddhist concepts of reincarnation, but done so clumsily. "Well, Sonya, when something dies something is born. It's a cycle." *Oh God*, I thought, I sound like I swallowed the New Age section at Barnes and Noble. But she got it, only better than me. "Ohhhh," she said. "You mean, the world starts over again?" Yes, I said, startled by her insight. "The world starts over again." That is the beauty of impermanence, and of a five-year-old's wisdom.

I tell Wayne that I'm going to walk back to my hotel and do so mindfully. "I'll feel the soles under my feet," I say.

"Good," says Wayne.

"I'm going to feel the breeze in my hair."

"There is no breeze."

"Right."

"You have no hair."

"Right again. But if there were a breeze and I did have hair I would feel the breeze in my hair. I'll take a taxi later today and it will be a bumpy ride."

"You're getting into the story. This is projecting, not mindfulness."

"Okay, well, right now my butt is a bit sore, from sitting."

"Good. That is close to home. Stay close to home."

"Okay, I'm going to shift my weight slightly, in order to get more comfortable."

"Yes!" says Wayne, the proud non-guru.

At this point, a young Nepalese man who has been watching us for some time approaches.

"Excuse," he says in halting English. "May I ask what you talking about?"

Wayne is about to answer but I stop him. "Let me answer this, Wayne. We've been talking about nothing. Nothing at all."

Wayne of Staten Island laughs, and together we experience a moment.

My last morning in Nepal. The air is crisp and fresh. I can see the snowcapped peaks of the Himalayas. They were always there, of course, but only now are they visible. I circle the Giant Marshmallow one last time, feeling the ground under my feet and the nubby texture of the beads along my fingers. I do five or six laps then climb the stairs to the Saturday Café and look for my seat. It's taken, so I grab another. I watch the synchronized prostrations going on. My coffee hasn't arrived yet. My mind takes off on its usual trajectory, and at a familiar velocity. *Where the heck is my coffee? I ordered seven minutes ago! How long does it take to make a simple cup of coffee? I'm going to go find a waiter; where the hell is the waiter?* Then a pause, a small, barely perceptible nano pause, like a break in the clouds on a solidly overcast day, emerges and I dive deep into this pause. And I relax.

Soon, my coffee arrives, along with my banana pancakes. I eat them slowly, mindfully. I could say they taste good but that's not quite what I experience. The pancakes are not good. They are not bad. They are not neutral. They are banana pancakes, resplendent in their banana-pancake nature. They couldn't be anything else, nor do I wish them to be. I feel the sun warming my face. I open *The Way of the Bodhisattva*, by now stained with honey and coffee, and read this:

> *Just like a blind man*
> *Discovering a jewel in a heap of rubbish*
> *Likewise, by some coincidence,*
> *An Awakening Mind has been born within me*

No mention of God. No talk of divine intervention. Just "some coincidence." The passage takes my breath away, not despite its godlessness but because of it. When coincidence works in our favor, unexpectedly, inexplicably, we can't help but feel blessed. Christians call this grace. Buddhists call this Suchness or, simply, the way things are. They don't make a big deal of it. Buddhism, I realize, is an unintentional religion.

This moment won't last. I know that. In a few hours, I'll be taking off my shoes at airport security then shoehorning myself into a metal tube commonly known as an airplane. The moment won't last, and neither will I. My body "is like an object on loan for but a minute," as the Buddha so bluntly put it. Does that fact make the moment less sweet? Not less, I decide, taking one last sip of coffee, more. Definitely more.

CWM, feeling empty inside.
Looking for a deity closer
to home. Are you the giving
type? Platonic okay.

Cities are like people. We think we know them, but we never do, not fully. There is always another side, a shadow city, lurking in the background like the eccentric cousin you studiously avoid at family gatherings. And so it is with me and New York. I thought I knew the city, but it turns out I only knew part of it. I knew the New York of bagels and thrift stores and yoga studios. The New York I am now speeding toward on the Number Two train is a very different New York. Different in precisely what way I can't say, for I have never visited this New York. Why would I? Reputation, reflected in, and to some extent forged by, movies like *Fort Apache, the Bronx*, formed a barrier between me and this New York, a barrier as impenetrable as any wall ever built.

Yet here I am, the only white person in a sweltering, crowded subway car, hurtling toward a homeless shelter that will be my home for a while. It's run by Franciscan friars—the Friars of the Renewal, they call themselves. They are attempting to renew an ancient and honorable path to God.

I've long been intrigued by the Franciscans. In India, they were the only ones willing to provide an education to a young orphan I had taken under my wing. Later, back in the United States, I'd occasionally see the friars walking in downtown Washington, DC, with their brown hooded habits, looking like they'd just stepped out of another century. What little else I knew about them I liked: their quixotic spirit; their uncompromised Christianity that takes Jesus's words, especially the difficult ones, seriously. Not that Franciscans care much for verbiage. As their founder, Saint Francis of Assisi, famously advised: "Preach the Gospel at all times. Use words if necessary." And so the Franciscans do: owning nothing, feeding and housing the poor, and doing so not in secluded monasteries but in intensely urban settings, the sort of neighborhoods people like me only witness when we take a wrong turn or our car breaks down.

The Franciscan life strikes me as difficult, wholly impractical, and that is precisely why I find it so compelling. What sustains them, I wonder, and might this be the God for me? I sure hope so. My depression has metastasized, spreading from scattered bouts of melancholy to something deeper and more sustained. Again, I wonder if my search for God is making me more depressed, not less. Alan Watts warns of a "karmic reckoning"—that as you dig into your own muck, detritus from your past (past lives too) rises to the surface. A Christian friend told me essentially the same thing, though in more colorful language: "The closer you get to God, the more the devil wants to get you."

As the train clamors past 125th Street, I take a few deep breaths. I am on edge. Something about that place, the South Bronx, is important to me. The thread of pain began there. My father grew up in the Bronx, dirt-poor. When he was five years old, his father abandoned the family. Then he did the same when I was five years old. I feel like I'm traveling to the heart of some raw, ancestral wound and now, as the father of a five-year-old myself, one that has taken on greater urgency. Ancestry is not destiny, I tell myself, as the train pulls into my station.

Not only am I apprehensive about the South Bronx and what awaits me there, I'm also worried my ignorance might be exposed. Somehow I managed to reach middle age knowing precious little about the Testaments, Old or New. Ignorance of Buddhism is one thing but we are a Christian nation, demographically at the very least, and there's no excuse for biblical illiteracy.

I arrive in time for evening mass. It's led by Father Louis. He has a shaved head and grizzly beard. He looks less like a priest and more like a retired member of ZZ Top. Which is not that far from the truth. Father Louis, I'd later learn, is a former saxophone-playing weight-lifting woman-chasing Wall Street executive and owner of a used-car dealership. He was, by his own admission, a very intense man. He has retained that intensity, only now it is channeled into the Gospel.

The chapel is small and simple with wooden floors, none of the gaudy ornamentation found in some Christian houses of worship. Up front, two candles flicker. One of the friars is playing a guitar, and playing it well. "We adore Jesus, like a girlfriend or a mother or a loved one," says Father Louis. "When you can tap into that love, torrents enter your life because you have opened a valve. Love like that can break down walls." Fingers to his lips, Italian-style, he adds, "It's a-nice," as if he were describing linguine Alfredo and not the divine love of Jesus Christ.

The Franciscans are a Catholic order, and I know nothing of the Catholic mass. Here I am again, among the devout, faking it. When everyone stands, I stand. When they sit, I sit. When they kneel, I kneel. When it comes time to cross ourselves, I fumble, my right hand flailing in various random directions. I must look like I'm having some sort of seizure. No one notices, or they do and are too Christian to say anything. Either way, I am grateful.

"Father, forgive them, for they know not what they do," Father Louis says, quoting Jesus's words on the cross. "I use that almost daily," he says, placing a worn leather Bible to his lips. Then he kneels, his bald head glistening. "We ask You to help us, to heal our minds, our bad thoughts, our addictions, our sinful inclinations." Guilty as always, I squirm slightly in my seat.

Next comes communion. "If you choose, you can come up for a blessing. There's no pressure," says Father Louis. I'm not sure about this. I watch others, carefully noting how they approach the altar, drink the wine, then open their mouths to receive the Eucharist. Sure, why not? I can do this. I wait for the right time then walk up to the small altar. Father Louis blesses me with a wave of his arm. I stand there, my mouth open, waiting. Anytime now, Father Louis, anytime now. But something is wrong. His eyes are trying to tell me something, but what? Is there something I'm supposed to do or say? Some password? The awkwardness is almost unbearable. Finally, he lowers his head and whispers, "I can't give you communion. I'll explain later." Then I remember. Only Catholics can receive communion. I should have known that. I slink away, realizing that, once again, I have managed to make a theological ass of myself.

The friary and the homeless shelter are separated by a small, pleasant courtyard. Brother Crispin, a cherubic friar with an intellectual bent, shows me my room in the shelter. It's on a floor designated for the lay volunteers who work here. The room is not air-conditioned, so I crack the window and fall asleep to the sounds of sirens and angry Spanish, the soundtrack of the South Bronx.

I wake early the next morning and forage for coffee. I find some across the courtyard in the friary and silently give thanks that the Franciscan vows of obedience, poverty, and chastity do not extend to caffeinated beverages. I spot a hooded figure. It's Father Louis.

From this angle, the morning light illuminating his dark, intense eyes, the medieval hood draped over his head, the muscles (still there, evident even under the loose robe), the coiled energy, I can't help but feel a shock of fear. There's something satanic about his appearance. I know that's not fair, but neither can I deny it.

I linger in the kitchen, savoring my coffee like it was mother's milk. The brothers are making breakfast; there's a relaxed collegiality here, like a frat house, only with considerably less beer and considerably more prayer. I like the way they call each other "bro." "Do you want eggs, bro? Thanks, bro." It's quite endearing. They don't call me bro, of course. I'm the outsider, as usual.

Over the centuries, the Franciscan vow of poverty has slipped, and this order, formed only twenty-five years ago, is intent on correcting that. They own nothing. No private bank accounts or credit cards or cellphones or, according to their charter, "popular electric gadgets manufactured simply for amusement and recreation." No beds, either. They sleep on the floor. The friary has no Internet connection, no TV, no dishwasher, no air-conditioning. All of these things, the Franciscans believe, are obstacles that stand between us and God.

When we're stripped of everything, what are we? As Pieter the dervish suggested, that is the essential question that all religions attempt to answer. If we were to wake one morning and find we have lost everything—our job, our house, our money, our reputation, our loved ones—would we roll over and die, or would we keep going? What would sustain us? The Franciscans don't merely entertain that question as some sort of intellectual exercise. They live it.

Their day begins with prayer. That's when they fill their tanks, as it were, and receive God's grace. Then they spend the rest of the day giving it away. The Franciscans don't hoard anything. "Freely ye have received, freely give" (Matthew 10:8). They call themselves "active contemplatives." They are in perpetual motion; they are needed. The doorbell rings and it might be someone wanting a pair of socks, or salvation. With the friars, it is all the same. It's all part of their apostolate work. I admire their usefulness, and wish I could be more like that.

In the kitchen, I find Brother Crispin pouring himself a large cup of coffee and digging into a bowl of Happy O's. He invites me on a tour of the neighborhood, and I accept. We step outside the friary, the heavy wooden door closing behind us with a solid and vaguely foreboding thud. He's wearing a baseball cap and, in one hand, holding a ceramic coffee mug, these two accessories clashing temporally with his thirteenth-century habit, held in place by a thick rope, just like in Saint Francis's time. We turn the corner and dip into Ralph's shoe repair. Ralph has been in the South Bronx forever, been mugged six times, which he conveys by miming a knife to the throat. We say our goodbyes, and walking south on Melrose Avenue, Brother Crispin tells me that Ralph repairs the friars' sandals for free. It is a favor they gladly accept. The friars have a reputation, richly deserved, for mooching.

They like to tell a joke about this. A Dominican priest walks into a barbershop. After his haircut, he tries to pay, but the barber refuses to accept money from a man of the cloth. The next morning the barber finds a bouquet of flowers at his doorstep. His next customer is a Jesuit. Again, the barber refuses payment. The next morning he finds a bottle of wine at his doorstep. Then a Franciscan friar comes into his shop for a haircut, and again the barber refuses payment. The next morning he finds twenty friars at his doorstep.

The friars never fail to laugh at this joke, though they've heard it dozens of times. It's funny because it's true. Yes, the Franciscans are tremendous moochers, but they are mooching for God, so all is forgiven.

We walk past a housing project—a dozen high-rise buildings, each identical in size and grimness. Brother Crispin points out the murals on the walls, portraits of young men killed in gang wars. There's been a recent spike in violence, including a shooting across the street from the friary. He tells me, matter-of-factly, how it is not unusual for families caught on the wrong side of a gang's wrath to find gasoline poured under the door of their apartment one morning and a note that reads, "Next time we light it." I can't imagine living like that, your fate in the hands of unseen, malevolent forces.

The police are out in large numbers, watching the comings and goings from portable cherry-pickers, like the kind used for crowd control at street fairs. They're wearing dark cop-glasses, and their cop-hands are twitchier than farther downtown. These are hands acutely aware of their exact location in relation to their holstered guns, and the exact number of seconds it would take to cover that distance.

Brother Crispin, like all of the friars, is street-smart. He can identify gang members by their tattoos and clothes the way an expert bird spotter can make out a yellow-rumped warbler from a hundred yards. Despite his thirteenth-century Umbrian outfit, he is very much attuned to the twenty-first-century South Bronx. "I have to have twice the street smarts as everyone else because, well, I'm a guy wearing a dress," he tells me. The truth is Brother Crispin is savvy and naïve *at the same time*, a rare combination.

A youngish man, smoking a cigarette and wearing black headphones, sidles up to Brother Crispin. This happens all the time. The habit necessitates a reaction. People, strangers, tell the brothers about their cancer or their kid's drug problem or some secret regret. The friars are therapists, aid workers, stand-ins for God, walking Rorschach tests.

"Brother, I always go for Christ," the man tells Brother Crispin, ignoring me. "I was in prison before, but now that I'm out I don't pray anymore." He goes on about how he lost his job and his girlfriend is pregnant, the kind of life details you'd normally convey to your closest friend, not a stranger walking down the street. Brother Crispin listens patiently as the man relays his life's story, before saying simply, "Just pray."

"I'll do that," says the man, who identifies himself as Ramón.

"I'm Brother Crispin." With that the man chuckles. Sometimes, explains Brother Crispin as we walk away, they laugh because they think he's saying "Merry Christmas."

I can't help but wonder about the encounter. What did he hope to accomplish by speaking with the man, who frankly seemed a bit unhinged?

"We hope we planted a seed. And even if he dies tomorrow, he'll die knowing he was loved."

We stop at a pizza place, a bit of a dive, but one of the best, Brother Crispin assures me. We order a couple of slices and I reach for my wallet. When you dine with a friar there is never any doubt about who is paying, no faux protestations: *Please, allow me. No, I insist. If you must.* None of that nonsense. I like the clarity.

We carry our slices to a table, and I'm about to dive in when Brother Crispin stops me. He needs to say grace first.

"Thank You, Lord, for this bounty."

I stare at the greasy mushroom slices, and am about to make some snide comment but restrain myself.

He goes on to thank me for my generosity, which makes me blush because it was only a few bucks, nothing really. There is a sweetness to the blessing, a sincerity, that touches me. If nothing else, it forces me to slow down, pause, taste the pizza rather than inhale it, as I usually do.

Brother Crispin has a sizable paunch, which doesn't seem to jibe with the ascetic lifestyle of a friar. I delicately inquire about that, and he tells me he's put on forty pounds since taking his vows. "All of that starchy food," he says, taking another bite.

We walk a few more blocks down Melrose, past storefront churches, their congregations overflowing into the street. People are sitting on folding chairs set up on the sidewalk. Yes, I think, this is an entirely different New York from the one I know. We stop at an ornate church. It looks like it's been here forever. Brother Crispin is going to his weekly confession. What does he possibly have to confess, I wonder. It is not this man but I who am a "foul stinking lump of sin," to borrow the colorful words of a fourteenth-century Christian mystic, the anonymous author of *The Cloud of Unknowing*. I say as much to Brother Crispin.

"Why don't you go in?"

"In there? The confession booth?"

"Yes. Why not?"

"But I'm not Catholic. I'm not even Christian."

"That's okay. If the priest has a problem with it, he'll let you know."

I hesitate. I think of confessionals as dark and shadowy and— I'm not sure where I get this from, the movies perhaps—having something to do with the mob. Yet my array of sins, large and small, weigh heavily on me, and I'm beginning to suspect that the attendant guilt lies at the root of my depression. Yes, I could use some forgiveness. As Paul Tillich says, "Nothing greater can happen to a human being than that he is forgiven."

And nobody does forgiveness like the Christians. They are number one in their field. Buddhists are not in the forgiveness business, for they believe there is nothing to forgive; no original sin, only bad karma. Jewish forgiveness comes once a year, and at a heavy price: twenty-four hours without food. The New Age movement promises self-forgiveness, and I've tried those exercises, talking to myself in the mirror and whatnot, but I always feel silly, and it never works anyway. No, we need forgiveness from God, nothing less will do. Christian forgiveness is complete and unconditional. It comes in the form of grace, a word that shares a common root with "gratis," as in free. Grace is a gift from God, and everything looks better when it is a gift. Crucially, forgiveness *causes* repentance and not, as is commonly believed, the other way around.

I glance at the confessional booth, maybe twenty yards away. Why not? If I can whirl like a dervish, meditate with Wayne of Staten Island, I can do this. I tentatively swing open the door and step into the little wooden cubicle. I can make out the profile of a figure shuffling behind a partition. I sense impatience, a bad vibe, and want to flee. But it's too late. He sees me.

"Forgive me, Father, but I'm not Catholic."

"Yes, that's okay," he says, but his voice betrays unease.

"I'm not even Christian. I'm Jewish."

"That's okay, my son, but..."

"Yes, Father?"

"I have to do the mass now. I'm already late. Can you come back in half an hour?"

Waves of relief wash over me. That and, surprisingly, disappointment too. Sure, I say, sure. I'll come back.

I do not come back. The moment has passed. I was so close, once again seven-eighths-assed. I wonder what would have transpired in that little wooden booth. Can a few words exchanged with some anonymous priest really wash away a lifetime of sin and guilt? Is forgiveness that easy? I'll never know. I feel like a failure at confessing, which is something else I will need to confess, eventually.

Brother Crispin invites me on a journey, a mission of sorts, to Brooklyn. He's delivering money—eight thousand dollars in cash—to an intermediary who will then dispatch it to Africa where he's helping build a school. I'm always game for a road trip, especially one that involves large sums of cash and shadowy go-betweens, so I agree. Brother Crispin stuffs the bills into his habit, where they instantly disappear like some sort of magic trick.

The friars have nicknames for each of their battered old cars, donations all of them. We climb into a 1993 Oldsmobile dubbed the Gray Ghost. They used to call it Gray Goose until they discovered that was a brand of vodka and therefore not entirely appropriate for a car of God. The Gray Ghost sports a clergy placard on the front dash, a baby-blue cross dangling from the rearview mirror, and a bumper sticker that reads "Women do regret abortion." Brother Crispin pulls out of the parking lot then, for no apparent reason, stops.

"Is there a problem?" I ask.

"Lord Jesus, bless us, protect us, in our works and in our attitudes. Thank You for giving us the ability to travel."

Barely, I think as the Gray Ghost jerks and strains and whines and wheezes, like an old pack mule that should have been retired years ago. It struggles to convey us across the Triboro Bridge. The air conditioner blows hot air over us, so Brother Crispin turns it off and rolls down the windows instead. The plastic cross dances in the warm breeze. Something about this scene—the beat-up car, the sense of divine purpose—seems familiar. Yes, of course: the Blues Brothers. I put on my sunglasses and announce: "We've got a full tank of gas, eight thousand in cash, and we're wearing dark sunglasses. We're on a mission from God." I redub the Gray Ghost the God Mobile, and Brother Crispin laughs. I like that about him and his fellow friars. They wear their faith lightly and, like their founder, Saint Francis, don't take themselves too seriously. (In fact, their vows require cheerfulness on their part.) The test of a good religion, as G. K. Chesterton observed, is whether you can joke about it. This is a good religion.

A mission from God. That becomes a running joke on our ill-fated journey. Whenever we get stuck in traffic or miss a turn or find ourselves hopelessly lost, I declare that all is well because "we're on a mission from God." This proves highly effective at defusing the tension—mine, not Brother Crispin's. He has no tension, at least none I can detect.

"How do you do it? How do you maintain your Franciscan composure in New York traffic?" I ask.

"I just leave it to Christ."

"But what if someone cuts you off?"

"I hit the brakes."

"Okay, that makes sense. Besides that, though. What do you do with your anger?"

"I pray for their conversion. Quickly."

With that, as if by divine providence, someone cuts us off. Brother Crispin leans heavily on the horn. I smile. It's nice to know that their vows of chastity, obedience, and poverty do not extend to honking. Everyone needs an outlet.

Brother Crispin has heavy bags under his eyes. He only got five hours of sleep; there was some problem at the shelter last night and he had to be up for the morning prayer at six. He's wiped out, he tells me.

He gets tired. He has bad days. He honks. All of these facts lead to one inevitable conclusion: Brother Crispin is a human being. Just like me, only with fewer possessions and more compassion. So often we see the habit and not the man or woman, as if taking vows somehow makes them less human, not more. We do this, I think, as a form of self-protection. If we see the friars as real people then they are more like us, and if they are more like us it begs the uncomfortable question: Why aren't we more like them? By sanctifying them we distance ourselves, and thus absolve ourselves of the possibility of such a life.

Brother Crispin speeds past a slow-moving car. The meek may

inherit the earth but not, it seems, the Brooklyn-Queens Expressway. We exit the highway and traverse the Crown Heights neighborhood, passing a clutch of Hasidic Jews wearing fur in the August heat. We miss a turn, again, and need to backtrack. Brother Crispin accomplishes this by making an illegal U-turn, shrugging sheepishly. It's okay, I say. We're on a mission from God.

As we turn right onto Atlantic Avenue, our conversation turns sharply theological. "Christianity is filled with contradictions," he says, pointing to several examples. Strength through meekness. Richness through poverty. Fruitfulness through chastity. Life through death. He's right, of course. All religions, in fact, contain that element of contradiction, of paradox. Zen koans. The Taoist classic, the Tao te Ching. They all contain seemingly contradictory thoughts. Richard Rohr, a Franciscan priest and author, goes a step further. Paradox, he argues, is a prerequisite for spiritual truth. "Any 'common sense' that doesn't have a certain paradoxical character deserves to be distrusted," he says.

Brother Crispin tells me about how he had to expel one of the men from the shelter yesterday. He was back on drugs, and the friars have a strict zero-tolerance policy. So he banished him to the street. It wasn't easy.

"I thought you guys were nice," I say.

"We're not nice. We're kind." There is a difference, he assures me. "Jesus told us to be wise as serpents and innocent as doves." I'm reminded of the Rinpoche in Kathmandu, who advised, "Wisdom first, then love." The Franciscans see no need for sequencing, though. Love always contains wisdom, they believe, or as Tolstoy says: "Love cannot be stupid." Usually, we think of love as an emotion, a blubbering one at that, but that is only one meaning of the word. Love is also a way of being, or as Aldous Huxley posited, a mode of knowledge: "We can only love what we know, and we can never know completely what we do not love."

Finally, we arrive at the church in Brooklyn and drop off the cash. Our return trip is no less eventful. After a series of wrong turns, traffic jams, and sundry other mishaps, we arrive back at the friary, exhausted but satisfied, and just in time for dinner.

The men are lined up outside the shelter. They are not allowed to stay in the building during the day. Each is searched and given an alcohol breath test. They shuffle into the cafeteria, where they sit on benches alongside long wooden tables. They display neither enthusiasm nor resistance. They are just here. Most have problems with alcohol and drugs. Many have criminal records, including homicide. Brother Crispin says grace, a short homily. The gist: We need God, we need help. We can't do this on our own. Then a few announcements. One of the residents (that's what they call the men, residents) has found a job, and everyone breaks into applause. My presence is mentioned and, unexpectedly, the men applaud for me too. Writerman, they call me. There will be a movie playing later, *I, Robot*, and a brief discussion ensues among the friars as to whether it is appropriate or not. (It is.) The food is good and plentiful. The men eat, and talk, but mostly they just eat. Afterward, one of the friars says a short prayer: "Allow us, Lord, to truly relax." Amen.

The men disperse. Some go to their rooms while others shuffle out to the courtyard where they play dominoes, smoke, gossip. As far as homeless shelters go, this is as good as it gets. No wonder there's a waiting list to get in.

I spot Father Louis in the courtyard. I am curious about his sudden and mysterious conversion. We carry two plastic chairs to a small clearing next to a tree. It is a bright, moonlit night, the air filled with the clicking of dominoes and the not-infrequent siren. I'm not sure where to begin. More than any of the other friars here, Father Louis displays the conviction of the converted. I find his intensity unnerving. I worry that at any moment he might hug me, or kill me. It could go either way.

Father Louis explains that he had two passions in life: women and weight lifting. The two fed off each other, supported each other. He would work out every day, for at least two hours, and with such intensity that no one got near him. Then in the evenings he'd prowl for his latest conquest. "Women were probably my first god," he tells me. "And the weights were just a means to get the women. My whole physique was exclusively to attract women. If I could have had three girls a day, I would have done it."

Then one day, his mother, Italian Catholic, said, "Louis, you must go to Bosnia."

"Say what, Mom?"

"You must go to Bosnia, to a holy shrine."

Louis couldn't have cared less about some shrine in Bosnia, nor could he have cared less about Catholicism. At that point in his life he was, as he puts it, "a practical pagan." But Louis loved his mom, so he agreed to go to Bosnia—specifically to Medjugorje, a pilgrimage site that has attracted millions of devout Catholics. He tacked on a few days in Rome afterward, figuring that once he fulfilled his Catholic obligation, made his mom happy, he would then party for three straight days. It was a good plan and, like all good plans, destined to fail.

Medjugorje was beautiful, stunning, but he couldn't wait to get to Rome. On his second day in Bosnia, bored during morning mass, Louis found himself killing time by engaging in an intellectual exercise. "So I'm thinking to myself, If Mary is my mother and God is my father, and if Mary is the mother of Jesus and God is also the father, can I consider Jesus my brother? It was, as I said, an intellectual thing." Louis thought about it for all of six seconds, and never mentioned it to anyone.

Later that day, he joined some other pilgrims on a walk up into the hills to see a church. One of those in the group, a young woman, was a locutionist, someone who supposedly receives interior messages meant for others. "When I heard about this girl's gift, I am thinking to myself she is just nuts. I mean, hearing voices in her head? She might need some medication."

Then, at precisely 5:40 p.m., the girl suggested they all kneel and meditate. Louis agreed, though he didn't know how to meditate so he just kneeled and faked it. After a few minutes, they began to hike again. Louis is taking in the scenic view when the girl pulls him aside and says, "Lou, while we were meditating, Jesus gave me a message for you."

Louis was skeptical. "I'm thinking, Well, she is probably going to tell me to be holy, you know, go to mass every Sunday. I figured it would be a very generic message that anybody can get anytime."

Instead, the girl said: "Jesus told me to tell you, 'Yes, I am your brother and I want to anoint your hands.'"

Louis was floored. She had given him the answer to a question she couldn't possibly have known he'd asked. "And in that moment, I was infused with this love for Christ, knowing that He was in my head, He was in my brain, He was in my heart. I knew He was real. I knew this was the man I needed to follow the rest of my life."

Louis continued to Rome, as planned, but went church-hopping instead of bar-hopping. When he returned to Newark, he was a changed man. He sold his businesses, stopped chasing women, and eventually joined the Franciscans. He walked into the friary with all of his possessions: a toothbrush and his saxophone.

"What happened to the old Louis?" I ask.

"The old Louis is dead and buried in a field. That is where he is. When I think about the old Louis, honestly, it is kind of frightening to me because I don't know who he is. God has taken that lust that was ever-present in my heart and transformed it into a pure love."

We sit in silence for a moment. I don't know what to think. I can't imagine such a dramatic transformation, and I silently question whether it is as complete as Father Louis portrays it. We are never fully born again; some vestige of our former self always remains. What keeps him from slipping into his old ways? Earlier, during one of his sermons, he had hinted at weakness: "A little disorder for me can be like a drug addiction." Is the old Louis still there, waiting for a chance to reemerge?

I also wonder why my experience in Tokyo wasn't equally decisive. I had seen the light, so to speak, yet turned away. Why didn't I make equally dramatic changes in my life? Perhaps it was because I had no context in which to place the experience, no way to connect that soaring moment of unprecedented joy to my everyday, terrestrial life.

"One day, you're going to make that connection," Father Louis says when I tell him my Tokyo story. "Jesus gave you a taste of something that might happen to you in the future. He was preparing the future for you." I have my doubts, God-size doubts, but I keep them to myself. It is late. We say good night, and I walk across the courtyard to the shelter, and my room. I sleep fitfully that night.

The next morning I find a stack of books and videos about Saint Francis, along with a note from Brother Crispin. My Franciscan education. I crack open one of the books and read.

Of all the Christian saints, Francis is probably the closest to Jesus, in his teachings and temperament. Like Jesus, the real Saint Francis is obscured by a fog of fable, hagiography, and tall tales. Which is a shame, because he was remarkable enough without the hyperbole. Francis is often portrayed as a harmless animal lover. He undoubtedly had a deep affinity for nature but to characterize him as only that, as some sort of Doctor Dolittle of Christianity, diminishes him unfairly.

Francis came of age in the early thirteenth century, a time, as biographer Hilarin Felder describes, "marked by ambitious cravings for aggrandizement, by a mad scramble for honors and fame." In other words, a time much like our own, only with less traffic and more leprosy.

As a young man, Francis fancied himself one of the troubadours, the wandering poets of the time. He was well dressed, a man about town, a playboy. He then changed into a knight's armor and went off to battle. As a warrior, he was an abject failure, captured by the enemy and held for a year. He was released only after his father paid a large ransom.

Back home in Assisi, he apprenticed in his father's lucrative cloth business, but his heart wasn't in it. Then one day, praying alone in a dilapidated church, he heard the voice of Jesus, commanding him, "Francis, go, repair My house, which, as you see, is falling completely in ruin." So he did, gathering stones and secretly selling some of his father's finest silk in order to pay for repairs to the church. Not surprisingly, his father was furious. He confined Francis to home, and beat him. When that failed to extinguish his son's rebellious ways, he took him to court in order to recover the money. At the hearing, Francis announced, in dramatic fashion, "You are no longer my father." Not only did he disown his father and forfeit his inheritance, for good measure he disrobed right there in the courtroom, practically throwing his clothes at his father.

It was a turning point for Francis. He had reversed his descent. This is how G. K. Chesterton, in his biography of Francis, described his trajectory: "A man going down and down until at some mysterious point he begins to go up and up. We have never gone up like that because we have never gone down like that." When I read those words, I wondered whether it provided clues to my own melancholy. Is the problem not my depression but, rather, that I am not depressed enough? Might even my melancholy be seven-eighths-assed? Do I need to plummet further in order to reverse my trajectory? It seems like a risky strategy; what guarantee do I have that Chesterton's "mysterious point" will actually materialize and I won't simply fall and fall into a bottomless abyss? There is no guarantee, of course, which is why there are so few saints.

Another turning point in Francis's life came when one day, riding through the Umbrian countryside, he heard the distinctive clapping sound of a leper. In those times, no one was more reviled and feared than lepers. They were required to carry small wooden clappers to warn of their approach. Francis was particularly disgusted by lepers, and would go to great lengths to avoid them. But on this day, in spite of his fear, he dismounted his horse and approached the man. Francis, as Mirabai Starr recounts, "wrapped his cloak tenderly around the man's bony shoulders. Stunned by his own impulse, Francis looked into the leper's grateful eyes and, his own eyes welling with tears, kissed the man's oozing face."

What to make of this story? Encountering lepers on the street isn't exactly a common problem these days, but the story, of course, isn't about leprosy. Francis wanted us to "love the leper within us," those parts of ourselves too hideous for even our own gaze. Our shadow selves.

Saint Francis was no theologian. He wasn't even a priest. He was a poet, perhaps the world's only happy poet, and one who expressed himself mainly through action. He was the first saint to smile. "What else are the Friars but joyous minstrels of God," he said on his deathbed. That joy continues today, among the Franciscans of the South Bronx. They're always smiling—more than most people, certainly more than me, despite my boatloads of stuff and "accomplishments."

If Francis had any theology, it was what Meister Eckehart, the German mystic, called "a spirituality of subtraction." Francis believed that we must empty ourselves—of possessions, of ideas, of pride—before God can enter our lives. For Francis, poverty represented not enslavement but freedom, for if you possessed nothing then you had nothing to defend. Even knowledge, Francis believed, could prevent God from entering our hearts.

Perhaps that's why the story of Saint Francis is usually told not as straightforward biography but in a series of parables. Over the centuries, many of these apocryphal tales have emerged. It's impossible to confirm their veracity; that's not the point. One story I can't shake is this one: Francis had congenital eye problems, and by his forties was all but blind. The "cure" back then was to cauterize the eye with a hot iron. Before the procedure, Francis said: "Brother Fire, God made you beautiful and strong and useful. I pray you be courteous with me." When the red-hot iron was applied to his eye—without anesthesia, of course—Francis didn't flinch.

Francis was prone to extreme behavior. His life was, as Chesterton put it, "one riot of rash vows"—rash vows that just happened to work out. He was, if nothing else, a great pragmatist. He was interested in results. "Every tree is known by its fruits," he said. That was essentially William James's philosophy of pragmatism. James believed that something was "true" if it proved efficacious. "Truth is what works," he said. Likewise, underneath Francis's seeming madness lay a deep reservoir of common sense. William James saw these two traits—common sense and a sense of humor—as the same principle, traveling at different speeds. Or, as he put it, "A sense of humor is just common sense, dancing." The Franciscans are wonderful dancers.

I am not, but nonetheless I've always had some of that Franciscan zaniness. Growing up, I would punctuate the long, hot Baltimore summers by wearing underwear on my head. Perhaps it was my way of turning the world upside down, like Francis, or maybe I was simply desperate for something, *anything*, to relieve the oppressive August boredom. Either way, it worked. I felt better, reenergized. Predictably, the neighborhood kids would cry, "Mom, Dad, Eric's wearing underwear on his head again." This was always said with a mixture of shock and reassurance, as if my underwear-clad head signaled a passing of the seasons. I also detected covert admiration for my unabashed willingness to make a fool of myself. I imagine the righteous people of thirteenth-century Assisi reacted similarly to young Francis when he, for instance, rolled around in the snow naked. True, Francis was filled with love of God and I was filled with an irascible loopiness. But this is how the religious impulse always begins, with a small act of insanity. Sometimes it leads to sainthood, and sometimes...not. The larger difference, of course, is that Francis converted his insanity into action, something useful, while I never progressed much past wearing underwear on my head. Maybe saints are simply neurotics who somehow manage to transform all that crazy, circular energy into forward momentum.

Sainthood is problematic, though. Saints can inspire but also discourage. We can never achieve what they did, never join them on the pedestal, so why bother? Indeed, nothing has done more to undermine spiritual progress than the pedestal. Sitting high on that loathsome invention, the saint drifts out of view. Unable to imagine ourselves inhabiting the same lofty world as the saint, we reach for the remote and another beer.

"One of the first signs of a saint," wrote Trappist monk Thomas Merton, "[is] that other people do not know what to make of him." That is a polite way of putting it. Another way is this: Saints are nuts. Nowhere is the line between saint and madman thinner than in the life of Francis of Assisi. He disrobed in public. He kissed lepers. He talked to animals. He heard voices. He deprived himself of food and water and basic comforts. He described suffering as "perfect joy." A modern psychiatrist would probably diagnose Francis with borderline personality disorder, possibly psychosis. Yet he *was* a saint, in spite of himself.

Those three words—in spite of—are the holiest in the English language. As Paul Tillich observes, the answer to every religious question always contains some element of "in spite of." We are forgiven in spite of our sins. We believe in spite of the lack of evidence. We love our neighbors in spite of their flaws. Or, on a more fundamental level, we get out of bed every morning in spite of the inevitable approach of death. (An act of faith if ever there were one.) There is a huge gap between "because of" and "in spite of," and in that gap lies the difference between a life of cold reason and a life of faith. Most of the time we operate in because-mode. Banks lend us money because we have good credit histories. Our employer pays our salary because we contribute to the bottom line. Economic life depends entirely on "because." The religious life, though, operates in "in-spite-of" mode, and so does family life. We love our children not because they are good and successful but in spite of their achievements, or the lack thereof. We love them in spite of their behavior. "In spite of" makes a mockery of cost-benefit analyses. It makes no sense, and that is precisely why we need it.

Sunday mass. A rainy day, and I'm dangerously undercaffeinated. Not a great combination. But here I am. For some reason, I feel obliged. Perhaps it's my Jewish guilt contorting itself to fit inside a new, Catholic container. Perhaps it's simply that the mind craves routine, and this happens to be the routine here. Both are plausible theories, but truth be told I actually enjoy the Catholic mass. The words, yes, but mostly the atmosphere. The service is—and I mean this with the utmost respect—a very sensuous experience. It appeals to our senses. The guitar playing, the incense burning, the candles flickering. All ritual contains an element of theater, and that is what I'm witnessing here. Yet I cannot fully enjoy it, for it feels like a betrayal. One of the advantages of catapulting oneself clear of the Judeo-Christian traditions, to the land of Buddhism and other exotic faiths, is that you approach them largely baggage-free. Not so with Christianity. I arrive with excess baggage. What am I, a Jew, albeit a gastronomical one, doing in a church, crossing myself (sort of), taking communion (nearly), and confessing (almost)? Is it possible to betray a faith to which you have not been faithful?

During an intermission, I sneak some lukewarm coffee from the kitchen. Father Louis sees me and looks me in the eye in that quasi-satanic way of his. He tells me that the Sunday mass is the holiest of the holies and that he's dedicating this mass *to me*. I know he means it as an honor but it sounds like a threat. Everything he says sounds like a threat. He scares me.

Back in the chapel, we pray. We pray for the pope. We pray for the sick. We pray for the homeless. And we pray for me. Me? I am touched. And also kind of freaked out. In the past, whenever someone said, "I'll pray for you," it was always said as a put-down, or at least that's how I perceived it. My usual reply, spoken or merely thought, was something like, "Yeah, well, you keep your prayers, buddy. I don't need your stinking prayers." But this is different. When these people say they'll pray for me, I can tell they mean it. Spoken sincerely, there are no sweeter words in the English language than "I will pray for you." Another human being, petitioning a higher power, not on their behalf but yours.

The service ends with Father Louis intoning, "As it was, is now, and will be forever," and something about that timeless sentiment, its sense of continuity and inevitability, melts away my guilt and my stress, lifts my spirits.

With eastern faiths, one can easily say, "It's not personal." These religions operate, as William James put it, on a wholesale, not a

retail level. Not so with Christianity. Christ is definitely into retail. For Christians, God is not some vague universal mushiness;
no pantheistic fuzziness here. Christianity promises a relationship,
a personal relationship, with God, in a way that no other faith
does. As one of the friars put it: "It doesn't get any more personal than one person entering into another. I mean, that's very
profound and that's very radical." Jesus *was* a radical, an extrem-
ist, a fact that is often overlooked given Christianity's mainstream
status today. This extremism is either a very good thing or a very
bad one, depending on whether you're ready for that sort of radical commitment. I'm not sure I am. The most radical moment in
my life, my Tokyo story, occurred years ago, and as my memory
of it fades, I'm starting to wonder if it really happened. Brother
Crispin has no such doubts. That sort of thing happens to him
all the time. The God moment, he calls it. "It is completely natural and supernatural," he said. "See, there was this cooperation
between you and God in that moment. There was a profound cooperation between what God wants and what you want. And that
cooperation is called union of heart. Communion. And when there
is communion there is joy. So for that brief moment you experienced a shadow of the communion of people in Heaven."

I sit there, taking this in. The problem, I realize, is that I am trying to do it all myself, to make something happen. Saint Francis
taught that this is impossible. He strived for a "radical dependency." We are not supposed to *do* anything. It has all been done
for us, by Jesus.

I am struck by a desire to help. Something is driving me to be
bigger than myself, to be useful. But the brothers don't know what
to do with me. I have no skills, at least not the kinds that are useful when running a homeless shelter. They ask me to help carry
some donated clothes, tied tight in Hefty garbage bags, to a storage room. I do that, and it feels good, but it's not enough.

Finally, Brother Crispin gives me an assignment. My task is to empty large bottles of shampoo into dozens of smaller, travel-size bottles that can be distributed to the residents. Okay, I can do that. It is time-consuming, tedious work. I keep spilling shampoo everywhere. After an hour, I smell like a cheap beauty salon. And all the while a refrain is playing in my head: *Eric is doing a good deed. See what a good person Eric is.* This is not the Franciscan way, I know. This is not the way of selfless love. I am not doing this chore for God, not even for the residents of the shelter, I am doing it for me. So I can feel better about myself. Is that so terrible? The men still get their shampoo.

Over lunch one day, I ask Father Rich, a man of slight build and fulsome Old Testament beard, about motivation. Does it matter?

Yes, he says, motivation matters, but "we can't wait for perfect motivation, or nothing would ever get done." In this sense, the Franciscans are very much aligned with William James. He believed that emotions stem from actions and not, as is commonly held, the other way around. "I don't sing because I'm happy; I'm happy because I sing," James said. Likewise, the Franciscans believe that action creates a new reality. "Fake it until you make it," they are fond of saying, just like James Hopkins in Kathmandu. Or, to put it another way, we act our way into a better way of thinking, rather than thinking our way into a better way of acting. The exact opposite of navel-gazing.

Personally, I have been gazing at my navel for so long it's a wonder it hasn't filed a sexual-harassment complaint. *Stop staring at me, you pervert.* So often in my life I have hesitated, forestalling action until I achieve the requisite state of mental clarity. That clarity, I now realize, may never come, and meanwhile I have forfeited so many experiences. Moreover, those experiences might have *created* the clarity I so desperately seek. Action precedes belief. "Just do it" is not only a clever marketing slogan. It is a philosophy.

I ask about gratitude. Are the men in the shelter grateful? Not exactly. The friars receive very little in the way of thanks. One brother explains that before coming to the friary he had a very romantic notion of helping the poor. In this fantasy, he's up in the hills of Bolivia helping the gentle and grateful locals. The fantasy was just that. "That has not been my experience here. Sometimes you get a thank-you, but there is also a lot of ingratitude and a sense of entitlement. That was, and still is, difficult. You find yourself trying to love someone who doesn't want to be loved." That would drive me nuts. I don't know how they sustain it.

Lunch is a leisurely affair, time being, in the Franciscan universe, an infinitely expandable dimension. They have plenty of time for my nagging questions. I want to know how they manage the chastity bit but that seems too invasive a question so instead I ask about another of their vows: poverty. Don't they miss stuff?

No, we don't, they tell me. Some of the friars, those young enough to have grown up in the digital age, can still recall what it was like to own a cellphone, to use Facebook. Sometimes they still feel a vibration in their pocket, like a phantom limb, a distant echo of a former life, one that, it turns out, they do not miss. "I had to learn how to pay attention again," says Brother Angelo, a smiley young friar. He has a steady gaze, and can carry on a conversation without periodically staring at a flashing screen. How refreshing.

I'm trying to wrap my mind around the notion that abject poverty is a source of joy. Brother Crispin calls the notion that stuff can make us happy "the big lie." Our rampant materialism, he says, is a form of addiction. "People think that things can fill the hole, but really it doesn't. You just want more of that thing. And you can shove the entire ocean into this hole and still it's empty."

Until now, I have viewed the friars' poverty as a form of self-denial, masochistic almost. But no one forced them to live this way and, as Gandhi observed, "Restraint self-imposed is no compulsion." For the friars, their material poverty represents freedom. By owning no stuff they are free from having to protect their stuff, free from coveting others' stuff (or others coveting theirs), free from constantly upgrading their stuff, free from worrying if they have the right stuff, free from finding a place for all of their stuff. Not only stuff. Also experiences. We can be attached to those too, and of this I am guilty. I collect experiences: the perfect meal, the perfect trip, each one more perfect than the last. The collection is never complete, and never will be, as long as I fail to heed the words of Ali ibn Abu Talib, the fourth caliph of Islam: "Asceticism is not that you should not own anything, but that nothing should own you." Our experiences can own us just as easily as our stuff, although they do take up less closet space.

With no TV or radio or Internet, the friars don't know much about what is happening in the "real world," yet they seem to manage just fine. They figure news of anything truly important will eventually reach them. I think of all the time I've invested in staying current and "up to speed" and wonder if it was a good investment. I am well versed in the problems of the world but do little about them. The Franciscans know much less but do so much more. In fact, they take a certain perverse pride in being so out of touch. "I'm so far out of the loop, I'm in the loop," is a favorite line of Father Glenn, one of the order's founders.

The noon bell rings. I point out that the correct time is twelve forty-five. The friars just shrug as if to say, "What's forty-five minutes? We're on Franciscan time."

The next day they ask me to man the front desk of the shelter. Mainly, this entails monitoring the security cameras and answering the phones. They get the strangest calls.

"Do you have room for two Siamese?" asks one caller.

"Hmm. Do you mean people from Thailand?"

"No, I mean two cats."

"Sorry, ma'am. We're not that kind of shelter."

Apparently, this is a common misunderstanding. For some reason, when you google "Bronx" and "animal shelter" the Franciscan shelter is the first thing that pops up.

The phone again. "Hello. Saint Anthony's Shelter. Eric speaking. May I help you?"

"I'd like a room for tonight."

"I'm sorry, sir, but we're full. If you like I could put your name on the waiting list."

"What waiting list?"

"It's this sheet..."

"What? I only get a sheet, not a blanket?"

"No, sir, a sheet of paper. I can put you on the list."

"I don't want no waiting list. It's because I'm Scottish, isn't it? That's why you won't give me a room."

"No, sir, it's not. We're full."

"You don't like Scots?"

"I like them just fine."

"Then why won't you give me a room?"

At this point, I'm getting uncomfortable and don't know what to do.

"I told you, sir. We're full. Even if you were from Mars, we wouldn't have a room."

"Oh, now you don't like Martians, do you?"

"No, sir, as I told you..."

"It's because I'm white. That's why you won't give me a room."

Now things are really getting uncomfortable. "No, sir, as I said..."

I hear laughter coming from outside the glass-enclosed office. It's Brother Oisin, an Irish friar, holding a phone. I've been played, and played well.

"Your goodness must have some edge to it, else it is none," said

Emerson. The Franciscans have plenty of edge. They are the merry pranksters of the Christian world. Who says God can't be fun?

One afternoon, I'm standing at the entrance to the main chapel at the friary. This one is much larger than the small, intimate chapel where mass is normally held. I prefer the smaller one. Architecture is more than a matter of aesthetics. It determines the substance of the service. I've never understood the appeal of the grand cathedral or synagogue. I suppose they're intended to evoke the grandeur of God, to reflect His greatness, but I find it only diminishes me. Houses of worship are supposed to bring us closer to God but most have the opposite effect. It's especially incongruous that Christianity, the most personal of religions, should hold its services in such impersonal spaces. History explains a lot. When Christianity migrated from the Middle East to Europe in the first century, services moved from small buildings, or simply outdoors, to massive and ornate basilicas. The priests then began to wear vestments to match the formality of the structure. Soon, the services themselves took on a more formal air. Ritual expands to fill the space provided.

It's hot. Latin music wafts in from the sidewalk, mixing with the liturgy, spicing it up. I see Father Louis seated, praying, his head swaying back and forth in the hot air. I notice a nun, a young woman, standing next to me, so I introduce myself. Her name is Caitlin. She has a degree in art history. I ask how she went from art history to the life of a nun and she tells me how she partied in college, "but it wasn't making me happy. It was self-centered yuckiness. I felt weighted down by my own self-centeredness." So she joined a convent.

"What is it about Christianity that you find so appealing?" I ask.

"Forgiveness. No other religion can do that. It's unconditional forgiveness. It's love."

I have nothing to add to that, so I resort to my lame habit question: "How do you feel about wearing a habit? Isn't it hot in the summer?"

"No, I love it," she says, and seems to mean it. Her hair is covered, of course, and she is not wearing any makeup, but still, I can tell that she is an attractive woman. This makes me uneasy. Religious garb has a strange effect on me. It gets me—how to put this?—interested. It's a real problem. There was the time I was in Kashmir, a predominantly Muslim region of India, interviewing a woman who was leading one of the many separatist movements there. She was covered from head to toe in a black *burkha*. All I could see were her eyes, peering through a slit in the *niqab*, face covering. Now, I'm not usually big on eye contact. As I've said, it makes me uncomfortable. But in this case, I could either look her in the eye or stare at a wall of black cloth. So I looked at her eyes, and—whoa!—it was unexpectedly, incredibly intimate. I knew such feelings were wrong, forbidden, and of course that fact only heightened my arousal. I was so flustered I could barely get through my questions. Later I'd learn that my reaction is fairly common. Say what you wish about the male libido, it is remarkably adaptable. It works with what is available. Men in Pakistan have been known to go bonkers over a bare ankle or, should they get incredibly lucky, a stray bra strap. Religion attempts to corral the libido but, it seems, manages only to relocate the object of its attentions. I'm not sure this represents progress.

Why do so many religions frown upon sex, at least for any purpose other than procreation? It is not, as is commonly thought, mere prudishness. Sex is pleasurable—the religious do not deny that—but there are other pleasures out there, they say, and these pleasures are accessible to us only if we redirect our Eros. Sex is not bad, per se, but it is a huge distraction, and like all distractions it exacts a toll. When our minds are preoccupied with the overtly physical act of sex, we are missing something. There is, as an economist would put it, an opportunity cost. Thus, followers of Taoism, the Chinese religion, often abstain from sex in order to preserve their vital energy, or *chi*. The Franciscans wouldn't use such terminology, but the idea is the same: They abstain from one pleasure in order to achieve another, higher pleasure. That, at least, is the theory.

So I'm talking to Caitlin, the hot nun, trying desperately not to make eye contact, when another woman, not a nun, approaches, reaching for her purse. She wants to make a donation. I look around for a friar but they're all busy praying. I try to put her off but she's insistent. She's already extracted a bill. "Please, take it," she says, practically throwing it at me. She has no idea who I am, except that I am talking to a nun so I must be righteous. (If only she knew.) I agree to take her money. Wow, I think, that was the easiest five bucks I ever made. No, that would be wrong, wrong, wrong. I snap out of it. I will give the money to one of the friars. Still, I can't help but appreciate the generosity this building attracts, and I get a taste of the temptation that men of the cloth must experience every day.

"Are you coming with us on Saturday?" asks one of the friars.

"Sure. Where are you going?"

"To the abortion clinic."

This makes me uncomfortable, even more than eye contact. I don't have strong views on abortion, but if forced to claim one, I would have to say I am pro-choice. I don't know anyone who falls into the other camp, probably for the same reason I had never been to the South Bronx. Our orbits never converge.

We hop in the Gray Ghost. I notice that the dashboard calendar is a month behind. "I'm surprised we have the right year," says Brother Oisin. We arrive at the clinic and, stepping out of the car,

Father Louis asks our small group to huddle. "Know that this is not a physical battle but a spiritual battle. The devil is all over this place." He then explains where we can stand and not stand. This is very important. "Don't touch the fence," says Father Louis. We walk to the front of the clinic, and Father Louis props up a picture of the Virgin Mary on the sidewalk. "If you don't mind, I'm going to put up a picture of your mother," he says to the escorts.

The escorts are pro-choicers who are here to ensure the women coming for abortions make it inside safely. They wear T-shirts that read "Escort" and stern expressions that say "Don't mess with me." They don't know what to make of me, standing alongside the friars, observing and taking notes.

Most of the friars quietly recite the rosary, but not Father Louis. He is in everyone's face. "Ladies, ladies, ladies, you don't have to do this; follow your conscience," he says. When a nurse, wearing green scrubs, steps out for a cigarette break, Father Louis says, "Hey, why don't you work at a real hospital?" He tells one of the escorts, a tough-looking woman, that she's invited to dinner at the friary. "I'm an organic vegan, so good luck with that," she snaps back.

I hate confrontation, so I walk around to the back of the clinic where Brothers Crispin and Oisin are quietly praying the rosary. "Holy Mother full of grace, the Lord is with thee. Holy Mother, forgive us our sins, save us from the fires of hell." This I can handle. But now Father Louis has joined us, and again, he is much more confrontational. He's talking to one of the escorts, a heavyset woman, but she's not listening. She's brought some sort of child's percussion instrument and is banging it in order to drown out the prayers and protests. She has her back to Father Louis and, at one point, puts out her palm, as if to demarcate her no-go line. Father Louis leans forward and kisses it. "That's sexual harassment," she says. "You can get arrested."

"I'm praying for you," says Father Louis.

"I don't want your prayers," the woman says.

I just stand there, clutching a Styrofoam coffee cup, wanting nothing more than to disappear. Finally, the friars pack up their signs and their rosaries and we climb back into the Gray Ghost. That night, lying in bed, trying to sleep, I hear a Good Humor truck, its childlike refrain clashing with the other, adult sounds of the night. I try to make sense of what transpired that morning at the clinic. I had encountered something that, so far, I have managed to avoid: the nasty, occasionally dangerous, intersection of faith and politics. I admire the Franciscans, but I do not approve of their abortion protests. Does one obviate the other? Or is this just another one of the paradoxes that define religious life?

One day, I tell Brother Crispin about my depression, and he is sympathetic, possibly empathetic too. "You should pray," he says.

"What? You mean meditate?"

"No, pray. Talk to God."

"He won't take my calls."

"That's not true. Just pray to God, however you perceive Him."

Prayer. It never occurred to me. I am not averse to other, more exotic spiritual exercises. I have meditated, masticated, masturbated. I have whirled, prostrated, cogitated, regurgitated, davened, pontificated, reflected, genuflected, and read (God knows I have read). I have not, however, prayed. A guy has to draw the line somewhere.

I don't know how exactly I have formed my views on prayer, if I could even call them "views." The fact is I have not given prayer much thought. In the jaded circles in which I travel, prayer, if it is discussed at all, is dismissed as a crutch for the weak and the deluded. It is one thing to watch one's breath or align one's chakras and quite another to pray. The word evokes images of a child, kneeling bedside, pleading with God to resurrect a dead cat or supply a certain toy, or perhaps smite a bully. I am above that sort of thing. Or am I?

I'm hearing voices. One belongs to Jewish theologian Abraham Heschel, who no doubt would diagnose me as suffering from a case of "religious bashfulness." Our prayer life has dried up, he argues, because we fancy ourselves too sophisticated. We need to get over that. Prayer is not for dummies.

No, it's not, Simone Weil, the French philosopher and Christian mystic, chimes in. Prayer is, at its most basic, simply about paying attention. Prayer is "absolutely unmixed attention."

True, says Mahatma Gandhi, but prayer also contains an element of self-deception, though not in the way atheists mean. The deception is that God is up there, outside of us. "We for a moment think of God as different from ourselves and pray to him," Gandhi says. There was nothing childish about Gandhi's prayers. He did not petition God to alter the material world but, rather, his attitude toward it.

The loudest voice of all belongs to Martin Gardner, the words plucked from his wonderful book *The Whys of a Philosophical Scrivener*. (Like all great books, readers swear it was written just for them.)

"Are you one of those dabblers in Eastern religions who likes to sit in a lotus position and meditate on a mantra, or on *om*, or on nothing?"

Yes, Martin, I am. How did you know?

"Let me recommend a more ancient practice. Try meditating about God. Say something to God. Give thanks for something. Ask for forgiveness for something. Ask for something you desire, remembering that God knows better than you whether you should have it or not."

But I can't pray. I feel silly.

"What can you lose? You might discover that at the heart of those old religious traditions, buried under the blood and balderdash, was something that gave them vitality, that held and still holds the allegiance of millions. You might discover that you have something in common with these believers after all."

The voices quiet. I return to my room and sit on the edge of my bed. I shut out the chorus of sirens, the airplanes overhead, the cries of "I'm gonna kill you, motherfucker," and I pray. What exactly transpired? Nothing spectacular, nothing that men and women haven't done for centuries. Beyond that, I'd rather not talk about it. It is personal.

I need a break. All of this asceticism and do-goodery is getting to me. I need to scratch my various materialistic itches, reconnect with my innate selfishness, and now. After morning prayers, I slip away, unnoticed, and hop on the Number Two train, feeling exhilarated and guilty in equal measure. At first, I'm the only white person on the train, but as we head south, that changes. We're like a giant MTA snowball, gathering whiteness until, when we finally reach Soho, virtually all color has been drained from the subway car.

I surface on Spring Street and am immediately overwhelmed. So much stuff! Trendy, minimalist stuff, trying so very hard to camouflage its stuff-ness, but stuff it is. I didn't realize how much my time with the Franciscans had recalibrated my tolerance for stuff. I am also struck by how self-conscious everyone is, how much of their mannerisms are a kind of performance, the sidewalk their stage. I feel like I have just arrived from the thirteenth century, which in a way I have. I am out of touch, out of step, literally. I get in people's way. I'm not keeping up. I'm moving at Franciscan speed, which it turns out is considerably slower than Soho speed.

I also notice how little people notice—anything. Everyone is twitchy, thumbing their iPhones, minds elsewhere. No doubt these hipsters, these younger versions of me, would consider the friars of the South Bronx hopelessly out of touch with the "real world." Yet I wonder: Who are the ones out of touch? The friars, unlike the denizens of Soho, are fully present. They know how to linger. They know how to look someone in the eye without silently calculating their social score. The materialism of Soho is particularly insidious because it is trying so hard to look like it is not. Army surplus bags that sell for five hundred dollars. Cargo pants that cost enough to feed the entire homeless shelter for a week.

I feel the urge to walk. Walking can be a deeply religious exercise. Whether it's Christian pilgrims walking the stations of the cross in Jerusalem; or a Buddhist monk, eyes closed, immersed in a walking meditation; or Muslims walking round and round the Kaaba in Mecca. Thomas Huxley, inventor of the word "agnostic," considered his mountain jaunts "the equivalent of churchgoing." Thoreau called his early-morning walks "a blessing for the whole day." The travel writer Bruce Chatwin took this sentiment a step further. Walking is not a path to God, it *is* God. "If you walk hard enough, you probably don't need any other God."

I like the way that sounds. So I walk. I walk north on Broadway, then angle west to Fifth Avenue. I keep walking. I walk past Steve Forbes, the billionaire, getting into his limousine. I walk past a beggar, and think: What would Saint Francis do? I know what he would do. He would disrobe right there on the street, as in fact he did in Assisi, and give all of his clothes to the beggar, then embrace him and apologize that he didn't have more to give. This is why I am not a saint. (One of the many reasons, actually.) But I do hand over a couple of dollars. As I walk away, the man says, "Thanks. This will help with my Viagra."

I walk and walk. My legs are tired, my mind shedding thoughts like Saint Francis sloughing his fine silk clothes. By Times Square

I have stopped thinking entirely, and yet I still walk, all the way to 86th Street, where I board a northbound train. When I finally arrive at the friary, I am exhausted but content. I feel as if I have come home.

I've grown tired of shelter cuisine. I want to go out to dinner but am intimidated by the South Bronx at night, so I invite two of the friars to join me. They are my protection. I recruit Brothers Angelo and Joseph. They don't put up much resistance. I suspect they're looking forward to a change of pace.

We make it only one block before encountering Jose. Jose is excited. Jose is agitated. Jose is drunk. He is a friendly drunk, but I sense the energy could pivot on a dime into something more ominous. I step back a few feet and let the brothers take the lead. They listen, for Jose has something very important to say—oh boy, it is so important but he can't quite get it out, owing to his inebriation. Jose glares at me. He senses my impatience. I know this because he says, "You're impatient, man." Nooo, Jose, I'm not. I'm just hungry (which is true). The brothers, though, are the pinnacle of patience. They stand there and listen to Jose while I slip down the hill and wait for them. Finally, Jose moves on, and the friars join me. How did you do it? I ask.

"We told him it would be rude to keep our friend waiting."

That was wise; they appealed to Jose's noble sense, allowed him to lift himself a bit higher. I learned my lesson, though. Never travel with a friar if you are in a hurry. Another lesson: Never turn to friars for dining advice. They don't have a clue. They eat out rarely and have, after all, taken a vow of poverty. These are not foodies. We wander aimlessly as the streets grow dark, and finally settle on a Mexican restaurant that, though two blocks from the friary, comes as a revelation to them. It's a nice place, the real thing. The neighborhood has been steadily improving in recent years. If it gets much better the friars may have to move to some-place worse, where they are needed more. They engage in a sort of reverse urban flight, always staying one step ahead of niceness.

We sit down and, over the guacamole and chips, they say grace, blessing not only the avocado but me, their benefactor. Once again, I like the way they say this sincerely, not by rote. But I have ulterior motives, as I so often do. I still don't know how to help. I still think of myself in the third person. *Eric is helping the needy. Eric is a regular Mother Teresa.* What is the right frame of mind? I still don't get it.

"If you do it for yourself, that's good," says Brother Joseph. "That's better than not helping at all. If you do it for the men you're helping, that's better. But if you do it for God, that is the best. Mother Teresa says, 'When you serve a person, especially a poor person, you serve God.'"

That is a very Christian idea, but not only Christian. All religions, to various extents and in various ways, preach altruism, but it is never simply about one human being helping another. The good deed is always part of some larger scheme. A Muslim who helps his fellow man is submitting to God's will. A Jew is engaging in *tikkun haolam*, repairing the world. A Buddhist is generating positive karma. Does any of this matter? Are Christians, for instance, in a way using the people they are helping in order to serve God? If so, does it diminish their good deeds, or magnify them? I silently ponder this while stabbing a tortilla chip into the guacamole.

Our quesadillas arrive, and they are good. Then we walk, and that is good too. When we arrive at the friary, my stomach is heavy with quesadilla, my heart heavy with regret. This is not good. Why did I eat so much? I confess my quesadilla regret to Brother Angelo, who says, "When in doubt, be thankful." What an unexpected response. When in doubt be thankful. When I'm in doubt

I worry, or spin my wheels, or resort to default sadness. Why not be thankful? The opposite of gratitude is entitlement, and that is a sure path to misery. Who says the universe owes me anything? I am here, aren't I? Why isn't that enough?

The next morning, I sleep through the morning prayers, and head to the kitchen for breakfast. I pour myself a bowl of Happy O's and sit in the dining room, alone, staring out the window at what is shaping up to be a fine day. I'm about to dig in when I stop myself, spoon hovering in midair. Something doesn't feel right. What is it? Ah, yes. "Thank You, Lord, for our daily bread..." Shit. I can't remember the rest. Oh, never mind. "Thank You, God, for the grub." I dive in. The Happy O's, for once, live up to their name. I, however, am not a Happy O. I still suffer, though not for my sins or anyone else's. I just suffer, for suffering's sake, I suppose, or perhaps like Saint Paul, who famously complained of "a thorn in my flesh." Yes, that's how I feel, only my thorn feels more like a branch, or maybe a redwood.

I ask Brother Crispin, the most psychologically attuned of the friars, about this. I don't understand the Christian—and especially the Franciscan—notion that suffering is a form of "perfect joy." I have suffered for many years now and find no joy in it, perfect or otherwise. Am I missing something? Or was Francis a masochist?

No, he wasn't, says Brother Crispin, and neither are his progeny. "Suffering is the experience of one's self being crushed and remade into the image of the divine love," he says, and again I wince at the violent imagery, like the Sufis' advocating annihilation of the self, or Wayne from Staten Island threatening to throw me back against my own experience. Why must God hurt so much? Because, says Brother Crispin, it is a necessary transition between suffering and love. "One suffers, at least a little, for love because the will to love destroys the narcissistic self." This is good suffering, he says. And bad suffering? "It's self-destructive, masochistic, or, worse still, a kind of macho spirituality." I know what he means by macho spirituality. I've met these people. Smug meditators who brag about how long they can sit in serene silence, devout Christians who take great pride in their humility. These are people so confident in their spiritual abilities they don't need anyone's help, thank you very much.

I am not one of these people, not by a long shot, so I'm not offended when, toward the end of my stay, Brother Oisin asks, "Would you like us to pray over you?" I don't know exactly what he means, but I like the way it sounds. I picture Franciscans hovering over me like angels. I agree.

He and two of his colleagues will meet me in the main chapel that evening. I arrive a few minutes early. The chapel is empty, the only sound the thwok-thwok-thwok of a ceiling fan. I take a seat in one of the pews. I feel like I'm in the reception area of a doctor's office. That same sense of doing the right thing, being responsible, but still dreading what lies ahead and hoping it doesn't hurt too much.

Brother Oisin arrives with two other friars. One of them is an Irishman, like him, only taller, with deeply recessed eyes and a large protruding forehead. I've never seen anything quite like it; his forehead arrives a few seconds before the rest of him.

"What seems to be the problem?" inquires The Forehead, sounding like a doctor examining a patient.

"I have a dull ache," I say but regret the words as soon as they leave my lips. They sound so lame.

"I see," says The Forehead, without judgment, as if dealing with a particularly challenging case.

I lower my head and close my eyes, as instructed, and then feel hands on me. Reassuring hands. All I hear is the ceiling fan, then The Forehead says, "Jesus, help this child."

"Jesus says He loves you, cherishes you. Please be clear, Lord, what is the source of this dull ache, this tip of a spear? Please remove it."

"I'm getting something," interjects Brother Oisin. It's a verse from the Bible. "For he who gives himself to pleasure, he is dead while he is alive." Not helpful, I think, not helpful.

"I'm getting an image," says another of the brothers. "This may sound strange, but you're a child at a birthday party. There are hats, and candles and a cake. But there's nobody there. You hear a sound on the other side of a fence, but you find nothing when you get there. Maybe the lesson is that there is nowhere you need to be."

"Lord Jesus," I hear another voice say. "help Eric find where home is. Offer him wisdom and guidance."

The Forehead is getting an image of me fishing off of a pier with a simple Tom Sawyer pole. I'm fishing, he says, with an air of expectation, not hopelessness. Someone else gets an image of me milking a cow. Nobody is quite sure what that means.

They bless me. They pray for my search, and for my family and friends. The Forehead says, "Thank You, Lord, for these images." And that's it. They're gone. I'm alone in the cavernous chapel. The fan is silent now. All I hear is the occasional airplane and my own heartbeat. I feel like crying, but the tears don't come. I don't know what to make of those images. I've never milked a cow and am not one for fishing. Maybe there is some hidden meaning there. Maybe not. Yet I am filled with gratitude, touched that these three men, one with a forehead the size of Mount Rushmore, cared enough about my indeterminate dull ache to seek divine grace. Unfortunately, there was none that warm evening in the South Bronx, none I could detect, anyway. There was, though, plenty of what Aldous Huxley calls "human grace." Maybe that is enough.

* * *

It's time for me to go home. The brothers give me the names of some places where I could volunteer. I vow to follow up, but know I probably won't. I will get busy. Life will intervene. I say as much to Brother Crispin, who tells me, "That's okay. Your wife and daughter are your apostolate." Of course. Charity begins at home. Why hadn't I thought of that?

I wonder, though: Could I take a giant leap and dedicate my life to helping others? Could I actually become a friar? In years past, I have occasionally observed two of their vows—poverty and chastity—though never voluntarily, so I suppose it doesn't count. (I've never cared much for the third vow, obedience.) Regrettably, as much as I admire the Franciscans, as much as I like them, I can't see becoming one of them. I lack the self-discipline. I lack the personal relationship with Jesus. Besides, I like my stuff too much. I like experiences too much. And, truth be told, I like sex too much.

Little do I know that, a few thousand miles away, a religion awaits me that not only permits such indulgences, but sanctifies them.

CWM, feeling deprived. Looking for a god that is fun and a bit wild. Willing to venture out of my comfort zone. Are you far out enough for me?

At first, I think I've taken a wrong turn. I must have stumbled across a gathering of Realtors or marketing executives or one of the other sundry conventions that sprout in Las Vegas like so many plastic flowers in the desert. There's the same too-plush carpeting, the same laminated name tags dangling from pale, suburban necks, the same banal haven't-seen-you-since-Houston chitchat.

This is different, though. Everybody is beautiful. And speaking French. And there's a large sign, in psychedelic Sergeant Pepper colors, that reads "Raëlian Happiness World Tour." Beside it are two tables. On one is a diorama depicting some sort of futuristic housing complex: dome-shaped buildings and gardens connected by manicured pathways. It's expertly done, with fine details: tiny cars and, atop one building, a little silver flying saucer. It looks like something Frank Lloyd Wright might design—if he had been abducted by aliens. A few feet away, on a matching table, are two wicker bowls, filled with variously colored condoms. Red, green, purple—a rainbow of prophylactics.

Then things start to get strange.

I'm standing in line, waiting to pick up my registration packet, when I feel a hand brush against my left buttock. The room is crowded, so I assume it was an accident, but then the hand—the same hand, of that I'm sure—lingers ever so slightly before gliding across my right buttock, where it also loiters for a nano second, just long enough to signal the intentionality of the gesture. I spin around and spot a tall blond woman crossing the room. Owner of the hand, I presume. The corners of her mouth turn upward in the slightest hint of a smile, and then she is gone. Was this, I wonder, some sort of salutation? Maybe this is how these people— the Raëlians, that's what they call themselves—greet one another. Maybe it's the extra-terrestrial equivalent of a handshake or a peck on the cheek. I sure hope not. Several hundred people have registered for the weeklong event, and that is, by any measure, an awful lot of buttock.

I can't say I'm totally caught off guard by this strangeness. I have done my research. The Raëlians are the largest UFO-based religion (yes, there is more than one). They believe that humankind—indeed all life on earth—was created twenty-five thousand years ago by an astonishingly intelligent and benevolent alien race called the Elohim. That diorama I saw was a mock-up of the embassy the Raëlians hope to build in Jerusalem in order to welcome our creators upon their return in 2035. Until then, the Elohim basically want us humans to have an outrageous amount of fun. (Safe fun, mind you, thus the condoms.) The Elohim built us for pleasure, a fact that most other religions have willfully overlooked. The Raëlians are determined to correct that oversight.

We can't see the Elohim but they can see us. With their superior technology, they are always watching us, and they send occasional messages via the Last Prophet, a diminutive French journalist and race-car driver once known as Claude but who now goes by Raël, or "the messenger."

Does this sound strange? I thought so too when I first read about it from my home near Washington, DC, but here in Las Vegas, I have to confess it seems markedly less strange. Vegas has a way of doing that, of tempering even the oddest of oddities into something more plausible. It's context, I suppose, oddness being a relative trait. The Raëlians, in fact, are only one of several groups gathered at the hotel. There's also a children's beauty pageant—five-year-old girls trembling under the weight of gold crowns and parental projections; something called a "smoke out," which is, as far as I can tell, a club of beefy gay guys who like to wear leather and puff cigars; a contingent of soldiers on leave from Iraq; and, of course, the usual quickie wedding crowd, young brides dressed in ironic white, overflowing with happiness and cleavage. People hardly notice the Raëlians.

To be clear: I am not in Vegas for mere frivolity. This is research. The Raëlians are a legitimate religion, as recognized by the highest of authorities: the Internal Revenue Service. The Raëlians have not only tax-exempt status but all the other trappings of a religion: a creation story, a clergy, a theology, rituals, holy days. The only missing piece is a steamy sex scandal, but there's a reason for that. Alas, though, I get ahead of myself.

A smiling Raëlian volunteer hands me a little manila packet and an ID badge (yes, laminated) that I'm told to wear around my neck at all times. Everything is well run. I walk past the embassy mock-up, past the bowls of condoms, and into a long corridor. I'm not sure where to go next when Lara (so says her name tag), a tanned and leggy Californian, greets me with a shiny Raëlian smile.

"First time?" she asks.

"Yes," I say, knowing it must be obvious.

"Welcome." She touches my shoulder lightly and leads me down the corridor. As we walk, Lara mentions that she first received "the message" thirteen years ago. I nod knowingly, though I'm not sure exactly which message she's talking about.

"When did you receive the message?" she asks.

"Oh, recently," I say.

She gives me a knowing look. We enter a large conference room with a stage in the front and, alongside it, two giant TV screens. The atmosphere is festive, in that forced Vegas way. Samba music is playing. My eyes are drawn to the stage, where several women, wearing bikini tops and short skirts, are dancing showgirl-style. Not for the last time, I remind myself that I am attending a religious gathering and not a bachelor party. Lara steers me to a chair then advises me to turn off my cellphone and be happy. And then she is gone.

Sitting next to me is a middle-aged woman with cropped, graying hair. She doesn't look like she belongs here. She looks like a CPA or somebody's aunt. Glancing around the room, I see many people who fit that description. Sure, there are plenty of the ponytailed and the tattooed, but there's also a fair number of the slacked and the jacketed. The music, meanwhile, has degenerated into disco. *Do a little dance, make a little love, get down tonight.* Presumably, everyone is stone sober. The Raëlian faith forbids the use of drugs or alcohol. Even coffee is banned, a prohibition that strikes me as perhaps the most bizarre aspect of Raëlian doctrine.

Inside the conference room, the anticipation builds. Everybody is clearly waiting for something, but what? My mind races. I eye the emergency exits in case a fire or an orgy breaks out. It's possible. I've read about the Raëlians' supposed penchant for orgies, and an orgy is the last thing I'm interested in. For starters, as I've said, I have this reflexive dislike of group activity, and you don't get any more group, or active, than an orgy.

The music fades. The lights dim. We hear a mellifluous French-accented voice on a loudspeaker emanating from deep in the cosmos. Or maybe from behind a curtain. Either way, it is a very nice voice.

"He has dedicated the last thirty-seven years to making the world a better place," The Voice says. "Please welcome: the Prophet."

A man enters the room—not so much enters as materializes— and bounds onto the stage. He is in his early sixties, I guess, trim and fit, with thinning white hair pulled tight into a Samurai top-knot. The most striking thing about him is what he's wearing: all white. White pants, white shirt, white shoes, and a puffy white spaceman vest. He looks like he just popped out of a *Star Trek* episode. Around his neck is a gold medallion the size of a small Frisbee. A couple of scantily clad women present the Prophet, Raël, with flowers. It's all very theatrical, perfectly stage-managed.

The crowd is on its feet, as am I, applauding. After a long while, they quiet down and the Prophet speaks.

"I have a question for you," he says, with a heavy Inspector Clouseau accent. "Are you Appy?"

"Yes!" everyone shouts.

"Okay," he says, "then I can go home. You don't need me." A titter of laughter ripples through the audience.

"What is that? Oh, you want to be *more* Appy?"

"Why have you come here?" Raël continues.

"To see you!" shouts someone from the back of the room.

"No, more," he says, brushing aside the sycophancy.

"To be more happy!" says someone else.

"No, more."

"To love!"

"More."

"To have consciousness."

"Yes, but still more."

"To feel the Elohim."

"Yes," says Raël, as if praising the smartest kid in the classroom. "To feel together with the Elohim. The Elohim have advanced technology; they are constantly looking at the earth. So they can see us, but it's easier if we're all together. We love the Elohim. We don't want to give them a hard time." More laughter.

It's not easy being Raëlian, the man formerly known as Claude says. People make fun of you. They laugh. "What? You believe in UFOs?" he says, doing a passable Bubba accent. "We need to escape the zoo," says Raël, the zoo being Out There. "When you come here you may be contaminated. Even the best Raëlians, we are contaminated. We need to be together in order to escape the zoo." Thus began a theme that would repeat itself throughout the week: Out There is the problem. If you are troubled, maybe addicted to drugs, the fault lies not with you but with your "programming," as Raël calls it. His use of that word is no accident. The Raëlians speak the language of science, albeit a garbled dialect, as I would discover.

Raël mentions the Buddha, one of his half brothers along with Jesus and Muhammad. "The teachings of the Buddha were the best," says Raël. "Almost perfect but not quite." Another theme: Others have almost grasped the truth, almost but not quite. Raël is not only the Last Prophet but the best.

The Raëlian message, strange as it may seem, is all about empowerment. We are told that we can achieve anything.

"You could all be a Buddha," says Raël. "You could all be another Raël. You can even be better than me," and with those words there is an audible gasp. Better than Raël?

"That's right. You have unlimited potential. Let's say, 'Yes.'" And we do. "Yes!" We shout it at the top of our lungs, and I admit it feels good.

Raël speaks for more than an hour before taking a break and sitting in an all-white chair especially reserved for him. He is shadowed by two muscular guys with earpieces and grim expressions. Raël takes his security seriously, though I can't imagine who would wish harm to this happy Frenchman.

I take stock of what I've just heard. To be honest, I agree with most of what he says. Not the alien story—I have serious doubts about that—and I'd wager he is not the Buddha's half brother. The rest, though, the bulk of his presentation, consisted of the most banal of self-help clichés. Raël on happiness: "Happiness comes from inside." Raël on taking chances: "Get out of your comfort zone." Raël on authenticity: "Be yourself." Raël on your future: "Dream big." Raël, I realize, is Tony Robbins in a space suit.

The Raëlians worship the Elohim, our alien creators, but they don't believe in God (although "Elohim" means "God" in Hebrew). "Our God is science," they say. Indeed, they are constantly citing one scientific study after another, using slides and Power-Point (the Raëlians love PowerPoint nearly as much as they love sex) to underscore the point about how, for instance, our thoughts mold our brains, altering neural pathways.

"We have a very small mission," Raël continues, back onstage. "We want to save the world." The crowd laughs. But Raël is serious. Raëlians *are* trying to save the world, though not in a typical way. No planting of trees or feeding of the poor for the Raëlians. Instead, they sponsor events like Go Topless Day and fund charities like Clitoraid, which runs clinics in Africa that specialize in mending the mutilated genitalia of young women. (Their website informs me I can "sponsor a clitoris.") And then there is the Raëlians' best-known venture: Clonaid. Its goal is to clone human beings. In the Raëlian world, this makes sense. The Elohim created us in their image, so now the Raëlians are attempting to emulate our creators. In 2002, the scientists at Clonaid made headlines when they claimed, prematurely it turns out, to have cloned a human being, a baby girl named, of course, Eve.

That failure hardly put a dent in Raël's reputation among his followers. Nothing seems to do that. Unlike the pope, or evangelical preachers like Jimmy Swaggart, Raël is virtually scandal-proof. He need not worry about getting caught with his pants down, though I suppose outrage might erupt among the Raëlian rank and file should the Last Prophet be caught with his pants *up*.

All of the newcomers are asked to line up and, one by one, stand on the stage and talk a bit about themselves. It is, I realize, an exercise in group bonding, the kind you'd see at any corporate retreat or AA meeting. Everyone seems normal enough. One guy tells us he lives in Syracuse and works at a restaurant. "Nothing special," he says meekly.

"But you *are* special," shouts a Raëlian, and everyone applauds.

Next up is a sixty-nine-year-old retired rancher from Texas who was in Vegas for the gambling but thought he'd check out the Raëlians, for reasons not entirely clear. More applause. A woman steps onstage and says, "I was always Raëlian. I just didn't know it." Hearty applause. A wiry middle-aged man with wavy dark hair is next. He's originally from Puerto Rico, he explains, and he's known since he was nine years old that he's always had protectors and now he's saying something about a near-death experience and how that raised questions, *huge* questions, about life and the universe and then he read Raël's books and all of his questions were answered. Applause. Except he's still talking. He won't stop talking. He's going on and on and won't leave the stage. Ricky, one of the "priest-guides," tries to steer the man to a soft landing, but this guy just keeps going. I squirm in my seat. This is uncomfortable. But I'm also fascinated. How will the Raëlians handle dissent? Is this when they unholster the phasers, set to stun? The resolution turns out to be decidedly less dramatic. Ricky gently but firmly persists, insisting that the man give someone else a turn and finally, reluctantly, he steps off the stage.

Now Ricky is trying to flush out the few remaining newcomers. I realize I am one of the holdouts. I feel like a fraud, which technically I am, since I am here undercover. The Raëlians have been burned by journalists before, mocked as crazy hedonists, and I didn't think they would take kindly to my presence. I feel eyes on me, though I might be imagining that.

I silently weigh the consequences of acting versus not acting. I decide to act. I walk onto the stage and instantly feel that jolt of fear and exhilaration that I always get in front of a large group. *I want to die; I want to stay here forever.* I say something about being a happiness consultant—which isn't far from the truth, given my previous book—and how a friend of a friend introduced me to "the message" (again, not far from the truth; I found the Raëlians on the Internet) and that I am here because I am curious. Which is exactly the truth. I *am* curious. Like many people, I believe we are not alone in the universe. On all of those billions of planets, surely there must be life on one of them. And perhaps that life is more advanced than us, perhaps these life-forms possess the ability to create other life-forms, just as we are beginning to do in laboratories here on earth, perhaps the Raëlians are onto something. Then there is the not-small matter of the caressing hands and plentiful condoms. I'm curious about that too—specifically, is it possible to base a religion on the pursuit of pleasure, rather than its denial, and, if so, is the resulting theology any less valid than, say, Christianity or Islam, faiths that take a much more proscribed approach to matters of the flesh? I'm also curious about Raël's nifty space suit and where I could get my hands on one.

None of which I mention, of course, while standing there onstage. Instead, I finish by saying how happy I am to be here. Which is true. Applause. All of those hands clapping for *me*, signaling their approval (their love?) for no other reason than the fact that I'm here and I'm me. I must admit, it feels good. Never mind that old Zen koan about the sound of one hand clapping, the sound of two hundred hands clapping is much more satisfying. Maybe this is what draws people to religion. Not the theology or the ritual or even the promise of Heaven but the acceptance, the unconditional love, or "collective effervescence," as French sociologist Emile Durkheim called it.

Odd as the Raëlians may seem, I find something about them surprisingly familiar. But what? Then it dawns on me: The Raëlians are caught in a 1970s time warp. They are me-first, disco-prone, and utterly enthralled by gadgetry. It's life imitating art, and in this case the art is Woody Allen's *Sleeper*. I can practically see the orgasmatron now. I was a teenager in the '70s and wish I had known about the Raëlians then. I would have joined in a heartbeat. Raëlianism is the perfect religion for sixteen-year-old boys. It has cool gadgets *and* hot chicks, and has elevated masturbation to an act of holy submission. The religion is mildly subversive, just enough to piss off your parents but not quite enough to get you arrested. Yes, between the Raëlians and my local synagogue it would have been no contest. Not even close.

We adjourn for a break. I grab a plastic cup of water, silently cursing the Raëlian prohibition on coffee. I stop by a small table where Raël's books are for sale. I grab a handful of titles: *The Message Given by Extra-Terrestrials, Extra-Terrestrials Took Me to Their Planet*, and *Let's Welcome the Extra-Terrestrials*. I also throw in a copy of *Sensual Meditation* for good measure. The books have wonderfully campy covers, retro illustrations of ETs with bald heads and glowing, mysterious eyes. I stash the books in my bag and decide to chat with some Raëlians.

The movement, for some reason, attracts many French Canadians, and quite a few followers with scientific or technical backgrounds. I meet a physician from Montreal, an economics professor from Ohio, and a few software engineers. They tell me they were drawn to the Raëlians because the message makes sense. "This is not for imbeciles," the economics professor tells me. Perhaps, but I have many questions. Why, for instance, did these aliens, the Elohim, choose a second-rate French journalist as their messenger? And given their presumably busy schedules, why did they bother to create the mosquito or the cockroach? I keep my questions to myself, though. I don't want to appear too confrontational and, besides, I'm having fun. Why ruin it with questions?

I'm downing my third plastic cup of water, hoping there's a trace of caffeine, or something, *anything*, in the Vegas water supply when I hear music: an original Raëlian score that goes like this: *Shut up and be happy, feeling sad is crappy.* Over and over and over again. That's our cue to take our seats. Raël has materialized back onstage. He's shifted gears and is now attacking U.S. foreign policy, though he clearly benefits from our religious freedoms. (Try being a Raëlian in Saudi Arabia.) He is especially piqued that women in this country cannot go topless. They must hide their nipples, Raël says, in the same tone of voice one might use when discussing, say, waterboarding. I admit this lack of toplessness disturbs me too, though not as much as world hunger or AIDS.

Raël is going on about this outrage, this oppressive mammary policy, when someone shouts, "Free your breasts free your mind." Someone else chimes in, then two, three, a dozen people—a hundred!—are all shouting, "Free your breasts free your mind." This is odd, I'm thinking, when suddenly people around me begin to do just that. They free their breasts. Women, as well as a few men, remove their shirts in one fluent motion and I find myself suddenly, inexplicably, afloat in a sea of fleshy, recently liberated breasts. Liberated minds, too, I presume, but I confess it's the breasts that get my attention. Tan, healthy breasts for the most part, but not universally so. Raëlian breasts, it turns out, are much like terrestrial breasts. They are beholden to the same law of gravity and with the same predictable results.

The day's events are over. We have several hours' "free time" before the evening event: Carnival Night. I use my time to find out more about the Raëlians. How did all this craziness start? I walk back to my room, dodging five-year-old beauty queens and gay cigar smokers en route, and plop down on my bed with Raël's books. I crack open *The Message Given by Extra-Terrestrials*.

It was December 1973. A twenty-seven-year-old Frenchman, Claude Vorilhon, was editing a little-known magazine for racing enthusiasts. One day he felt compelled, drawn, to visit a volcanic crater in southern France. He was walking when suddenly he saw an object in the sky. At first he thought it was a helicopter, but it didn't make any noise. Not a sound. Then it landed about thirty feet from Claude, who regretted not taking his camera that day. A door opened and stairs descended. Two creatures emerged, each about four feet tall with almond-shaped eyes and long black hair.

"You regret not having brought your camera?" asked the creatures in perfect French.

"Yes, of course," said Claude.

The Elohim knew everything about Claude. They had been watching him since the time of his birth "and even before." They had chosen him to convey their message to humanity.

The aliens told Claude to return the next day, with a Bible and a notebook. He did. They went through the Bible, line by line, not disputing the events that took place but explaining them in terms of technology and science. For instance, the Genesis flood was caused by exploding nuclear missiles. Noah's ark? It was actually a spacecraft that floated high above the earth. Crossing the Red Sea? Repulsion beams made that possible. Jesus's healings? Those were performed by concentrated laser beams fired from a faraway spaceship.

Why, asked Claude, did you come to earth? A long time ago, the Elohim explained, they were a lot like humans are now. They were experimenting with creating new life-forms. A debate erupted on their planet, with some Elohim in favor of the experiments and others warning that such meddling might create dangerous monsters. So they agreed to conduct their experiments someplace else: earth. And thus began what was most likely the very first case of intergalactic dumping.

I close the book. I don't know what to think. I'm fairly certain none of this ever happened, and that Raël, aka Claude, is either lying or deluded, possibly both. But how to explain his eighty thousand followers? Are they all deluded? Many seem quite sane—some, frankly, saner than myself. Besides, if a factually true creation story were the sole gauge of a religion's validity, then there would be very few religions. There are other kinds of truths, though. Moral truths. Truths of the heart. The Raëlians might be wrong about the whole alien encounter but right about other things, such as the need to inject a bit of fun into religion, the wonders of science, the proper use of condoms. One falsehood does not render the entire enterprise worthless.

I'm reminded of what a senior bishop at the Vatican, someone close to the pope, once told a former religion reporter for *The Washington Post*. "I can no more believe in the virgin birth than I can believe in Santa Claus," he said. "But I love my faith." In a flash of honesty, the bishop articulated an ethos, a way of being, that hard-core rationalists overlook—namely, that we can derive great benefit, tangible benefit, from myth. Not a myth in the sense of a lie, but myth in its original meaning, as a story that helps guide us through this thicket of thorns otherwise known as life. Joseph Campbell puts it this way: "Is it true? Who cares? This is the source of my life. Question the cosmological authenticity of a clergyman's archaic image of the universe, his notion of the history of the world [and he's likely to say—] 'Who are you, pride of intellect, to question this wonderful thing that's been the source of all my life?' "

Many Americans sense this intuitively. When asked in a recent survey what is most important about their religion, only 40 percent answered, "I believe it is the source of truth." That leaves an awful lot of people who derive some other benefit from their faith. What might that be? Psychologist Chana Ullman's landmark study of religious converts offers some clues. She found that what mattered most to the convert was not belief but experience. The converts were not appropriating a new ideology so much as a new form of "emotional relief." The Raëlians, deluded or not, are getting plenty of relief, emotional and otherwise.

Frankly, it's refreshing to find a religion that is not opposed to ejaculation. You'd be surprised how many are. It's not only the Catholics who believe that sex distracts us from God, but Taoists too. They believe that ejaculation is a waste of precious *chi*, or energy. The Jains, an ancient ascetic faith in India, believe that ejaculation is murder, since so many sperm die in the process. When I first heard that, I shuddered with guilt, as I recalled one particular day when, at age sixteen, I committed my own personal genocide. The Raëlians, though, are solidly pro-ejaculation. Yes, they want me to ejaculate, and soon. Well, not *too* soon but, still, it's refreshing.

Something isn't sitting right with me, though I can't put my finger on it. It's not the aliens or the liberated breasts—well, not that only, but something else about the Raëlians that makes me uneasy. I don't think they're dangerous. They're not about to concoct one of those group suicides, not when they're having this much fun. That is the problem, I realize. Fun. Is it enough?

The next morning, I walk into the conference room and find everyone lying on the floor. I join them, using my backpack as a pillow. New Age music is playing over the loudspeaker. The Voice is back, as French and mellifluous as ever. Breathe in deeply, The Voice tells us. And I do. The Voice is telling me to feel the cells in my toes. I'm not sure how to feel individual cells but I want to please The Voice so I try.

"Now focus on your arms. Gently contract your arms. Now move up to the intestines." I do as I'm told, traversing my intestines, then hanging a left at my spleen and making a beeline for my gallbladder. I feel like I'm in that old Raquel Welch movie *Fantastic Voyage*. That's the one where a team of scientists boards a miniaturized submarine then journeys through some guy's body. The movie worked on many levels, appealing to the anatomically curious as well as those who liked the idea of Raquel Welch scooting through their capillaries, which pretty much covered all of America.

"You are an amalgam of cells," The Voice tells me. "Every cell is in deep relaxation. You are at peace." And the funny thing is— I am. I'm not sure why. Maybe it's because I'm focusing on something, anything, besides my usual litany of worries. The Voice sends us into a spiral—clockwise, of course—deep into our brains. This makes me a bit dizzy but it is not an unpleasant sensation. "All is energy," The Voice says, and who am I to argue. "All is movement. You are movement. For eternity. Even when standing still you are moving, vibrating. You are the universe becoming aware of itself."

I'm trying to wrap my spiraling mind around that one when The Voice announces that the meditation is over. I slowly open my eyes, as The Voice instructs, and am surprised to see a woman standing over me. She is wearing a maroon toga and holding a small bowl of fruit. She kneels down so that we are at eye level and removes a strawberry from the bowl. I'm not sure what to do—The Voice has fallen silent just when I need it—and so there is a moment of awkwardness. At least it's awkward for me. She doesn't have an awkward cell in her Raëlian body. Then it dawns on me. She is here to feed me. Of course. I open my mouth and she inserts the freshest, juiciest strawberry I've ever had. Then the toga lady is gone, off to feed someone else.

I look around the room and take in the scene. All around me toga-wearing pleasure-bots, as they call themselves, are feeding people fresh fruit while gentle, New Age music plays and on the two large screens images of nebula and swirling galaxies flash like so much space porn. I find the tableaux strange, of course, but also oddly familiar. Where have I seen this before? Documentaries about ancient Rome spring to mind. No, that's not it. Of course! I'm in one of those *Star Trek* episodes where Captain Kirk and his landing party have just beamed down to some planet and found that the inhabitants want nothing more than to please Kirk and his crew. It's Eden again. Everything is perfect. Bones has run off with some sultry native while Chekov lies in the sun reading poetry. Spock, as usual, remains skeptical. There must be a catch, and of course there is. The fresh fruit turns out to contain sulfuric acid, or the beautiful inhabitants are secretly plotting to kill the crew and commandeer the *Enterprise*, or something awful like that. And that's the way I feel now, lying on the floor with these beautiful French-accented Raëlians so selflessly feeding me fresh fruit: What's the catch?

The next morning and that same infernal song, *Shut up and be happy, feeling bad is crappy.* It's driving me nuts. Raël is back, and this time he is serious. No joking. No masturbation tips.

"How many of you have had problems with alcohol?" he asks.

Many hands go up.

"How about drugs?"

More hands.

"How many of you have considered suicide?"

I'm surprised how many hands go up. I'm even more surprised that one of those hands belongs to me. Why have I just confessed such dark thoughts to this group of libidinous UFO junkies? Again: context. When bombarded with such outlandish notions as "aliens created us" and "coffee is bad," then I suppose "I want to kill myself" becomes just another outrageous idea thrown up for grabs.

Only for me it is not quite so outrageous. A history of suicide attempts, some failed, others successful, lurks in my gene pool like a bogeyman waiting to strike. Sometimes, when the darkness comes, I briefly consider the option, or at least the *idea* of the option. I have never made actual plans, never measured the height from an overhead rafter to the floor or lingered in the rubber-hose section of a hardware store. When I'm feeling generous, I tell myself that my dark thoughts make me a better person. That, unlike most people, I have considered the alternative and actively chosen life. Like I said, that's when I'm feeling generous. Usually, such gloominess only inspires more self-loathing.

We put our hands down and, as I look around, I realize no one is judging me. How liberating, to confess your darkest thoughts and emerge unscathed, unjudged. I still question the existence of the Elohim, but I like the idea of such a tolerant Creator. I make a mental note to add that to my list of requirements.

On day four of the happiness academy, I discover what the catch is. I walk into the conference room that afternoon and find a large sign that reads, "Welcome to the gender-switching workshop." Oh no. I eye the exits nervously. The point of the workshop, we're told, is to see the world through the eyes of another gender. This is the most important seminar of the conference, a guide says, and I'm thinking, I really don't want to do this, when the guide adds, "The more you don't want to do this, the more you need it."

We are told that in a few hours we will gather for a cross-gender mixer. The women will come as men and the men as women. This is no costume party, the guide says. We are to transform ourselves in every way, to go to an extreme. "We're going to open all of our emotions," the guide says. "We're going to cry," and for once I do not doubt.

We have a few hours to prepare for the event. The men are led into a room that looks like the backstage of a theater. There are dresses and shoes and wigs piled everywhere. I choose a nice blue polka-dot number, a blond wig, some necklaces, and, ambitiously, a size 34C bra. I stuff all of this into my bag and head directly to the hotel bar where I attempt to fortify my resolve by downing two vodka martinis, extra dry, in quick succession.

Back in my hotel room, my nerves calmed somewhat by the vodka, I plop down on my bed and assess the situation. I could skip the exercise—no one would know—but that seems like a cop-out. I've come this far; I might as well go through with it. I have questions, though. Practical questions—like do red pumps clash with a blue dress? Metaphysical ones, too, like what in the world does cross-dressing have to do with aliens, or happiness, or my search for God? The Voice didn't say, so I have to fill in the blanks myself.

The feminine side of God, the anima, is an important yet often overlooked aspect. The Creator is not all fire and brimstone and manly miracle making. He has a softer side, too. From nearly the beginning of civilization, mankind has worshipped the mother-goddess figure, and in fact nearly every theistic religion contains a feminine aspect of God. The Jews have the Shekinah; the Hindus, Shakti. Rumi said, "A woman is God shining through subtle veils." So I suppose the Raëlians' gender-switching exercise is about getting in touch with that eternal feminine quality. Or am I giving the Raëlians too much credit?

Never mind that. I have more-pressing concerns. I have two

hours in which to transform myself from Eric to Erica. First order of business: shaving my legs. This does not go well. The razor keeps catching on my hair. I bleed. I curse. I try again. I bleed some more. I curse. How do women do this? I put on my dress, which takes longer than I imagined, and walk over to a room where others are getting ready. One of the guides, a nice woman named Monica, applies makeup and lipstick and then does my nails. I am amazed at how much is involved—space shuttle launches don't require this much preparation. Now for the tricky part: my breasts. Monica grabs some toilet paper, balls it up, then stuffs it into my dress. At first, it's not right. They're either too lumpy or too flat or one is bigger than the other. Eventually everything fits and I achieve something resembling cleavage. Monica slips a pair of pumps on my feet, and the transformation is complete.

I look at myself in the mirror and can hardly believe my eyes. I look good, *really* good. My thick blond hair falls nicely across my ample bosoms. My freshly shaved face is smooth, and the rouge lends a subtle yet healthy glow to my complexion. Yes, there's no doubt about it: I am hot. Looking in the mirror, something strange happens. I find myself attracted to myself, or at least attracted to this feminine version of myself. I briefly consider the implications of this but don't like where that particular thought thread is heading so I drop it and walk over to the mixer.

I'm halfway out the door when Monica stops me.

"You're doing it all wrong."

"Doing what all wrong?"

"Walking."

How can this be? I've been walking for more than forty years now and always assumed I was rather good at it. Apparently not. I am walking like a man, explains Monica. I need to walk like a woman. She gives me a brief lesson in how to do this. Elbows in tight. Palms down. This, she explains, forces me to sway my hips, something that until now has not exactly been a priority in my life. I practice a few times until Monica declares that I've got it.

I arrive at the mixer. Apparently, there is something about putting on a dress and shaving your legs that makes you instantly catty. I find myself commenting on the other "women" here, and not always kindly. I don't like her dress. Look at the outfit on that one, *you have got to be kidding me*; this one is wearing flats instead of heels, *oh my God*. I sit down but my sitting—something I've been doing even longer than I've been walking—is apparently all wrong too. It's the way my legs are crossed, exposing my crotch. A lady doesn't sit that way, I'm told.

The "men" are more convincing. Some are wearing suits and ties while others are dressed more casually. One guy, wearing sweatpants that droop halfway down his backside, keeps eyeing us women as if we were pieces of meat or something.

I'm making small talk with the other "women," some of whom frankly could use a shave, when a "guy" named Jim asks me to dance. This goes about as well as my attempt to shave my legs. The shoes make my feet hurt and, worse, my breasts keep migrating, no doubt trying to liberate themselves, and it's all I can do to corral them. Thankfully, Jim doesn't seem to notice. He's too busy telling me about how he is some big-shot Hollywood producer. I smile even though I doubt his story and think he's a blowhard. The music moves uptempo and then, out of the blue, Jim starts to dry-hump me. Right on the dance floor! I excuse myself and go to the restroom. I'm about to walk into the men's room when a guide stops me. No, I should use the women's restroom since I am a woman. Right. So I do, and I have to say, the women's room is much nicer than the men's. It's cleaner and there's a nice little table with a box of Kleenex. Several hours into this gender adventure and, finally, I have found an advantage to being a woman.

I return to the dance floor and find that Jim has moved on and is now chatting up some brunette with a beard. Fine. Let her fend him off. I decide to leave with my virtue, if not my dignity, intact. Back in my hotel room, I dismantle my feminine persona, removing the wig, unlooping the necklaces, and discarding my breasts, which I find, after a lengthy search, loitering in the general vicinity of my kidneys. I have returned to my original factory setting. Well, nearly returned. There's still the matter of my bloodied, partially shaven legs. It would take days for them to heal.

The next evening is the Raëlian synagogue. That's what they call it. A synagogue. At first, I thought it was some sort of Jewish-Raëlian hybrid ritual, but it turns out that it's just a chance to ask questions. I guess that's what the Raëlians think Judaism is all about: asking questions, and in a way they're right. In any event, I have many questions.

The lights are dim, so dim I have trouble seeing my notebook. On the floor are large white sheets on top of white air mattresses, and pillows (also white), all encircled by colored glowing beads. In the center is a small Buddha statue and a larger Raëlian symbol—the swastika inside the Star of David—and candles everywhere. It looks more like the setting for a rave party than a synagogue, but I have to admit it's relaxing, except for the swastika part; that does not relax me. (The Raëlians point out that the swastika is actually an ancient Indian symbol that the Nazis later appropriated, and they're right, but still, guys, can't you come up with another symbol?)

We are told that we can ask any questions, anything at all. Everything is on the table, or in this case the air mattress. I'm tempted to ask the Big Question, the meta-question that would penetrate to the core of Raëlian theology and something that's been on my mind for several days now: Are you guys nuts or what? But I don't. Why? It's not necessarily that I'm afraid of being rude—I'll never see these people again—nor is it a case of

Stockholm syndrome, the psychological phenomenon where captives bond with their captors. No, questioning the premise of the Raëlian theology, such as it is, strikes me as an act of cruelty, of arrogance, and who am I, pride of intellect, to commit such a barbarous act?

So instead I ask another question: Why? Why did the Elohim create us—and, for that matter, all other life-forms on earth? If they are so advanced, surely they had better things to do than create some flawed creatures like *Homo sapiens*.

"They created us for their pleasure," says a female guide. "The purpose of all life is pleasure."

I'm not buying it. Pleasure may be an agreeable side effect of a life lived well but, as philosophers through the ages have pointed out, it makes a lousy primary objective.

Another guide, perhaps sensing my skepticism, jumps in. "Are you a father?" he asks.

"Yes," I say, and smile at the thought of my daughter.

"Well, it's like that. The Elohim have the same desire to procreate. They created us not only for their pleasure but out of love."

I find this answer more satisfying. Nobody would say that they endure the trials of parenthood for pleasure, and indeed research consistently finds that parents are no happier than childless couples. So if the Elohim did create us then I'm sure they were motivated by something greater than pleasure.

Time and again the Raëlian leaders remind us: We do not believe in God. Science is our religion. It is, though, a selective reading of science. The Raëlians do not subscribe to evolution but, rather, a kind of intelligent design. We were designed not by God but by aliens. Nor do they believe in the big bang theory. As for Einstein, we're told, he was a genius but he got a few things wrong—the theory of relativity, for instance.

The parrying, the questioning, does vaguely resemble what

takes place at a real synagogue but there's considerably more touching going on here, and an absurdly attractive couple on the air mattress adjoining mine is engaged in some heavy petting. The funny thing about the Raëlians' incessant sensuousness is how quickly it grows tiresome, annoying even. There is a reason why bedrooms have doors.

As if picking up on my thoughts, a guy with graying hair and slumping shoulders asks, "What if you believe in The Message but you're not ready for all of the, you know, sensual stuff. What happens to us poor suckers?"

The synagogue-goers giggle. But it's a good question, and I'm eager to hear the answer. One of the female guides answers: "Just give yourself time," she says coyly. More laughter, but the man with the slumping shoulders does not appear satisfied with the answer.

"Look," she adds, "what do you think sensuality is?"

"Sex and stuff," he answers.

A chorus of "ahs" from all of the guides. A rookie mistake. "The problem," says a guide, "is that people have confused sensuality and sexuality. They have sex without sensuality so they are like rabbits"—and with this she makes a high-pitched sound that I presume is the sound of rabbits having mindless sex. "Refinement is a fine-tuning of the senses. When you approach someone"—she caresses the guide sitting next to her—"sexuality is fun," she says, as if it were a matter of dispute. "We're like toys for each other."

The couple on the adjoining air mattress certainly think so. It's a regular Toys R Us over there. The guide, meanwhile, is finishing her thought. "We were created for pleasure, so there's no reason to feel guilty. Besides, you can always opt out."

That last part finally seems to please the guy with the slumping shoulders. He can opt out.

The sequined blonde next to me, one-half of the Toys R Us couple, as I now think of them, untangles herself just long enough to ask a question. She asks about the twenty-one-gram theory. A body supposedly weighs twenty-one grams less after dying than before, proof—in occult circles—of the existence of a soul.

"That is an old rumor," says a guide, his voice rising in anger. "Show me the proof. We should not even be talking about this. It's a waste of time. Science is our religion." He's really worked up now. "The Message is very scientific and we have to stick with the science and not expose two hundred people to this mumbo-jumbo." I am floored. Why, I wonder, is this twenty-one-gram theory mumbo-jumbo but the existence of the Elohim hard science? In fact, the Raëlians consistently mock other UFO groups, suggesting they are a bit unhinged. One person's insanity is another's theology, and vice versa.

I've heard enough and am about to leave when one of the guides says, apropos of nothing, "Look, this philosophy enriches my life." He says it so utterly sincerely and with such conviction that I feel pangs of remorse for my inner snarkiness. If this craziness does enrich their lives then who am I to mock them? Tertullian, the Roman writer and theologian, once said, "I believe because it is absurd." Not despite its absurdity, but *because* of it. That is, of course, an absurd statement but one that, oddly, makes sense. Huck Finn was wrong. You *can* pray a lie.

The next morning I notice a few women who are always seated up front and who tend to flock together. They're all wearing silver necklaces with white feathers attached, and they are, without exception, beautiful, even by Raëlian standards. Who are they, I ask a person near me.

Oh, those are the Angels, he says.

The Angels?

Yes, Raël's Order of Angels.

The Angels were created some fifteen years ago after Raël received a telepathic message, via his Samurai topknot, from the Elohim. The Angels take a vow of celibacy, with two exceptions: the Elohim, upon their return to earth in 2035, and the prophets. The only living prophet being, of course, Raël. When I tell women friends about this they get an *aha* look in their eyes, as if they've just figured out the last clue in a particularly difficult crossword puzzle. All of the pieces fit now. The riddle has been solved. Raël is in it for the nookie. Nothing else I tell them about the Raëlians matters.

That strikes me as possibly true but not the whole story. It's like saying that because the pope gets a spacious rent-free apartment in Rome, he's in it for the real estate. There might be something else going on.

The pope is on my mind because Raël mentions him often, and not in a flattering way. The Raëlians, many of whom are former Catholics, are unabashedly, unrelentingly anti-Catholic, "pitting the UFO against the crucifix," as sociologist Susan Palmer, who has studied the Raëlians, puts it. Raël deliberately provokes the Catholic Church—by handing out condoms in front of Catholic high schools in Canada, for instance, or holding "masturbation seminars," or writing, as he did once, that "the family is a dangerous sect."

But we never fully escape what we actively combat; indeed, the more we combat it, the more we entangle ourselves in it. Hatred is not so much a fire that consumes us as it is a glue, a crazy glue, that binds us to that which we ostensibly disavow. The Middle East is living proof of this phenomenon, and so too are the Raëlians. They are locked in a death hug with Catholics. In fact, the entire movement is a sort of mirror image of the Catholic Church. Catholics have baptism; Raëlians have the "transmission." Catholics have orders of nuns; the Raëlians have Raël's Order of Angels. The Raëlians are engaged in what psychiatrists call "reaction formation," and the rest of us call going to the opposite extreme. They are so vehemently anti-Catholic they don't realize how tightly they are yoked to the church.

The Raëlian emphasis on pleasure is clearly a reaction to Catholic teachings. The Raëlians believe that if it feels good it must be good. The assumption is that if only we were free to pursue pleasures of all sorts, unencumbered by the Catholic Church or guilt or anything else, then we would be happy. But as the Buddha has convincingly shown, the satisfaction of desires only produces more desire, not happiness.

At first, giving the Raëlians the benefit of the doubt, I assume they are like the Tantrists I encountered in Nepal. They too employ pleasure as a means to spiritual development. There's a difference, though. In Tantra, pleasure is a means to an end, a vehicle. For the Raëlians, pleasure is an end in itself, a destination, and that never works. Pleasure, like happiness itself, is always a by-product of a life lived well. If the Elohim are so advanced, I wonder, how could they have overlooked this basic fact of human nature?

I meet John, who strikes me as exceedingly normal. He owns his own consulting business and does a lot of work for the State Department. He has not yet "taken the transmission," but I can see that he is drawn to the Raëlians. I wonder: How can someone so seemingly normal join a movement like this?

I want to talk to John, but think it is best to do so off campus, away from Raëlian eyes. We agree to meet for lunch at a nearby Mexican restaurant. It's a warm day, so we sit outside and each order a Corona. The waitress brings a basket of tortilla chips and a tub of salsa the size of a small swimming pool.

I'm not sure how to broach the subject. What I want to say is this: "John, you seem like a normal guy. Why are you becoming Raëlian? Do you really believe all of this Elohim nonsense?" That seems too confrontational, so instead I ask John to tell me about his childhood.

He grew up in rural Virginia, horse country. He had a happy childhood, he says, and I practically choke on my salsa. A happy childhood? Sure, I knew such a thing existed, in theory, much like life on other planets, but I've never met anyone who described their childhood as happy, at least without a boatload of qualifiers, as in "a relatively happy childhood," or "a happy childhood, given the circumstances."

John and his happy family went to church three times a week. The preacher was a devoted man, prone to fiery sermons. "Jesus Christ!" he would yell, but young John misheard him; he thought he was yelling "Jesus crashed!" That image seared itself into John's young mind: Jesus in a spacecraft, wearing a white space suit and crashing to earth. Then one day the church held a Nativity play. They dressed up John as a shepherd and gave him a doll to hold. It's baby Jesus, they told him. No, said John, it can't be. Jesus crashed. In a spaceship.

That's when they called John's parents, who took him home and set him straight on Christian theology. From then on, John toed the party line, but still, the seed was sown: God came from outer space.

Actually, it's not so far-fetched. Religion and outer space have long been intertwined. Nearly all of the early polytheistic faiths, from Africa to Australia, included a powerful "spirit of the sky" or "sky god." In fact, one of the meanings of *anthropos*, human being, is "to look up." And so we do: at the heavenly bodies, at God Himself.

In the twilight of his brilliant career, Carl Jung wrote a little-known book about the UFO phenomenon called *Flying Saucers: A Modern Myth of Things Seen in the Skies*. On the question of the existence of extra-terrestrials, Jung remained agnostic (or perhaps

Confusionist), but he was clearly fascinated by the outbreak of UFO sightings and their psychic significance. Jung concluded that UFOs represent a religious impulse. The aliens are "technological angels" who have come to save us from ourselves. These angels, being more advanced than us, have lessons to teach. Technology, they've learned the hard way, can destroy life as well as promote it. UFOs may be new but the story they tell is old, Jung concluded.

As John grew so did his doubts about the faith he had inherited. When families in his town had problems—a son with a drug addiction, a pregnant daughter—the last place they went to for help was the church. That seemed wrong, John thought. And increasingly, he began to question Christian beliefs. Some just didn't make sense to him. How could all of humanity, all the various races, have sprouted from Adam and Eve alone? And what about this battle in Heaven where Lucifer was expelled? If Heaven is a perfectly peaceful place, how could a battle have taken place there?

John's questions ran deeper and deeper. It struck him as an accident of birth that he was Christian. If he were born in Israel he'd likely be Jewish; in Japan, Buddhist or Shinto. In India, Hindu. John's faith in God, or some sort of transcendent state, never wavered, but he increasingly began to question organized religion. He still prayed every day, as he has since his happy childhood, but always alone. Now he is looking for a way to pray publicly.

So why the Raëlians?

John was living in France a few years ago when he stumbled across one of Raël's books. Something about extra-terrestrials creating humans. He couldn't make it out. John's French wasn't very good so he showed the book to a French colleague. "This is a cult," he said. "Stay away." John didn't give it much more thought—until he moved to Vegas and contacted the Raëlians' local representative, Thomas. John was impressed with Thomas, who exuded vitality and optimism. He invited John to a meeting.

John liked what he saw. There were about thirty people at the meeting and they all seemed "very balanced and intelligent." One thing that appealed to John was that with the Raëlians everything was out on the table, nothing was hidden.

The waitress brings our food: Mine is a burrito the size of my head. I just stare at it for a moment, formulating a plan of attack. I'm also formulating another plan. I want to ask John a more direct question. How does he square Raëlian theology with the obviously well-developed rational part of his brain? Where is the proof?

John has clearly given this some thought. The way he sees it, the Raëlians are no different from any other religion. They ask their followers to accept the tenets, the story, on faith. Christians don't demand proof of the Virgin Birth; Muslims don't demand proof of Muhammad's revelations at the Cave of Hira. The only difference is that Islam and Christianity are at least a thousand years old and the Raëlians have been around only since the Ford administration. And, adds John: "Jesus in His lifetime was considered a villain, a cult leader, and everyone who was affiliated with Him had to be careful. Their lives were in danger."

He's right, of course. Time has a way of transforming wild tales into received wisdom, madmen into sages. Might that happen with Raëlians? A few thousand years from now might millions of people around the world give thanks to the Elohim for creating us and start their mornings with a sensual massage? As unlikely as that seems, we'd be foolish to dismiss it out of hand.

But still, I ask, aliens who created us in a laboratory?

"Let me ask you a question," says John as I wrestle with my burrito. "If tomorrow everyone were Raëlian, would the world be a better place?"

"Well," I say, "people would certainly have a lot more fun."

"I have to say," says John, "in my heart of hearts, against everything I've been taught, I'd have to say yes, the world would be a better place. There would be no war and you'd probably have less people going postal at some shopping mall with a machine gun. Your whole life, it builds up inside you," says John, and at this point I wonder if he is speaking of himself, "and then you wake up one day and you're older and you think, 'My whole life I've been a good guy and where has it gotten me?'"

Now I'm fairly certain that John is talking about himself. He's the nice boy who went to church and followed the rules and denied himself pleasure because, well, that's what nice boys did. But John is now north of forty and he's tired of being the nice guy. He wants to have fun. How, though, does nice John, the Virginia-bred, baptized John, handle something like the "gender-switching work-shop"? Come to think of it, I didn't see him there. John is a man of considerable girth, and I'm fairly certain I would have recognized him, even in drag. Where was he?

"Ah, there's a story behind that. Do you have time?"

My burrito remains formidable. Yes, I have time.

The evening started off with a hitch. None of the dresses in the Raëlian wardrobe fit John, so he borrowed one from a friend. He added an "atrocious wig" and some makeup to the ensemble and hopped in his car for the short drive to the hotel. He was changing lanes when his mascara started to run, stinging his eyes and causing him to swerve wildly. He heard a siren and, in the rearview mirror, could make out flashing blue lights.

"License and registration, ma'am."

"Ah, not exactly," John told the officer in his booming baritone.

Now, the Las Vegas police have no doubt seen it all—perhaps they even have a special task force assigned to deal with cross-dressing alien worshippers—but this officer must have been new to the force, judging by the way his eyes grew *really* wide.

John reaches into the glove compartment and next thing he

knows there's this loud ripping sound as his friend's dress tears along the seam.

"I don't suppose you want me to step out of the car, Officer?"

"No, ma'am, uh, sir, that will not be necessary."

In a flash of sympathy, or maybe shock, the officer let John off with a warning, but not before asking where he was heading dressed like that.

"Believe it or not, Officer, I'm trying to save the world."

Later, John told that story at the Raëlian conference, in front of everyone. People laughed and, when he finished, the entire ballroom erupted into applause. John enjoyed the attention, the acceptance—who wouldn't?—and once again, I couldn't help but think that maybe this is what it is all about. Never mind the crazy talk about UFOs and aliens and genetic engineering and even sensual voyages. The Raëlian movement, like all faiths, provides its followers a sense of community, of belonging, of human grace. Their beliefs are almost irrelevant.

As the days went by, I noticed that John shifted pronouns from "them" to "we" when speaking of the Raëlians. Then, one day, I spotted him wearing a Raëlian pendant around his neck. He was turning Raëlian.

As the Happiness World Tour draws to a close, I reach an uncomfortable but unavoidable conclusion: The Raëlians are more like us than we might care to admit. They are a caricature of us, and every caricature, of course, contains some truth. The Raëlians worship technology *in extremis* ("Science is our religion"), but don't we all? Don't we view technology—not a particular technology but the very idea of technology—as an almost divine force for good in the world? Technology is not only our religion, it is our magic. We might think, as we smugly thumb our smartphone, that we are light-years more advanced than our primitive ancestors who believed in hidden spirits and fairies (as some still do),

but when you think about it, what's the difference? Yes, we can see
and hold our smartphone, and not the spirits, but we have imbued
these technologies with all sorts of magical powers: the power to
transcend time and space, to connect (that is, to bond, *religio*) us,
to educate our children, to heal the sick.

And the pleasure part? We may laugh at the Raëlians, with their
sex games and pleasure-bots, but we too bow before the god Pleasure. My wallet is overflowing with various "rewards cards" from
every establishment imaginable. They all carry the same implicit
message: Treat yourself. You deserve it. Do I? Really? What exactly have I done to deserve such fulsome rewards, other than
spending $24.75 on a new juicer that I don't need? Again, the
Raëlians have merely taken our own tendencies to a ridiculous
extreme. So perhaps, as sociologist Susan Palmer suggests, the
Raëlians are actually social satirists. Maybe they've established
this wacky movement to help us see the folly of our ways.

I don't think so. I think they are well-meaning people, a bit
wounded and lost, perhaps more so than most of us, but we're
talking about a matter of degree not of kind. I do not think they're
a cult. Nobody asked me for a dime. Nobody coerced me into doing anything I didn't want to do. And I have to admit: I had fun.
My depression has lifted slightly, stunned into submission, I suspect, by the Raëlian shock troops.

Alas, though, I leave Vegas, as so many have before me, un-
fulfilled, and in need of a very long shower. Don't get me wrong.
I've learned many things during my week with the Raëlians. I've
learned that religion and fun can mix. I've learned that collective
effervescence is a powerful force. I've learned how to match a nice
pair of pumps with just the right skirt.

The problem, I conclude, is not that the Raëlians are radical but,
rather, that they are not radical *enough*. They don't ask their followers to make any significant sacrifices. Restraint is for fools and

Catholics. The Raëlians' creed is: Have fun. Enjoy yourself. That may work for a theme park, or a city like Vegas, but it is an insufficient basis for a religion. Hedonism is a lifestyle, not a theology. Religion, *good* religion, is more than some frothy tonic for our everyday neuroses.

In southern France, not far from where Raël encountered his aliens, is one of the world's great wonders: the caves of Lascaux. Inside the vast, multichambered recesses are hundreds of elaborate drawings dating back to the Paleolithic era, at least twenty-five thousand years ago. The drawings depict elaborate hunting rituals, leaping bulls, droves of trotting ponies, a shaman dressed in a bird costume. What I find most fascinating, though, is not the sophistication of these depictions but *where* these ancient humans chose to draw them: in the most remote corners of the labyrinths. The artists had to navigate blind passages and sudden, perilous drops in order to reach these places, sometimes more than half a mile in depth. Why did they choose these locations when it would have been so much easier, and safer, to create their art near the entrance to the caves?

Good religion makes demands on us. It is *supposed* to be hard. Good religion pushes, as well as pulls, and in so doing tackles head-on Heschel's urgent question: "How does a man lift his eyes to see a little higher than himself?"

The Raëlians, for all their talk of extra-terrestrials and flying saucers, don't lift their gaze much above breast level. Regrettably, that is not high enough. Not even close.

> **CWM**, tired of the insanity, and just plain tired. Loves Chinese takeaway. Let's move slow and see what happens. No game players or cross-dressers, please.

Energy is delight," writes Blake. A Chinese poet would never pen those words; they are self-evident. For the Chinese, energy is life. *Chi* is the Chinese word for the vital, delightful energy that animates us, envelops us. We are nothing without *chi*.

I have a *chi* problem, I suspect. Not a lack of *chi*, I'm fairly certain, judging by the speed at which my mind races and my heart pounds, but more of a flow issue. Perhaps my *chi* is clogged. That would explain why I exert a lot more energy than normal people do just to get through the day. Mine is not the satisfying fatigue of a man who has put in a hard day's work or run a 10k but, rather, the unconsummated weariness of a man who has been running in place for a very long time. I need to find someone who can unclog my *chi*. A Chinese plumber, of sorts.

That's where Bill Porter enters the picture. Bill isn't Chinese, but he's close, about as close as a white guy from Washington State can get. Bill lived in China for years, married a Chinese woman, speaks fluent Chinese. People say he has a Chinese soul. Bill has translated the Tao te Ching, the classic Taoist text. He also wrote a book about Chinese hermits and when I meet him at his house in Port Townsend, I am immediately struck by how, with his feral beard and wise, crinkly eyes, he actually *looks* like a Chinese hermit. This makes me wonder if writing books is like owning a dog; do we start to look like the people we write about?

We're huddled in Bill's den, a cozy space. He pours us tea, and does so expertly. Gurdjieff, that wily Georgian mystic, once said, "If you can serve a cup of tea right you can do anything." That may be true, but the same principle does not apply to coffee, a workaday beverage that possesses none of tea's mystical qualities. Someone who can pour a cup of coffee right can't do anything—except pour coffee. I don't know why this is so, but it is.

Bill publishes his translations under the pseudonym "Red Pine." I ask him about that. When he was living at a Buddhist monastery in Victoria, British Columbia, he explains, he was called Victoria's Cloud. That was his name. Then he left the monastery and knew he couldn't run around calling himself Victoria's Cloud, not if he wanted to be taken seriously. So he invented Red Pine. Six months later he discovered that "Red Pine" was the name of the first great Taoist master. As we sip tea and talk, I think of Bill as Red Pine. He sounds wiser that way.

I'm dancing around the subject of my clogged *chi*. I don't know how to bring it up—it's embarrassing—so instead we talk about Taoist philosophy, which is something else that is troubling me. I can't get a handle on Taoism. Of all the religions I've explored so far, Taoism is proving to be the most slippery. It's like Los Angeles; there's no *there* there. I've read all the classics, even taken a *tai-ji* class, but I still can't say what Taoism is, beyond some vague notion of going with the flow. Trying to "get" Taoism is like trying to hug a seal lathered in sunscreen. Why is this so difficult?

"Because Taoism is an amorphous religion," says Bill. It's intentionally vague. The Tao te Ching is a work of monumental vagueness or, as Bill puts it, "one long poem written in praise of something we cannot name, much less imagine." That something is the Tao. It's normally translated as the Way, but also the Universe, Nature, God, the Great Void, the Great Mystery, or simply "the way things are." As for the Tao te Ching, every stanza can be read in seemingly infinite ways. That's why there are so many translations and commentaries about it, more than any other holy book besides the Bible. Everybody thinks they know what the Tao te Ching means, but nobody does.

We're not supposed to know, not in the usual sense of the word. For Taoists, knowledge is the enemy, a hindrance to spiritual progress, just as it was for Saint Francis and Rumi. Taoism is not promoting ignorance, not exactly, but rather a different kind of knowledge, one that is based not on concepts, or cold logic, but on an intuitive sense for things. In other words: wisdom. If Lao-tzu, the enigmatic author of the Tao te Ching, were to materialize today, he would no doubt spare a few words for the Internet, and they would not be kind ones. All those bytes of data, the blogs, the chatrooms—so much information, so little wisdom, Lao-tzu would no doubt say.

Poor Bill had to immerse himself in the world of knowledge—learning Chinese, for instance—in order to translate these texts that advocate an utter lack of knowledge. If you think that's a contradiction, you ain't seen nothing yet. More than any other faith I've explored so far, Taoism sits on a mountain of paradoxes. So many paradoxes it will make your head spin. And not.

Lao-tzu teaches us to fail, says Bill, pouring more tea.

He wants us to fail. Why?

"So we can succeed. It's like the moon. Better to be like the new moon than the full moon, because if you are the full moon then you are doomed to suffer. You are going to wane. But if you can always be the new moon then you'll constantly experience growth."

I like how that sounds—and am reminded of Wayne's meditation advice to "start over"—but wonder how we can possibly remain the new moon, which by definition is always moving toward fullness. "It's like surfing," says Bill, shifting metaphors as effortlessly as he pours tea. Lao-tzu is like the surfer who keeps moving to the lowest point of the wave.

Another cornerstone of Taoism is the concept of *wu-wei*, literally "non-action." When I first heard this I assumed it was a clever justification for laziness dreamed up by some Chinese slacker of centuries past. Bill assures me that is not the case. *Wu-wei* is actually "effortless action." It's the difference between making things happen and letting them happen. For Taoists, resistance is not only futile but silly. Gratuitous exertion. *Wu-wei* means approaching life less like warfare and more like navigation. That's the theory, at least. As the Buddhists would say, I need to investigate.

Speaking of Buddhism, there are some obvious similarities between the two faiths. Over the centuries, they have borrowed heavily from each other, but there are clear differences. If Buddhism is about the mind, then Taoism is about the body, in the largest sense of the word. It is a philosophy of the body, expressed through practices like *tai-ji* and *qi gong* and ultimately in the Taoist quest for immortality—not in Heaven but right here, on *this* earth and in *this* body.

"It's about getting your body in tune with thoughtless action," says Bill and, not for the first time in our conversation, I am confused. Usually we think of "thoughtless" as something negative, as in "He acted thoughtlessly," but Taoists mean something else entirely: action unencumbered by thought. Once you achieve that, says Bill, the *chi* begins to flow. This is my opening. "What exactly is *chi*?" I ask.

"It's a force, a coherent energy, like the couple of times I saw it—"

"Wait. You saw *chi*. Actually saw it?"

"Yes. Twice."

"This is amazing. What did it look like?"

"It looked like luminous sperm, glowing sperm, moving all around me. Like I was on drugs."

"Now, just to be clear, Bill, and I'm not making any accusations, but *were* you on drugs?"

"No, I wasn't. I was in a Buddhist monastery."

I'm dumbfounded. Here is someone who actually saw *chi*. "What did it look like?"

"Imagine sperm flowing all around you, just like the shape of sperm but with lightbulbs inside."

I'm trying to picture that but am having a hard time. I've got the lightbulb part, it's the sperm part that is causing trouble.

Bill pours more tea.

"Was it frightening, these DayGlo sperm?" I ask.

"No, it wasn't frightening. I was just confused. So later I asked some Taoists and they said, 'Oh, that's *chi*. Normally, it's invisible. But sometimes we see it.' "

Bill does not doubt what he saw. I don't know what to think. It is certainly plausible. We need not understand a phenomenon in order to experience it. We need not understand the workings of electricity in order to marvel at a flash of lightning. Likewise, acupuncture works, we know this, but not why. Bill says it is based on the manipulation of *chi* or, as he puts it, "the coherent flow of luminous sperm."

I love that phrase! It sounds like something from a Walt Whitman poem, or the name of a 1980s punk band. There's something about Bill—maybe his hermit-like appearance or the fact that he spent years in deep meditation—that subdues my skepticism. Also, I've met Chinese people who practice *tai-ji*, who cultivate their *chi*, and they possess the vitality and suppleness of people half their age.

I need to know more about *chi*, the DayGlo sperm of the universe. And I need to know—*know* in the intuitive sense—the Tao, the Way. I sense that amid the paradoxes and the vagueness there is something here for me. The poetic brevity of the Tao te Ching, the raw physicality of *tai-ji*, and the tantalizing prospect of a life free of the usual frictions and futile strivings that we mistake for normal. All of this appeals to me, but how to take the next step?

China. I must go to China, and I must go now. I am well and truly obsessed, and once I get obsessed about something I'm like a dog with attachment issues. I can't let go. In a paradox that Lao-tzu would no doubt relish, my search for the way of non-action begets action—frantic, teeth-gnashing, wheel-spinning action.

I had been to China once before, years ago, and that experience was hugely disappointing, spiritually speaking. I had braced myself for the neon and the impossible traffic and the skyscrapers that looked like something from *The Jetsons*. I was prepared for all that. I was not prepared for the look in people's eyes: harried, multitasking eyes with all the soul of a fifty-inch plasma screen. Where was the China of teahouses and ancient wisdom? It's still there, people told me, people who know, but you'll never find it on your own. Not in a million years. Now, if it were Buddhists I was looking for, no problem. The Buddhists are very well organized. There are Buddhist retreats, Buddhist magazines, Buddhist tour operators, Buddhist products. The Buddhists practically throw themselves at you. Not the Taoists. The Taoists are terrible at organization. I don't know if it's part of their philosophy or simply sloppiness, but I can't find any Taoists. Zip.

Then one day I see it—a magazine called *The Empty Vessel*. I like it already. Both words—"empty" and "vessel"—appeal to me; together they ooze crinkly wisdom. So I call *The Empty Vessel* people and it turns out that the vessel really *is* empty, or nearly so.

Inside is only one guy, an aging hippie from Eugene, Oregon, who used to be named Herbert but now, for reasons not entirely clear, goes by Solala. Solala tells me that his magazine is running a Taoist tour of China in a couple of months. The group will do some sightseeing, but this is no cushy temple tour. Not by a long shot. The centerpiece of the trip is an intensive weeklong course in *qi gong*. We're talking serious *chi* manipulation, Solala says, and at one of China's holiest mountains. I sign up right there on the spot.

I fly to the city of Wuhan. It's all concrete and traffic and raw ambition, about as un-Taoist as a place can get. My bags are heavy. I'm weighed down by all these books on Taoism. It's wrong, I know, but I can't help myself. I feel naked without my books. (And, no, I'm not ready to trade them in for a Kindle. To me, books are like people; they yearn to be touched and smelled.)

Walking through Wuhan's shiny new airport, I spot them—an earnest-looking group of about eight Americans and one slightly nervous-looking Chinese woman, our guide. Her name is June and she's wearing jeans and a sweatshirt. She's talking to Solala, who, despite his American-ness, looks like something out of the Qing dynasty. He's wearing one of those silk Chinese shirts, with beads looped around his wrists. But it is his forearms that rattle me. Tattooed on one are Chinese characters, the first verse of the Tao te Ching, "The Way that can be named is not the Eternal Way." It's a very famous line, widely read, though usually not on forearms. Tattooed on his other arm is a Tibetan Buddhist verse. There's also some Hindu scripture somewhere on his body, though I'm afraid to ask where. He's a one-man ecumenical society. The tattoos kind of freak me out and, as I would soon discover, they freak out the Chinese, too. Every time Solala rolls up his sleeves, the Chinese get all bug-eyed and say something like, "Wow. We may be crazy but you Americans are even crazier." Even if they don't say it, they think it.

So we all hop into this small bus. I don't normally like group travel, owing to the group part of the equation, but this group is small enough and everyone is easygoing. Not surprisingly, the group skews heavily herbal: massage therapists, acupuncturists, and assorted tree huggers. Then there is Bob, a retired engineer from New Jersey, who is here because his wife dragged him along. Bob helps keep the group grounded. When Solala used his *chi* to bring a pair of dead batteries back to life, rubbing them in his palms, Bob pointed out that it was actually the warmth of his hands that did the trick. Then there's the enigmatic Sandie. She's the only one in the group who is not coupled off, and I have trouble fitting her in a box. She's in her sixties, works in the high-tech field, and is on her third Taoist pilgrimage to China.

The darkness of Wuhan soon yields to open highway. Everyone is tired, and slumps into their seats. Solala, though, sidles up to me and tells me strange things. He tells me that when we get to the mountain we'll be doing "spinal twists," and I don't like the way this sounds. Then he tells me that we'll be swallowing a lot of saliva—the Taoists call it "heavenly nectar"—and I *really* don't like the way this sounds until Solala reassures me that it is our own saliva that we'll be swallowing. Solala tells me of a Taoist meditation practice called "sitting and forgetting" and I *do* like the way this sounds. In fact, I think I spent my sophomore year in college engaged in such a practice, though at the time I was unaware of its religious significance. No, explains Solala, this is different. It's called *zhowanglun*, and it's a way of disengaging with the world and finding "the still, empty space within."

We stop at a little convenience store. It's called "Easy Joy." Everyone likes the way that sounds, so much more relaxed than, say, Quickie-Mart, and we snap a few photos before loading up on snacks. June is herding everyone back onto the bus, though it's not easy. This is a group of lingerers, which drives June nuts. She is very well organized. She is not a Taoist.

Back on the road, I gravitate toward Sandie. She's less herbal than the rest. She smokes. She drinks. She checks out the young Chinese guys in their tight jeans. About twenty years ago, Sandie fell in love with the Chinese. Not one in particular. All 1.6 billion of them. She loves China, loves everything about it, and can't get enough. Some irresistible force keeps drawing her back. Her husband stays at home, says he "doesn't get involved in other people's religions." He does notice, though, that whenever Sandie, normally a clumsy person, returns from one of her China trips she moves more gracefully. Back home, she writes a blog about Taoism and life. She calls it Tao 61, partly because she likes that Bob Dylan song "Highway 61" and partly because she likes the sixty-first verse of the Tao te Ching. It's about the female overcoming the male through stillness.

"You can turn on the wind," says June, twisting her wrist in what I assume is some ancient *qi gong* movement that harnesses the forces of nature. No, she means we can turn on the air vents above our heads by twisting them. A common mistake. Profundity is all about context. If you're looking for profundity, chances are you'll find it. Foreign-ness helps. Anything foreign, especially Asian, increases the odds of profundity by a factor of three. A Chinese person could order a Big Mac and fries and sound like he's revealing some deep metaphysical truth.

We arrive at the base of Wudang Mountain. It's the holiest mountain in China, and the Communist Party has transformed it into a national park, if you're feeling generous, a theme park if you're not. All of the shops are constructed in identical pagoda style, with the same signboards. The tea shop is called "Tea Shop" the sword shop "Sword Shop." It does not exactly represent the pinnacle of Chinese creativity.

Sandie notices that a few of these "old buildings" weren't there three years ago, and in fact, as we're waiting to travel up the mountain, we notice several more old buildings under construction. Fake cultural heritage, though, is better than none at all, I suppose, certainly better than another Cultural Revolution.

We switch to a larger bus—no private vehicles are allowed on Wudang Mountain—and suddenly we're switchbacking along the road, and everywhere I look I see lush green mountains illuminated by golden light. Not a construction crane in sight. The other China at last. I glance at Sandie and notice she is smiling. It's the smile of someone who has come home. I love Chinese road signs, with their accidental profundity. I see one for "Carefree Valley," the very words sending my blood pressure plummeting, then another for something called the "Mind-Changing Hall," and picture a large room filled with indecisive people.

Mount Wudang holds a special place in the Chinese heart. There are dozens of Taoist temples scattered across the peak. Legend has it that *tai-ji* was invented here centuries ago. A man was watching a crane and a snake fighting and instinctively began miming their moves. That's the story anyway. Nobody knows if it's true; nor do they seem to care. It's still a good story.

We arrive at our hotel, sort of. The entrance is down a steep embankment. With one exception, nobody in our group has packed light, and we struggle to haul our trolley luggage down the mountainside. The straps of my book-laden backpack dig into my shoulders. It's damp and cold. Everyone is tired and grumpy.

"Who's in charge?" someone barks.

"The Tao is in charge," says Solala, and that lightens the mood.

The next morning we assemble in the dining hall for breakfast. Solala has added a black beret to his Chinese ensemble and looks even more ridiculous. Sandie is wearing a T-shirt that reads, "That was Zen. This is Tao," and black-and-white yin-yang earrings.

The concept of yin-yang is probably the most famous aspect of Taoist philosophy, something that has seeped into western discourse. Except, as usual, much was lost in translation. We tend to use yin-yang to mean opposites—"She is the yin to his yang," that sort of thing. But that's not exactly what it means. Yin-yang describes polarity, not opposition, and there's a difference. Both poles need each other and, in fact, couldn't exist without each other, any more than up could exist without down, hot without cold. They are mutually dependent, and complementary.

Breakfast looks an awful lot like dinner. Lots of dumplings and noodles swimming in indeterminate sauces. I pine for the banana pancakes of Kathmandu. More crucially, there's no coffee, confirming what I've heard about China's abysmal human-rights record. Bob the engineer has come prepared. He's brought these coffee bags—they look like tea bags only with coffee inside—and, in an act of extreme compassion, hands me one, which I grab like a junkie in need of a fix.

Properly caffeinated, I join the group as we walk up the hill for our first *qi gong* session. It's misty. The Chinese love mist. A misty day is much better than a sunny one, and there's no better way to view the temples of Mount Wudang than through a thick, egg-drop-soup mist. This mist, though, seems almost too perfect, like something out of a movie, and then I find out that's because it *is* from a movie. *Karate Kid*, the remake, was filmed here and the producers couldn't count on natural mist so they made their own. They built this elaborate mist-making system, with vents carved into the side of the mountain, and when they finished filming gifted it to the people of Mount Wudang. So now every day in Wudang is a perfect misty day.

We enter the temple grounds through a gate, men on the right, women on the left. Solala tells us we're not supposed to exit the way we enter. "It's like those airport bathrooms," he says. We climb some stairs, stopping to bow to the God of the Mountain, then meet our teacher: Master Zhong. He's tall and thin, with a wispy black beard and long black hair pulled tight into a topknot, held in place with a little wooden stick. A classic Tao-do. He's dressed in all white. He's young, though probably not as young as he looks. We're not about to ask. Taoist masters are like women over forty. It's bad form, possibly dangerous, to ask their age, for they are on the road to immortality.

We're gathered in a beautiful courtyard, with birds chirping and the sun streaming through the Hollywood mist. There's good energy here, we're told. Ancient masters used to practice in this very courtyard. Maybe it is the energy, or simply the pleasant surroundings, but I do feel an alien sense of peace creeping up on me. We spread out, close enough that we can see one another but not so close that we might whack one another in the face. Instinctively, I find a spot toward the exit. Just in case.

We'll be learning basic *qi gong*, something called "the eight brocades," Master Zhong explains. *Qi gong* is similar to the better-known *tai-ji* but it is less about movement and more about cultivating *chi*. Master Zhong demonstrates the first brocade. Eyes closed. Arms raised. Fingers intertwined. Then he twists side to side. It looks easy enough, like stretching when you get out of bed in the morning. We are "balancing Heaven and earth, man and woman, midnight and noon," he says. That seems like an awful lot to ask of a simple stretching exercise but, again, I suspend my disbelief and pray it doesn't snap.

We do the exercise while Master Zhong circles like a drill sergeant inspecting the troops. When he gets to me, he stops and tells me to relax. It's very important to relax, he says, and of course this makes me even more tense. "And stand up straight," he adds, sounding less like a *qi gong* master and more like my mother. I feel like I'm being watched, and that's because I am; a few Chinese

tourists have poked their heads into the courtyard and are surveying us as if we were animals in a zoo.

We take a break, and everyone uses the opportunity to offer me
advice. Solala tells me to breathe more quietly. Steve, a rugged outdoors type from Colorado, tells me to stand in the middle of the
group. The group pushes you along, he says, like one giant organism. A discussion ensues about when to inhale and when to
exhale. No definitive conclusions are reached but everyone agrees
that breathing is important, and I don't disagree.

Back in formation, we try the first brocade again, and this time
it feels better, more natural. I don't see the luminous sperm, but
I do feel my mind settling with each twist. The next brocade is a
lot more complicated. Zhong squats like he's on horseback, then
cocks his elbow as if firing an arrow. He does this incredibly slowly
and fluently. I've never seen anyone move like this. Every tilt of his
head, every pivot of his hip, every muscle contraction, is perfectly
aligned with his intention. No motion is gratuitous, or lacking in
any way. Nor is there anything mechanical about his deportment.
These are the movements of a fully sentient being.

Now it's our turn. I feel, and probably look, like a drunken
elephant. I keep landing wrong-footed, and wrong-armed too. I
expend much precious *chi* unknotting myself. My physical awkwardness is compounded by an intense self-consciousness, similar
to what I experience whenever I attempt to dance in public or kiss
a woman I've just met on the cheek. This time Master Zhong looks
at me like a doctor diagnosing an especially sad case, and says simply, "Practice, practice."

It's time for lunch. We walk down the temple steps, past the little gift shops selling Taoist talismans and yin-yang jewelry. It's here
where I encounter my first trash-can wisdom. All the trash cans at
Wudang have signs with little snippets of advice and encouragement. This one reads, "You are helpful to Mount Wudang, which

is proud of you." I like that. The mountain is proud of me. That's so much nicer than "$500 fine for littering."

Back at the hotel, we sit down for lunch, which looks an awful lot like breakfast, and autopsy the morning's efforts. Everyone is kind, and tells me I have great *qi gong* potential. I just need to relax. Suddenly Peter, a thin, earnest guy from New Mexico, is all excited. "Look," he says. "It's the yin-yang symbol!" Sure enough, someone has spilled soy sauce on the table and it has pooled into what is definitely the yin-yang symbol. We all stare at it in amazement. It's the Taoist equivalent of finding a two-week-old grilled-cheese sandwich that looks like the Virgin Mary. The Tao being the Tao, though ("gain is loss, loss is gain"), we do not attempt to sell the soy-sauced table on eBay but instead wipe it off and return to our noodles and conversation.

We're talking positions. There is a Taoist position for everything, even for sleeping (something like the fetal position but different). Someone mentions the tree meditation. That's where you stand still like a tree for an hour. Sandie says she knew a guy who crouched for an hour. Then he had a stroke. I stare at my noodles.

Later that day, Sandie and I decide we need a drink, so while the others sip tea at the hotel we slip into a little restaurant up the hill. It's just a shop, actually, with one table set up and a couple of plastic chairs. On the TV, two guys are pummeling each other in a kickboxing match. Sandie orders two beers in Chinese. She doesn't speak real Chinese but, rather, a kung-fu dialect she's cobbled together from watching Taiwanese movies. This she supplements with energetic hand gestures and, oddly, French. Every time Sandie tries to speak Chinese her college French pops up like an old boyfriend she hasn't thought about in years. Anyway, it works, and shortly two large bottles of Purity beer arrive.

We down them quickly then the shopkeeper, a smiley red-eyed

man, brings us two shot glasses filled with a murky liquid. "Medicine-alcohol," says Sandie. I sip mine; she empties hers with one flick of the wrist. The proprietor, who clearly partakes of his own product, does not speak a word of English but, employing an imaginative use of hand gestures, props, and facial expressions, conveys this sentiment: "What, are you a wimp or something? Your lady friend here just downed her booze and you're sipping yours like some kind of wuss. Man up, sir." So I do. One big gulp. It tastes like month-old antifreeze. At this point, things get a bit fuzzy. But Sandie and I are talking about the Tao, of that I'm fairly certain. What exactly is the Tao? I ask.

"It's the Way," says Sandie.

"Yes, I know, but what does that *mean*?"

"It's influenced by Zen."

"Yes, but what *is* it?"

"It's about going with the flow. And telling funny stories."

"Is it a religion?"

"Yes. No."

"Is it a philosophy?"

"Yes. No."

That's the way Sandie answers many of my questions. It becomes a running joke, only she is not joking. In Taoism, everything is yes and no—or, more precisely, as Sandie points out, yes/no, without the conjunction, for both the yes-ness and the no-ness occur simultaneously, not sequentially. Everything with Sandie is yes/ no. Except when the opportunity to imbibe cheap Chinese booze presents itself. Then it's just yes.

"What we're doing right now is very Taoist," she declares.

"What? Smoking cigarettes and drinking alcohol of dubious vintage?"

"Yes. We're being in the moment."

We order another round of medicine-alcohol in order to solidify the moment. At one point Sandie gets up to go to the bathroom and spots the big tank that holds the booze. She's staring at it and while I can't see the tank I can see her eyes growing very large.

"What is it?" I ask.

"You don't want to know. Do *not* look at this."

But of course I can't resist. I walk over to the tank. She's right. I didn't want to see this. It's a fish tank, only there are no fish, just this milky white liquid and, at the bottom, giant mushrooms. Coiled in one corner is a snake. I decide then and there to lay off the medicine-alcohol.

The shop is closing and it's just as well. My head is whirling. "To be continued," I say to Sandie, and we stumble down the hill back to the hotel where we discover that the group was worried about us, in a vague Taoist way.

The evenings are cold, and there's no heat in the hotel so I sleep with all my clothes on, not just the clothes I was wearing that day—*all* of my clothes. My muscles are sore from the day's contortions, my mind a blur of alcohol and Taoist philosophy. I slip under the covers and, flashlight in hand, read the Tao te Ching. Brevity is the soul of wit—and wisdom, too, it turns out. The book is one short ode to conciseness. Only five thousand words long, you can read the entire text in forty-five minutes. Or a lifetime.

About Lao-tzu there is virtually nothing to be said, and I suppose he'd like it that way. He may or may not have written the Tao te Ching alone. He may or may not have been a contemporary of Confucius. What is certain is that he didn't preach. He didn't organize. He just wrote a few pages on request (or so legend has it), then rode off on a water buffalo, and that was that. All in all, a mere blip compared with Jesus's itinerant preaching, or the Buddha's forty-five years traveling the dusty roads of India, spreading the *dharma*.

I read but, uncharacteristically, without a pen at the ready. The

Tao te Ching is the only book that I don't underline. That's because to underline a passage is to sequester it, contain it, and Lao-tzu defies such containment. Yes, he is vague but not in the same way that, say, a politician is vague. Politicians are vague because they don't want to say anything. An absence of meaning is their goal. Lao-tzu, on the other hand, has everything to say, and aims for multiple meanings. Each verse can be read several very specific ways, depending on readers' frame of mind, what they had for breakfast, how the light strikes the pages, a million variables. The book is like one of those trick photographs where every time you look at it you see a different image.

Having just traveled halfway around the world, I can't help but sigh when I flip open to verse 47: "The farther you travel, the less you know. Thus the wise person knows without traveling." I decide to ignore that verse and turn to verse 15: "Clarity is learned by being patient in the presence of chaos." China teaches us that lesson every day. It's easy to be calm in the quiet countryside. It is the chaos of urban living that puts that calmness to the test. Stillness in motion. That is the goal of the Taoist practitioner.

Stillness, and softness, too. "The soft overcomes the hard in the world as a gentle rider controls a galloping horse," writes Lao-tzu. That is not our approach. We favor the hard over the soft, and our language reflects this bias. We admire those who are "hard as nails" or "hard-bitten," or even "hard to read." Softness is seen as a liability, a character flaw. "Don't go soft on me," we beseech our friends. Even when soft is served up as a compliment—by describing someone as an "old softie," for instance—it always contains a dollop of derision. The old softie is a fool.

If you think about it, our hard bias makes little sense. A newborn baby is soft; a corpse is hard. Soft things bend; hard ones break. The Taoist sees the hidden strength in softness. Water, for instance, is as soft and pliant as any substance, yet over the centuries a flowing river can carve the Grand Canyon. Soft power at work.

Some of the verses sound oddly familiar. Like this: "Die without dying and you'll endure forever." That echoes Jesus's call for us to "die unto thyself." The Taoist emphasis on humility and self-effacement mirrors Jesus's proclamation that "the meek shall inherit the earth." I find many other examples where Lao-tzu echoes Jesus—or the other way around. Lao-tzu lived several centuries before Jesus. Taoism also shares a core belief with Islam. Both faiths preach submission. In the case of Islam, to Allah; in Taoism simply to the Way. I briefly reflect on how the world's faiths brush up against one another, however briefly, before heading their separate ways, but I'm tired, and soon yield to the warmth of my comforter and the softness of my pillow.

The next day we have an appointment with the Bee Hermit. He's an old Taoist who lives in a cave up in the mountain and raises bees. There's a long tradition of hermits in Taoism. They meditate and cultivate their *chi* in solitude, though a hermit is not supposed to remain a hermit forever. It's like graduate school. A few years is fine, but any longer and it looks like you're avoiding something.

We trudge up a steep hillside, Sandie holding my arm for balance. Her guide dog, she calls me, and I don't protest. And there he is: a gnome of a man bristling with happy energy. Bill Porter's doppelgänger. He has no teeth but big, healthy gums, which he flashes often. He hands us each little plastic medallions and handfuls of sunflower seeds. He says that we are all like classmates, following the Tao together. "We have the same purpose, the same way." The group is eating this up. The Bee Hermit fulfills their western notion of the wise hermit. He may very well be wise but everyone is so busy projecting wisdom onto him that we'll never know for sure.

He gives us a guided tour of his cave. It's rough but not quite as rough as I expected. The Bee Hermit has stuff: a small collection of books, toothpaste, little shampoo packets, a smiley-face trash can, a radio, a newspaper, a flashlight, a calendar opened to the correct date. The Bee Hermit takes off his boots and crosses his legs, which he does remarkably nimbly for someone his age—whatever that is. He's not about to tell. Over the sound of a drip-drip-drip from a nearby bucket where he collects water, we talk.

"Is there any moment other than the present?" someone asks.

I suppose he could answer, "Yes, a week from Tuesday. That is much better than the present moment," but of course he doesn't. He just smiles a gummy smile and says, "I'm happy," eliciting a chorus of ahs from the group. The Bee Hermit utters snippets of wisdom but mostly he just smiles and laughs. He has a wonderful laugh.

Our discussion shifts to immortality, one of the goals of Taoism. How to achieve it? Meditation alone is not enough, he says. "You must be of service, have compassion, only then will people come to respect you."

I realize this is the first time I have heard a Taoist mention the word "compassion." Unlike other faiths, Taoism does not hold it as a central focus. The Tao te Ching mentions compassion only once or twice. It says nothing about love. Which is not to say that Taoists aren't compassionate and loving, of course, but theirs is an approach different from, say, Sufism, which is all about love.

"Are you lonely?" someone asks.

"Hermits can live with loneliness. That's their greatness."

"Can you show us your practice? What should we do?"

"The important thing is to be comfortable," he says, contorting his body into a position that doesn't look very comfortable at all.

"Concentrate on your navel," he says, pointing to his, just in case there was any doubt.

"Are you meditating now?"

"Yes. I'm always meditating."

More ahs.

"Is there a Heaven?"

"Yes, without Heaven there would be no earth."

Someone asks how we can save the bees. Apparently, they're dying back home, but the hermit doesn't seem terribly concerned. "Some die, some are born," he says. Solala asks a technical question about Taoist positions and the hermit doesn't have a clue what he's talking about. He's too busy following the Tao, I suspect, to worry about such arcane matters.

"You cannot see it but everywhere there is *kai-shin* [loving heart]. I'm always mediating on *kai-shin*."

"How do we develop *kai-shin*?"

"Release."

"Release what?"

"Release everything." And with this, the Bee Hermit picks up an empty plastic water bottle in order to demonstrate. Only if you're empty first can anything worthwhile enter.

We're all sitting on these tiny wooden chairs—they look like children's chairs—absorbing this wisdom as best we can when all of a sudden Sandie's chair gives way and she crashes to the ground. She's okay, just embarrassed. The Bee Hermit finds it very funny and he's laughing and laughing. He is not laughing at her, or even with her but, rather, *for* her. It is a compassionate laugh. Maybe this is how Taoists express love: through laughter. It reminds me of the laughing clubs of Mumbai that I once joined, on assignment for NPR. Daybreak at a park on Malabar Hill and two dozen people laughing. No jokes. Only laughter. Microphone in hand, serious expression on my face, I tried to maintain my professional distance. I lasted about thirty seconds.

It's time for us to leave. The Bee Hermit has a five o'clock. He shakes our hands, in that Chinese way, palm cupped over palm.

He was a big hit with everyone, even with Bob the engineer. "I love that guy!" Bob says, in an uncharacteristic outburst of enthusiasm. I like him too. I think he does possess a certain wisdom, independent of our group's projections. His is not a bookish wisdom, or even a wisdom centered in the mind at all. The Bee Hermit is wise the way a cat is wise when it effortlessly finds the most comfortable two square feet in a two-thousand-square-foot house. The Bee Hermit is wise the way a child is wise when she points out that sometimes it's okay to have dessert *before* dinner. Which is not to say the Bee Hermit is a child or a cat, but simply that he is more attuned to his own needs (genuine needs, not manufactured ones) than most of us. I suspect his isolation has something to do with this. No one is telling him what he needs, or wants, so he figures it out on his own.

Master Zhong has joined the group now and we've convened at a nearby "power spot" for our afternoon *qi gong*. The air is soft, and music wafts from Master Zhong's cellphone, like magic. This time, I do much better. The movements feel more natural. I don't know if it's spiritual or not, but it feels good. "Move as if you're holding Heaven in your palms," says Master Zhong, and while I don't know exactly what he means the words inspire me. Something has changed. I'm looser. Still no sign of the luminous sperm but I feel a buzz of energy (is it *chi*?) when I do the brocades. The image of water comes to mind, like I'm rafting down a gentle river in one of those inflatable inner tubes. I am not *doing* the brocades so much as riding them, brocading.

The next day Sandie tells me she needs to break away from the group again and invites me to lunch at a restaurant she remembers from her last trip. We hop on one of the official buses and arrive in no time. The restaurant is still there, perched at the very summit of Mount Wudang. The proprietor is a smiley, rotund woman who remembers Sandie, or at least pretends to. Sandie deploys her kung-fu Chinese, and a few minutes later heaps of tofu and vegetables, along with two bottles of Purity beer, arrive at our table.

Food. This is how her love affair with China began. Sandie loved Chinese food, more than most people, and bought a cookbook—nothing fancy, your basic *kung pao* and such. She soon mastered several dishes and took delight not only in the flavors but also in their geographic origins. This dish is from Sichuan province, this one from Hunan. The food took her places.

Then came the kung-fu movies. Not the watered-down American versions but the real thing; several times a year, videos from Hong Kong and Taiwan would arrive at her home in Honolulu. Then came the Chinese painting. She loved the vague, misty representations of nature. If people appear in a Chinese painting, they are always dwarfed by a mountain or forest. Sandie took lessons and soon was producing her own work. (She shows me photos of her paintings and I'm struck by how good they are.)

Then came the books: the I-Ching, the Tao te Ching (she has fourteen translations), and many others. One day, she met a *qi gong* instructor. He didn't call it that, though. He called it "energy work" so as not to spook people. His day job was to drive blood samples around to labs, not terribly demanding, and that was fine with him. He just wanted to do the energy work. Sandie learned at his side.

Then she stumbled across an ad in one of the martial arts magazines she subscribed to. It literally fell out of the magazine and landed on her lap. "Come study Taoism on Mount Wudang." So Sandie, having just turned sixty (an important age for the Chinese), her son now grown, went to Mount Wudang. And then she went again. And now here she is again. Friends ask why she keeps going back to China. What is she trying to work out of her system? Again, the assumption, so common, that our spiritual urges are like some sort of intestinal parasite we need to flush out of our system so we can get on with our "real lives." Were all of these incremental steps, I wonder, the gradual conversion that William James called "the religion of healthy-mindedness"? But Sandie didn't think of Taoism as a religion, not in the usual sense of the word. There was nothing she had to believe in. It was just "the way things are, and it was so obvious." That's a common sentiment. People tell me: I was always a Buddhist/Wiccan/Kabbalist/Whatever, I just didn't know it. Their conversions represent not a dramatic shift to a new worldview but, rather, confirmation of one they already held.

Sandie now considers herself an "aspiring Taoist." Why aspiring? I ask.

"I guess because there are things I still need to let go of."

An interesting choice of words. Not things she needs to learn, or understand, but let go of, drop. Taoism, even more than Buddhism, more than any other faith, is about emptying ourselves of attachments, knowledge, concepts, ambition—all of that, and more, until we become empty vessels. Taoists fill their God-shaped hole with a hole-shaped God. It's not the emptiness of Buddhism, which is actually everythingness, only without the thing, the self. In Taoism, emptiness is indeed nothingness. The Great Void. But that Void is essential to the creative process, to life itself. From nothing springs everything or, as the Chinese emperor Hsüan-tsung said: "Less is the ancestor of more."

Since we've dived deep into the Great Void, I figure I might as well go for broke. I drop the G-bomb. "Do you believe in God?"

Sandie takes a big swig of her Purity beer before answering—dodging, actually.

"Wittgenstein says, 'What you can't speak about you must pass over in silence.'"

"Forget Wittgenstein. He's dead. Do *you*, Sandie, believe in God?"

"I need to know what you mean by God. The minute you say 'God' people have an image in their mind of what they think God is. I believe in something but I'm not sure I can tell you what it is. Some of the early translators translated 'Tao' as 'God' but that's not right. Tao is not God. It is the Way. There's a difference."

"Okay, but does Taoism provide the answers you've been looking for?"

"I'm not looking for answers. I'm just looking to experience."

I ponder that one while wrestling with a slippery slab of tofu. This is what separates all the eastern faiths from Judeo-Christian ones: the emphasis on experience rather than belief. Taoists, Buddhists, Hindus, Jains. They don't ask questions like "What do you believe?" That is a western—specifically a Christian—bias. Action. Experience. Results. Those are the eastern bywords.

Our conversation eventually, inevitably, turns to *chi*. No sign of the DayGlo sperm yet, and I still can't get a handle on just what it is.

"It's energy, almost like electricity but not quite."

"Is it like a good cup of coffee in the morning?"

"No, not that."

"And you're sure it exists? It's not just your imagination?"

"I have no doubt."

"You've seen it?"

"No, but I've felt it."

Sandie has a bum finger, injured in a car accident. It's permanently dislocated, always bent at an odd angle, as if clenched in a fist. One day, on one of her previous trips to China, she was meditating with her teacher Master Hu and she felt someone, some*thing*, probing her injured finger. It didn't hurt, this probing, but felt kind of nice. Tingly.

"Okay, if *chi* is real why can't everyone feel it?"

Because, says Sandie, they've decided it doesn't exist. We experience what we expect, or at least what we are receptive to the possibility of. Or, as William James said, "Sometimes faith in a fact can help create the fact."

Sandie's progress along the Way, like all worthwhile journeys, comes in fits and starts. "You reach a level where you say, 'Yes, I understand all this,' then you realize you don't understand anything, then you reach another level of understanding, and so on." Sandie relays this with a sense not of frustration but, rather, of wonder. And mystery. That's another word we have debased. A mystery is not a puzzle waiting to be solved, but rather something for which there is *no human solution*. Mystery's offspring is not frustration but awe, and that sense of awe grows in tandem with knowledge. The more we know, the more we wonder. The Great Mystery.

I fear our conversation has drifted into the stratosphere, which is where I am naturally drawn. I feel more comfortable up there, in the thin air, than I do down here on earth. Whatever the opposite of grounded is, that's me. So it is Sandie who, thankfully, steers us to a soft landing.

Taoism is a practical path, she explains. Almost every day, in ways large and small, she finds it useful. Like the time she endured some particularly unpleasant dental work by separating her mind, her attention, from what was going on in her mouth. Or when she's stuck in traffic and instead of stressing out goes into *tai-ji* mode, slowly turning her neck side to side, loosening her death grip on the steering wheel. Or the time someone stole her car radio. At first, she was furious. She loved to listen to the radio during her commute. But then she discovered she enjoyed the quiet time alone with her own thoughts. Now she daydreams, practices sitting and forgetting, or simply relishes the tactile pleasures of driving a car. It's been two years now and she still hasn't had a new radio installed.

Being a Taoist is like being a dog, she says. "The dog sits here, the dog sits there, the dog wags its tail. If the dog is hungry it eats. If it spills something all over itself it just shakes it off," and Sandie shakes her body side to side like a dog. Sandie thinks of herself as a basset hound and, yes, I can see her as one. All jowls and good intentions.

Since embarking on the Way, Sandie has streamlined her life. She's canceled her subscription to *Vogue*. It could be that she is now, as she puts it, of a certain age, but there's more to it than that. She just doesn't care about such vanities anymore. There is, in fact, much that Sandie no longer cares about. She doesn't care about keeping her house neat. She doesn't care about her job—not in the same grasping way, at least, as if her very life depended on a good performance review.

Normally, we think of the religious as people who care *more*, not less than the rest of us. This is not true, not exactly. The truly religious care more deeply about fewer things and don't give a hoot about the rest. As old William James put it, "The art of being wise is the art of knowing what to overlook." Sandie overlooks much these days and that, she says, makes it easier to make decisions.

I perk up. "I'm terrible at making decisions. How do you do it?"

"Because I don't care."

"But don't you want to have the best experience?"

"The best experience isn't what I'm looking for. If a group from the office is going out to lunch, I'm the one who steps back and says 'Whatever you guys want.' "

"Isn't that being passive, or maybe passive-aggressive?"

"No, I don't complain. There's always tomorrow and another lunch. As long as you learn, either this was good, or I'm never coming back here again."

I whip out my copy of the Tao te Ching and read aloud the

passage that Sandie loves, the sixty-first verse. "The feminine can always conquer the masculine by yielding and taking the lower position." Like much of Lao-tzu it takes conventional wisdom and turns it on its head. Normally, we think of yielding as something negative, a sign of weakness. Never yield an inch to your enemies, fight the good fight, get what you want, what you deserve. I ask Sandie what Lao-tzu would say about that mind-set.

"He'd tell you that the way to make it happen is by not trying to make it happen, *wu-wei*."

"Does that work for you?"

"Yes. Now, you need to know when to push. It's not total passivity. You know just when to exert that power. Like now, I said I want to go up the mountain, break away from the group, and be open to something, listening to my guidance. I knew there was something available here. I didn't know how fine it would be."

As if on cue, more food arrives. A big heaping plate of fish. We dive in, devouring it in silence, only pausing long enough to declare it The Best Fish Ever.

It's time for us to move on. Sandie asks for the check, in French. After that bit of linguistic confusion is rectified, we pay and amble up to a clutch of souvenir shops. She's looking for a sword, the bigger the better. She tests several, holding them in both hands, gauging their heft and feel. This is the sort of decision that would take me forever. I'd go back and forth, afraid of choosing the less-than-perfect sword. Sandie, though, takes only a few minutes before finding one she likes, one that feels right, and after some halfhearted haggling closes the deal. It is a truly intimidating sword, a good three feet long and sharp as a butcher's knife. I ask Sandie if it's used in her Taoist practice. Not really, she says. She wants to bring it to work one day and just lay it down on the conference table. "I figure that will get me some respect," she says. Sometimes a sword is just a sword.

The next day I'm sick. I become intimately acquainted with my bathroom. The group is concerned and offers me all manner of homeopathic remedies—roots extracted from deep inside the Amazon and stuff like that. One person is an acupuncturist and offers to stick me. All I really want is antibiotics, but this isn't the antibiotic crowd. I sip green tea and try to practice sitting and forgetting.

The next day brings blessed relief, and rain. A heavy, natural mist hangs over the mountain. The Chinese staff love it, and so does Sandie.

"Look at it," she says, pointing to a vista that resembles a misty Chinese painting. "Look how vague it is." She says this like it's a good thing.

"Do you find vagueness beautiful?"

"Yes. No."

Sandie may be soaking up the beautiful vagueness, but the rest of the group is uppity about their brocades. What are we going to do? We have three more brocades to go. It's decided that we'll hold our morning session indoors. It's not the same. Something about the awful fluorescent lights throws everyone off. The *feng shui* is all wrong. Our *chi* is depleted.

In the afternoon we attend a philosophy lecture by Master Hu. I like him, but I don't understand him. Partly it's his heavy accent, and partly it's the subject matter: esoteric aspects of Taoist philosophy, impenetrable diagrams. I'm getting maybe 30 percent of what he says. At one point, Master Hu says, "Good intestines are very important for the spiritual life." He says this with great conviction, and I have to agree, given my colonic escapades. Others, though, look skeptical. Good intestines? Master Hu repeats himself and only then do we realize he means "Good *intentions*." Which I suppose are also important.

We wrestle with other metaphysical puzzles like: Where were

you before your parents were born? We talk about the different kinds of energies; *chi* is only one. There's also *jing*, which is a coarser form of energy, something like Freud's id, and *shen*, which is more refined than *chi*. Taoists see the human soul as a kind of energy-processing machine that takes the coarsest form of energy, our most animal ways, and constantly refines it so that we become more fully human, closer to the gods. The process is called "internal alchemy."

Much of the Taoist literature is written in code, he says, and scrawls on the blackboard: "The Iron bull tills the land." Translation: Our minds should be free of stray thoughts. This I do follow. Taoism, like Buddhism, believes that this world, the world of dust, is about as real as a dream. Enlightenment, the Taoist as well as the Buddhist version, is about waking up from that dream. When we in the west say someone is "living the dream," we see it as the ultimate sign of success. Taoists don't see it that way. Tell a Taoist that you are living the dream and a likely response is: "I'm sorry to hear that. I hope you wake up."

We're up to six brocades now. We've added a head roll, something called the "kidney rub," which is just what it sounds like, and a punching maneuver that I quite like. Feet shoulder-width apart. Arms at waist level. Eyes wide open. Punch! Punch! Punch! I can feel a lifetime's worth of latent anger drain away. My movements are more fluid, though still too fast, says Master Zhong.

"God is a direction," says the Austrian poet Rainer Maria Rilke. The Taoists would agree with that, though they'd add that He is a velocity too, and that velocity is much slower than you think. For Taoists, slowness is next to holiness. They do everything slowly. I, however, wrestle with slowness and its cousin, patience. I want to get everything over with, which makes sense for something like a root canal but the problem is I also want to get the pleasant things in life over with as soon as possible. My favorite tense is past. This is crazy, I know. I wonder if my depression isn't somehow tied to my lack of patience. If I want to get everything over with as quickly as possible, it begs the uncomfortable question: Why live at all?

"You need to relax," says Master Zhong again. I know, I know. I am trying very hard to be effortless. That is, of course, the problem. I have only two modes of being: frantic and catatonic. I'm either forcing life or giving up on it. There is a third way, the Taoists say, *wu-wei*: effortless doing. What did Lao-tzu say? When nothing is done, nothing is left undone. I wish I could believe that—or, better yet, live it.

To describe *wu-wei* as simply "going with the flow" is to cheapen it. Going with the flow requires real skill and a very specific kind of intelligence, one that is fundamentally different from how we normally think of intelligence. It's not knowing something, as in knowing how to program a computer or bake a peach cobbler, nor is it merely sensing something, a gut feeling. It is more of an alignment, an orientation. A sense for "the way things are."

Our last evening on Mount Wudang. I'm in Sandie's room eating chocolate and drinking Black Label from these little airline bottles that she's tucked away in her luggage. We drink to a wonderful week. And the weather, you couldn't ask for better. Such nice, vague mist. We drink to that too. Our teacher was a true master. "He's so slow and graceful," says Sandie. "It's just sickening." And we drink to Master Zhong. I can't say whether he is enlightened or not (and, really, who am I to judge?), but he definitely walks the walk. Slowly, very slowly.

The next morning we put all the pieces together, all eight brocades. We've assembled in our hotel courtyard. The rain has cleared; sunlight illuminates a lucid sky, free of mist and vagueness. I'm distracted, though. My mind is racing ahead to the next day's journey, my reentry into the world of dust. But the movements pull me out of my head and into my body, and by the time we get to the kidney rub my inner mist has cleared too. It feels good. My back is straight, my movements fluid, and slow. The slowness no longer feels like a burden. It is a relief. Time is my friend. I breathe. I move. Not discrete movements but one uninterrupted movement. No notes, only the song.

I don't see the *chi*, not a DayGlo sperm in sight, but I feel it, I swear. Maybe it's my mind playing tricks on itself—my own private magic show—but I feel a buzz pulsing through me, as if someone had just upped my voltage. Afterward, Master Zhong invites us to tea. The Chinese don't merely drink tea. They perform it. It's an enthusiastic, messy ritual, with much splashing of tea over frog statues and sloshing everywhere.

"First, smell the tea," says Zhong. "Then sip it, the fragrance will stay with you longer."

Someone asks if different teas evoke different states of consciousness.

"No," says Zhong. "But only people who live well can taste real tea."

The group peppers Master Zhong with other questions about the metaphysics of tea, which he answers patiently until announcing: "We don't have to be that deep. Let's just drink tea." So we do.

We lug our inappropriate luggage up the steep stairs and onto the bus. June announces that "we're cool" and, soon after, we're on the open road. I notice a sign along the highway that reads "Curve continuously" then another one: "Notice your velocity." Roadside Taoism at its finest. None of our fellow travelers share this philosophy, though. They're honking and riding our bumper. "These people need to meditate," says Sandie.

We're humming along on the highway, curving continuously,

noticing our velocity, when all of a sudden—boom!—a blowout. The driver pulls over, inspects the damage, and promptly spits. This is not good. He gets back into the bus and decides to limp to a little town. It's a real dive, and everyone is eyeing us like we just landed from Mars. The group, meanwhile, gets all philosophical, attacking the problem from different angles.

"It's just a flat," says Bob.

"Shit happens," says Solala.

"Maybe yes, maybe no," says Sandie.

I'm going to miss this bunch.

Sandie sets off for beer and a few minutes later, judging by the smile on her face, she's scored. It's awful, piss-warm beer, but never mind. Popping one open and sipping it here in this dusty nowhere town, with a flat tire and a long trip ahead of us, Sandie declares, "God, I love China." The strange thing is: I can tell she means it.

We say our goodbyes. The group is heading to Beijing to do some sightseeing. I'm flying in the opposite direction, west to the city of Chengdu. My ultimate destination is Mount Qingcheng, a peak that rivals Wudang in holiness and where I hope to experience a more hermit-like existence. When I told Master Zhong of my plans, he nodded his approval. "That mountain has a different voice," he said.

On the flight, I think of Sandie. She has found her God, it seems, though He has no name, and I don't think she would quite put it that way. She has not upended her life, does not live like a hermit, does not, as far as I know, have any scripture tattooed on her body, yet Taoism nourishes her in profound ways I don't fully understand. I'm going to miss her. The pain of parting, though, is eased by the large tin of candy-glazed macadamia nuts she generously bequeathed to me.

* * *

I arrive at the Chengdu airport and, as I was instructed, stand under the giant rotating panda. There's no sign of Daniel, my interlocutor, a Canadian student who has somehow managed to master the Chinese language in a few short years. So I sit in the sun, watching the panda rotate and the newly wealthy Chinese scurry at an American pace, oblivious to their velocity. Finally, Daniel arrives, along with his ridiculously beautiful Chinese girl-friend. We attempt to load my suitcase into the trunk, but there's no room. It's filled with shoe boxes, dozens of them. I haven't seen so many shoes outside of a shoe store. Jimmy Choo and Manolo Blahnik and Christian Louboutin. All of the major designers are represented in Daniel's trunk. His girlfriend apologizes, mumbling something about a little shopping expedition. The country that brought the world the philosophy of less is more now seems to live as if more is more.

Our destination is a mysterious retreat in the foothills of the mountain. It's called the Book Palace, which sounds like Heaven to me, and is run by the even more mysterious Madam He, or Madam H., as I would come to think of her. That's all I know. Bill Porter, aka Red Pine, had set this ball rolling months ago, and I trust Bill and his Chinese soul not to steer me wrong.

"Do you mind stopping at a wedding?" asks Daniel.

"Sure."

Daniel's girlfriend's cousin is getting married, and no frivolity has been spared. The food and drink flow faster than the Yangtze during a flash flood. Nobody seems to mind my presence. On the contrary, they treat me like their long-lost American cousin, pos-ing to have their picture taken with me. The rest of the wedding is a blur of dubious alcohol and curious cuisine. "You've got all of your major organs here," says Daniel drily as a conveyor belt of pig brains, chicken livers, and sundry viscera circle in front of our bloodshot eyes like some sort of nightmarish carousel.

A few hours later, we arrive at the foothills of Mount Qingcheng. Daniel parks the car and we walk along a pathway bracketed by thick foliage. Then the trees part and there it is: the Book Palace. Maybe it's the way the late-afternoon light sets the place ablaze with colors, or maybe it's the wedding juice still swirling in my head, but I feel like I have arrived in my own personal paradise. The compound consists of several old buildings—genuinely old, not Wudang faux old—beautifully restored, and gardens everywhere. Music—real music, not Muzak—filters through the air, emanating from invisible speakers, like magic. And of course, there are books everywhere. They are objects of beauty but, for me, a cruel tease. They're all in Chinese.

Until now, Madam H. has remained an enigmatic figure, so when I actually meet her I feel that familiar pang of disappointment. She looks so...ordinary: a fit woman in her late sixties, with alert eyes, and a kind face. What was I expecting? I withhold judgment, though, recalling a Sufi *sheikh*'s advice I received many months ago: Distinguish between the outer and the inner.

Daniel and I are the only guests at the Book Palace. It's not open to the public. "The reason you are here is the reason it was built," Madam H. tells me. And that's exactly how I feel: as if this entire world has been created just for me. I'm reminded of that John Fowles novel *The Magus*, where a young malcontent finds himself the guest of an enigmatic tycoon on a Greek isle, and a psychodrama ensues. The Book Palace is good, too good to be real, and a small voice in my head whispers, "Where's the catch?" But this is not Vegas, and the inhabitants of the Book Palace no Raëlians. The risk of spontaneous cross-dressing seems minimal.

Later, with Daniel translating, Madam H. tells her story. She is a former Buddhist nun, lived eight years in a Buddhist monastery, but "didn't reach the level I had hoped for." The rituals and rhythms of monastic life left her feeling empty, distanced from her true passion: books. I hear this and think, Here is someone I can relate to. She had doubts and "you waste energy with uncertainty," she says, and I'm thinking, Yes, here is definitely someone I can relate to. She then moved to Hong Kong and made a living as a fortune-teller, quite a famous one, but the noise of the city, combined with the burden of knowing other people's fates, wore her down. So one day she sold everything, moved here, and founded the Book Palace, renovating what was once an abandoned Buddhist temple. She could run it as a hotel, but money no longer interests her. She opens the Book Palace's doors only to invited guests. She rarely leaves the compound. "A high-class hermit" is how she describes herself. She sleeps only four hours each evening; otherwise, she meditates, and reads. At age sixty-eight, she began studying architecture.

Madam H. subscribes to Chinese philosophy, but her somatic pleasures skew western: coffee, wine, Celine Dion. During one of many sumptuous meals, she gestures to me and asks, "What do you think of this path to enlightenment, with feasts and wine?"

"*Yawl-de*," I say, parroting one of a dozen Chinese words I've picked up. "It's all good."

"Stay for a few more days," she says. "I will teach you to be an Immortal." She's kidding. I think she's kidding.

During the day, Daniel leaves to teach English in town. That leaves me alone with Madam H. and the staff of the Book Palace, none of whom speak English. My twelve words of Chinese take us only so far ("Me like coffee? You like coffee? No problem"), so I spend my days in solitude. After all of that group activity on Mount Wudang, it's a pleasant change of pace. I slow down, I do nothing, and yet, as Lao-tzu would say, everything is done. He also said: "He who knows does not speak. He who speaks does not know." I know very little. My constant stream of verbiage, I think, is a kind of self-soothing behavior. For me, words are like pacifiers. My loquaciousness represents, I think, a clumsy effort to hold fear at bay, and there is no greater fear, of course, than the fear of death, of nonexistence. *I speak therefore I am.* If I just keep talking, I figure death can't get a word in and I'll achieve some sort of immortality, albeit a verbose and annoying one.

But here I stop talking. Admittedly, this is mostly a bow to reality—nobody here understands me—but I'd also like to think that some of this Taoist wisdom is seeping in. Silence, I realize, is another way of emptying ourselves, of aligning ourselves with the Tao. This insight hits me like a thunderclap, and of course I feel the need to share my revelation. I can't say enough good things about silence. Really, I could go on and on but, alas, there is no one to talk to, no one who speaks my language at least, so I find myself in the odd though not entirely unpleasant position of keeping a thought—a good thought at that—to myself.

The human mind craves routine, even when that mind finds itself, inexplicably, ensconced in paradise, so a routine I devise. I wake early and promptly perform the eight brocades I learned on Mount Wudang. I don't want to lose that momentum. Much as it pains me to admit, it's tough going without the group, that giant organism, pulling me along. Then I walk across the compound to the dining room and fix myself breakfast. I offer silent thanks to Madam H. and her passion for coffee. Then I find a spot, curl into a chair, and read. I've dropped Lao-tzu and moved on to Chuang-tzu. He is the second-most-famous Taoist philosopher and, in style if not substance, the exact opposite of Lao-tzu. Chuang-tzu is a traveler, a free and easy wanderer, as he says, and most of all a storyteller. His tales are populated with larger-than-life characters with names like the Crooked Man with No Lips and the Man with a Jug-Size Goiter. The core lesson, though, is pure Taoist: Cling to nothing, especially your own ideas, and follow the Tao the way a hawk rides the wind.

One afternoon, I'm sitting and reading Chuang-tzu and watching not a hawk but a butterfly. I watch this butterfly for longer than I've ever watched a butterfly, possibly any animal, in my life. I watch it flutter and land, take off again, nose-dive. Maybe this is what the Taoists mean by sitting and forgetting, though the practice might better be called sitting and remembering—remembering what life is like when we notice our velocity. Chuang-tzu was a big fan of butterflies too. Once he dreamed he was a butterfly. "Suddenly, I awoke, and veritably, was Chuang-tzu again. But I do not know whether I was dreaming that I was a butterfly, or whether I am a butterfly dreaming that I was Chuang-tzu." A beautiful, intriguing passage, but what to do with it? Much of Taoism is like that. It sounds wise, and part of me knows it *is* wise, but what to do with it when there are bills to pay, and the "engine check" light is on again, and where the hell are my keys?

I awake the next morning to the rat-a-tat of rain drops striking the metal roof of my building. Later, when the rain clears, Madam H. teaches me her version of *qi gong*. She had declared my eight brocades unduly complex. Standing in the courtyard, with Daniel translating, she shows me a pared-down routine. It's looser than what I learned at Mount Wudang, with much waving of arms, gathering the *chi*, and robust inhalations.

"This is very important," says Madam H. "You must tighten your anus."

"Daniel, are you sure you translated that word properly?"

Yes, he did. My anus is too loose. This explains a lot. My *chi* isn't clogged, after all. It's leaking, and out of an unexpected orifice. The deeper life lesson I extract is this: There is energy all around us—love, too. Our challenge is holding on to it. Perhaps this is an overly generous interpretation, but why not?

And so my days at the Book Palace unfurl with Taoist ease. One day, I'm reading Chuang-tzu. He's describing "the true man of old," an archetypal figure who followed the Tao unswervingly. Writes Chuang-tzu: "The true man of old did not hold on to life, nor did he fear death. He arrived without expectation and left without resistance." Reading that, it dawns on me how little I resemble the true man. I hold on to life tightly (so tightly I practically strangle it). I certainly fear death. I have great expectations and much resistance. I put the book down and ponder the implications of this. What Chuang-tzu describes sounds impossible. Does anyone live their life like that, with no expectations or resistance? I feel lost.

I think of Chungliang Al Huang. He is a Chinese American who has been teaching *tai-ji* for decades. He's known as "the wild man of *tai-ji*," for his approach is very different from the mechanical moves favored by most teachers. Chungliang is fond of saying things like "There's no excuse not to move," and "Every movement has a meaning; never move meaninglessly." And my favorite: "If you want to understand the Tao, you dance it." Chungliang is a *tai-ji* dancer, a *tai-ji* genius. He moves and looks twenty years younger than his seventy-four years. As far as I'm concerned, the man is living proof of *chi*.

I took one of his classes before coming to China, and it was going well, except I kept getting lost. Each morning, on the drive from my hotel to the college campus where the workshop was held, my GPS betrayed me, dispatching me into cornfields, mountains, the Pacific Ocean. I'd arrive late, apologizing. It became a running joke. Here I was following the Tao, the Way, and yet I kept losing mine. One day, Chungliang, who is also a master calligrapher, drew (the verb does not do justice to the explosive, full-body way he paints) the Chinese character for "lost," and told me that it also means "mystery." I like that. I am not merely lost on the back roads of Olympia, Washington, I am deeply immersed in mystery, the Great Mystery, the "whirling emptiness" that is the Tao, the

Way. Throughout the ages, no one has ever found themselves without losing themselves first.

Sadly, it's time to leave the Book Palace. Life is beautiful here, but it is the beautiful life of a hermit, albeit a high-class one, and I feel it is time to reenter the world of dust. I say goodbye to Madam H., promising to return. She leaves me with these words of advice: "You don't choose a religion, it chooses you. You'll know when you're ready." And with that, Daniel and I load up the car and are soon subsumed by the impatient, unyielding China that lies just beyond the gates of the Book Palace.

Have I gotten hold of this slippery seal called Taoism? Yes. No. Certain unifying words spring to mind. Softness. Inaction. Simplicity. Yes, Taoism counsels all of this, but the word that rises to the top of my list is "trust." At its heart, Taoism is about trusting "the way things are." Going with the flow sounds nice but works only if you trust the flow—trust it to carry you to a better place and not, say, over Niagara Falls. And I realize for the first time how little I trust. I have, consciously or not, answered Einstein's meta-question—Is the universe a friendly place?—and my answer is no. It is a hostile place, a place where I must constantly remain vigilant and, should I drop my guard for even a second, all will come tumbling down. How exhausting. How arrogant.

I wonder: Is Taoism a kind of antidepressant? If I could meet Lao-tzu, what would he prescribe for my dark night of the soul? In my mind's ear, I imagine the conversation.

"Please help, Lao-tzu. How can I fight this ghastly depression?"

Lao-tzu, a slow talker, would pause before answering: "Your melancholy is not a monster, an aberration outside the Tao, for that is impossible. Nothing is outside the Tao. Don't resist your sadness, accept it, fully and unconditionally, and it will dissipate of its own accord, like water evaporating on a hot summer day. Trust the universe. It is indeed a friendly place; otherwise, you wouldn't be here right now questioning whether it is. Your very existence presupposes a benevolent force. We cannot name this force and need not try."

For once, I would say nothing, for there would be nothing to say.

CWM, looking to put a little magic in my life. Perhaps I need more than one deity to meet my needs. Open to a multiple-god relationship. Let's get creative together.

It's a bit tricky finding me," says Jamie the Witch when I call to arrange a meeting. "My house has two addresses." A vast and vaguely uncomfortable silence ensues as I mull over that statement. A house occupying two points in space simultaneously. Some sort of black magic?

No, some sort of mix-up with the local zoning department, Jamie assures me. Don't bother using MapQuest, either, she warns. You'll get lost.

Of course I don't heed her advice. I place my fate, as usual, squarely in the hands of our modern and supposedly benevolent god: technology. As it so often does, though, this god disappoints. The house with two addresses befuddles my GPS, which promptly recalculates itself into a highly agitated state. In an act of mercy, I switch it off, and follow Jamie's directions.

We approach all religions with preconceptions. Say the word "Muslim" or "Buddhist" or "Rastafarian" and certain images instantly materialize. Few religions, though, arrive as fully loaded as witchcraft. The word "witch" evokes all sorts of associations, none especially positive: spells, hexes, cauldrons, fire. Even my five-year-old daughter was intrigued when I told her I was traveling to the Seattle area in order to hang out with a few witches. "Do they ride on broomsticks?" she asked. The modern witch bristles at such cartoonish depictions yet, owing to the playful nature of her faith, also derives a certain degree of pleasure from them.

A good witch is able to laugh at herself and, Jamie assures me, she is a good witch. She does not worship Satan (Satan being a Christian device), she does not sacrifice anybody or anything, other than her time, which she does often and with a reckless generosity. She does not turn people into toads, though she has met her share of toad-like people, and even married one once. In her spare time, she writes a blog called Witchful Thinking. It's an advice column. Like Dear Abby, she says, only with a pointy hat.

That default question when investigating a new faith—What do you believe?—was of little help with the Buddhists and Taoists. It gets me absolutely nowhere with witches. They're hard to pin down. "I dare you to find out what Wiccans believe," my friend Alan Cooperman, a former religion reporter for a major newspaper, told me over a sushi lunch in Washington, DC. "I dare you. It can't be done," he said, practically spitting raw fish at me, so adamant was he.

I love nothing more than a good dare, but that temptation alone doesn't explain my interest in witchcraft, a subset of Wicca and, more broadly, neo-paganism, a loose category that includes Druids and Heathens, among others. My time in China did wonders for my *chi*, and there is much wisdom in its philosophy of effortless action, but Taoism makes no room for God, only the mysterious and ineffable Tao, the Way. Try praying to that when storm clouds gather. Wicca, on the other hand, dangles not one God before me but hundreds. It is a very new religion, and also very old. Largely unfettered by hierarchy or dogma, it promises a world of nature and magic—and just enough danger to keep things interesting.

I arrive at a gravel parking lot. Is this it? I spot a rusting washing machine marooned out front, like an artifact from some now extinct civilization. No signs of life. I must be lost, and not in the Taoist sense. I'm about to pull away when I notice the "No Trespassing" sign that Jamie the Witch said I would see. And there are the rickety wooden steps leading to a tired-looking shack, "not the nicest of houses," just as she warned. I knock, and there is Jamie Lewis. No pointy hat. No broomstick. Just a young woman with a kind face and the zaftig figure of an Anatolian goddess.

Around her neck dangles a pentagram, a five-pointed star, the Wiccan symbol. Posters depicting phases of the moon adorn the wall of her bedroom. Otherwise, it is not the nicest of houses inside, either; the walls look like they're made of cardboard, and the entire structure feels like it might collapse at any moment. Jamie's boyfriend is planted on the couch and looks like he's been there since the Clinton administration.

Rather than disturb the boyfriend, Jamie and I drive to a local eatery. It's a content place, unburdened by ambitions to be anything other than what it is: a hole-in-the-wall diner with tuna melts for five dollars and waitresses who will cheerfully refill your coffee until you float away. We order, then slow-dance our way into conversation. Jamie seems incredibly normal, which, of course, disappoints me. I was expecting someone a little witchier.

How, I wonder, does one become a witch? I assume witches are made, not born, and that turns out to be the case with Jamie. She grew up in a secular household—her family attended church maybe once a year—but from an early age she displayed spiritual proclivities. At age eleven, she studied Zen Buddhism. She dabbled in Mormonism. She was a Muslim for a day. (She bought a Koran, delighting in the subversiveness of it, but her interest in Islam never took root.)

Why such feverish God shopping?

"I had questions," Jamie says.

I know that is an understatement. Jamie strikes me as one of those people who desires more, always more. These are greedy people, in the best sense of the word, and their greed takes on a religious nature.

In high school she fell in with the Dungeons & Dragons crowd. At the time, she didn't know why but now, looking back, she realizes they were all wounded souls, broken. Like her. Ever since age sixteen, when a close friend committed suicide. After the funeral, Jamie left candy at her grave. They both liked candy.

Jamie blamed herself for her friend's death. A few days before the suicide, Jamie had seen her friend on the lunch line. "Hey, how's it going, Jamie?" the friend asked. But Jamie, more interested in the color and texture of her french fries, sloughed off her friend. Why didn't she stop and talk to her? Maybe it would have made a difference. Maybe she could have stopped her from going through with it. Racked with guilt, Jamie slipped into a deep depression.

Then one day, while attending a counseling seminar at school, talking to some guy who was saying nothing especially interesting, Jamie saw her.

"Saw who?"

"My friend. As clear as day, standing next to this guy."

"Your *dead* friend? You saw your dead friend?"

"Yes."

Then her friend, her dead friend, says to Jamie: "It wasn't your fault. I was going to do it anyway. Thanks for the candy." Jamie began crying uncontrollably and ran out of the room.

I nearly choke on my tuna melt. "What did she look like?"

"She looked like herself, except she seemed healthy and happy. And kind of transparent."

I don't know what to think. Jamie doesn't strike me as crazy, though I may not be the best judge of sanity. The obvious question—was the ghost real or not?—doesn't seem to concern Jamie. Real or not, the ghost was helpful. It permitted Jamie to stop blaming herself for her friend's death and move on with her life. *Truth is what works*, as William James said.

A piece was still missing, though, a big piece. Jamie needed a mechanism, a theology (though she wouldn't have put it that way) that enabled her to make sense of the ghost experience, to incorporate it into her evolving worldview. This proved difficult. Traditional religion didn't offer much help in the ghost department. Then one day she stumbled across a book. It was called *Teen Witch*. An embarrassing book, Jamie says, but one that, like the ghost, proved useful. *Teen Witch* is where Jamie first encountered the goddess—not a particular goddess, but the idea that deities come in genders other than male. Jamie was intrigued. Growing up fatherless, she never could relate to God as the Cosmic Male Parent. In Jamie's small, fatherless world, her mother was god. The goddess.

Not long after, Jamie was Christmas shopping with her grandmother. "Get whatever you want," her grandmother said, so Jamie bought a book on witchcraft and a deck of Tarot cards. The book depicted all sorts of rituals: ritual nudity, ritual sex, ritual whipping. No explanations, just these bizarre rituals. Jamie already had plenty of bizarre in her life. She didn't need this. So she checked out. She stopped shopping for gods or goddesses or any other deities that might be lurking out there and busied herself with schoolwork and boyfriends.

Then came college and that old Wiccan itch surfaced again. Again, a book was the proximate cause. This particular book,

Wicca: A Guide for the Solitary Practitioner, resonated with Jamie. As the title suggests, it prescribed a do-it-yourself faith. This appealed to Jamie, who was never much of a joiner.

"And so one day I was self-initiating in my bedroom, in the nude. Of course my roommate walked in."

"I hate when that happens."

"Yeah, so there I am with a knife in the air, naked, and I'm like, 'Um, can you knock next time?'"

Nudity and knives. This does not sound like any ritual I'm familiar with—except one in which I was an unwilling participant at eight days old, but I've blocked that from my memory. I'm curious about the mechanics of this ritual Jamie was performing in the nude, but it sounds awfully personal, so I don't inquire further. Suffice to say, she dispatched her roommate and resumed her self-initiation, officially achieving witch-hood. That was a decade ago. She hasn't looked back since. She found fellow witches, joined a coven, but still finds her solitary practice the most rewarding. Wiccans, perhaps even more than mystics, cut out the middle man. "It's between you and the gods," she says.

"Okay, but what do Wiccans believe?"

"We don't believe anything," she replies, and I can hear Alan Cooperman's self-satisfied voice: *See, I told you. Impossible.* "We experience. The only thing you can trust is your experience," says Jamie, sounding very much like Sandie the Taoist.

Jamie considers herself "a logical witch" and has no patience for "these kids who want to be Wiccan but don't want to do the work." Wicca is not a fad or a free-for-all, she tells me. It is a religion, and "absolutely valid." Wicca tackles the big questions. It helps people understand where they are in the universe and what happens when they die. Questions don't get any bigger than that.

I wonder, though, if it's a religion for the indecisive, like me. There are hundreds of gods from which to choose: ancient Greek gods, Egyptian gods, Druid gods, Norse gods. Why so many gods? I wonder. What's wrong with the One? I, like most people raised in a monotheistic tradition, reflexively view polytheism as inferior, atavistic, a throwback to the days when Man (and Woman) worshipped idols and thought leeches and bloodletting were covered under their HMO. That is not how pagans see it. To them, monotheism is, as the Tibetan lama said of my search for God, "a bit limited." Dangerous, even. As any economist knows, one-crop economies don't fare well over the long term. Pagans choose not to put all of their spiritual eggs in one theistic basket. They have a diversified portfolio, in a way that, say, Jews don't. If Hashem tanks, has a bad year, Jews have no recourse. We're screwed. Not so with Wiccans. There is always another god.

It's not simply that Wiccans are hedging their bets. Polytheism also renders God more accessible. This is how Jamie sees it: God, singular, is like a big diamond. Too big and incomprehensible for "our puny monkey brains" to comprehend. So Wicca breaks down the diamond into facets. These parts—God, plural—are easier to grasp than the unfathomable whole. Polytheists worship a tapas God, small platefuls of distinct appetizers that, together, make for a satisfying meal.

Wicca, as Jamie sees it, is a very democratic religion. You choose the gods and goddesses you wish to worship, choose which part of the diamond to look at, and nobody is offended by your choice. No jealous gods here. The best part, Jamie says, is "if a god isn't working for you, you can fire him or her."

"You can fire a god?"

"Sure."

Part of me loves the idea of multiple, disposable deities—*The Apprentice* meets *Big Love*—but another part of me is offended. To my Judeo-Christian ears, this sounds blasphemous. Fire Hashem? Sack the Almighty? How is this possible? I mean, without inviting some serious, biblical repercussions. Jamie has an answer for that. "It's just like having a friend you always play poker with. That doesn't negate the friendship you have with someone else you always play bridge with; each person brings a richness to your life." In other words, Wicca is the perfect faith for people with commitment issues. If it doesn't work out with one god, you can always hook up with another. Jamie, for instance, flirted with the Celtic gods for a while. She thought they might hit it off. After all, she loved Irish dance and culture, music. But no sparks flew. She didn't understand their cosmology and, as she recounts, "When I talked to them they weren't that interested in me." So she dumped the Celtic gods and moved on. No hard feelings.

Another surprising aspect of paganism: The gods are not perfect. They possess human frailties, and Jamie isn't beyond critiquing these lesser gods. Aphrodite, for instance, can be "bossy." How, I ask, can you worship an imperfect, lowercase god? I always thought that was why God existed in the first place: to be better than us, to give us something to aspire to. Otherwise, I might as well worship the guy down the road with a gut the size of a small refrigerator and a propensity for scratching his ass.

Jamie has an answer for this too. "We're perfect in our imperfection, and so are the gods. Zeus, for example, was a pedophile, adulterer, and tyrant, but we aren't expected to act like him." The pagan gods exist not as perfect beings but as object lessons. Thou shalt not make a royal mess of things like we did.

Jamie, as I said, dabbled in Buddhism but it didn't resonate with her. The problem, as she sees it, is that Buddhists aim to extinguish the ego. Jamie didn't want to kill her ego; she wanted to heal it. Also, the newness of Wicca appealed to her. Unlike more established religions, Wicca is a work in progress, just like Jamie. She felt she could actually shape the faith in a way that is much less likely with, say, Catholicism.

Witchcraft is often cast in opposition to Christianity, but the two faiths share some common ground. Both emphasize kindness and consideration to others. Both adhere to the Golden Rule: Do unto others as you would have them do unto you. Wiccans perform rituals and pray, just like Christians. The difference, Jamie says, is that Christian worshippers are more or less passive. The priest or minister does all of the work. Not so in Wicca.

"The thing that bothers me about Christian prayer is that it is, 'Please, God, I beg You, I am so pitiful. I can't do anything by myself. Can You please do this for me? Because You are so almighty and wonderful and I can't do shit.' And for paganism it is, 'I am powerful. I can change my life.'"

On this point, Christianity and paganism are irreconcilable faiths. One says, I can do anything. The other says, I can do nothing without You. One advocates a radical dependency, the other an equally radical independency. Is there no middle ground? I wonder. A radical interdependency, perhaps?

Wicca is the perfect faith for anarchists and nonconformists. While there are covens and a few Wiccan churches, these are loosely organized. There is no governing Wiccan body, no Wiccan pope or Wiccan rule book to follow. There is simply the Wiccan Rede: "A'in it harm none, do what thou wilt." Or, in more contemporary English: Do what you wish as long as it doesn't hurt anyone. (It sounds wonderfully simple, but it is not. How do you define harm? Does squashing an insect count as harm? What if I apply for a job and get it; haven't I harmed the applicants who did not get the job?) Witches take a nonjudgmental, almost libertarian, approach to life.

Stripped of all pretense, pagans stand naked before their gods. Sometimes, literally. They call it "sky clad," which sounds considerably more noble than "buck naked." Jamie has performed more than her share of sky-clad rituals. Women, like herself, not size 6, *nowhere near size 6*, standing in the woods naked. "When you get to see nudity in our culture it is pornography or it is in a film with movie stars. Well, most of us don't look like that. You don't really get an opportunity to see what regular people look like. And so there is this curiosity."

No, Jamie, there is not this curiosity. I have no desire to see what regular people look like naked. I haven't fully recovered from my close encounter with the Raëlians, who, while not exactly regular, were quite naked. I am, though, intrigued by Wicca. Like Buddhism and the mystical paths, it emphasizes experience over doctrine. In Wicca, there is no such thing as sin, original or otherwise. It is mildly subversive.

A retired British civil servant named Gerald Gardner is widely credited with inventing modern Wicca. Gardner was an amateur anthropologist, folklorist, and nudist who spent much of his career in Asia. In 1936, he returned to England, where he joined an occultist group called The Fellowship of Crotona and, as legend has it, in 1939 was taken to the house of a wealthy woman named Dorothy Clutterbuck, "Old Dorothy," and initiated into "The Craft." Gardner, a natural promoter, wrote several books on witchcraft that attracted a lot of attention. He called his new religion Wicca, an Old English word for witchcraft. In *Drawing Down the Moon*, her classic account of neo-paganism, Margot Adler says the word "derives from the Indo-European roots 'wic' and 'weik' meaning to bend or turn. According to this view, a witch would be a woman (or man) skilled in the craft of shaping, bending and changing reality."

In other words, magic. And now we have stumbled across probably the most controversial aspect of this controversial faith. We're not talking about pulling rabbits out of hats. So what is Wiccan magic? Many Wiccans like to cite Aleister Crowley's famous definition: "The Science and Art of causing change to occur in conformity with Will." Is that change supernatural? No, witches tell me. But it sure seems that way to me. I hear tales of money that is needed for, say, college tuition, suddenly arriving, right on cue, or the skies all of a sudden clearing in time for the big festival. In my experience, such propitious happenings are not natural at all. I make a note to find out more about magic.

To this day, some Wiccans go to great lengths to "prove" that theirs is not some newfangled faith concocted by a retired British civil servant with a vivid imagination but, rather, part of an ancient, unbroken chain. That is a highly dubious claim. "The Wiccans know this. They're not stupid," says Alan Cooperman. "They know it's bullshit." Which is not to say that Wicca is not a valid and meaningful path to God, plural. Again, the value of a religion does not depend on the veracity of its creation myth—or, to put it another way: Bullshit is no deal breaker.

It's been said that you're not really a Wiccan until you do something Wiccan. So when Jamie invites me to a coven, a gathering of fellow witches, I eagerly accept.

I pick her up at the house with two addresses and we head east toward the small town of Index, Washington. As we drive, we discuss the split in the witch community. On one side are those who believe The Craft, as Wiccans sometimes call their faith, should remain secretive, and on the other side are people like Jamie, who believe that it's time to come out of the broom closet. The way Jamie sees it, her religion has made great strides from the days when Wiccan books were stashed behind counters and witches hid their beliefs. Today estimates of the number of Wiccans and other neo-pagans in the United States vary from one to three million, and the religion is recognized by, among others, the Pentagon. Wiccan service members killed in the line of duty can have their faith's symbol, the pentagram, engraved on their tombstone at Arlington National Cemetery.

Soon the strip malls fade, and then so do the drive-up espresso stands, replaced by mini churches, similar in appearance and purpose: small, squat buildings selling a quick hit of salvation to fellow travelers. We pass a reptile museum, and then...nothing. Jamie announces that we've officially reached the end of civilization.

The conversation turns to ritual. All religions practice ritual, even those that are atheistic, like Buddhism. Children seem to naturally understand the importance of ritual. My daughter derives great pleasure from the few Jewish rituals we sporadically engage in, the lighting of the Sabbath candles, for instance. Are we hardwired for ritual? Researchers have found that the part of the brain where religious thinking is located is the same part where children play with ideas and express creativity.

Wiccans certainly know how to express. They approach ritual the way a musician approaches jazz, improvising, riffing, and simply making it up as they go along. They see no shame in that. Ritual is especially important to them, perhaps because they have so little liturgy and so few temples. ("The forest is our temple," they are fond of saying.) All ritual may be simply "myth enacted," as Joseph Campbell says, but Wiccans believe that not all ritual is created equal. "There's a lot of bad ritual out there," Jamie says, sounding like a guy at Woodstock warning about "some bad acid out there."

Bad ritual? What can that possibly mean? At church or synagogue, I suppose flubbing a line of prayer or expecting communion when one is not Catholic, or perhaps forgetting to stand (or sit) on cue might constitute bad ritual. But, no, Jamie is speaking of something else entirely. Bad ritual is not bad form but bad content. "The energy isn't grounded or people invoke a bunny or something. I mean, what is the point of that?" Good ritual elevates us; bad ritual diminishes us. *By their fruit you shall know them.*

For Wiccans, ritual is not some heirloom they dust off on special occasions. It is fluid, malleable. Alive. Wiccans are constantly inventing ritual. Which sounds blasphemous at first, but when you think about it, it makes perfect sense: The religious impulse is, at its heart, a creative one, and like all creative enterprises demands a high tolerance for failure. "You can try rituals and they can be total flops. That's okay," says Jamie. Wicca is the perfect faith for imperfectionists, experimenters, and people willing to make total asses of themselves. I just may have found my God.

Then again, maybe not. As we turn off the main road, Jamie warns me that the church is experiencing "a bit of a public-relations crisis." I'm thinking, Oh, some problem with their finances probably. The IRS can be so picky.

"What sort of crisis?" I ask.

"One of our members murdered another, chopped up her body, and burned it." I nearly swerve off the road. "Say what?"

Jamie explains how this guy who went to the church occasionally—everybody thought he was strange—got jealous and one day murdered his girlfriend, who was also a member of the church. He told the police he killed her because she had violated a "Wiccan blood oath." There is no such thing as a Wiccan blood oath, Jamie assures me. The guy was clearly deranged.

I believe her, I do, but I'd be lying if I didn't confess I'm just a bit concerned driving out to this end-of-civilization town for a pagan ritual with a witch I just met. We turn down a dirt road then see a small sign that reads "ATC" and beside it, a pentagram. We've arrived at the Aquarian Tabernacle Church, which looks more like a budget ski lodge than a house of worship. We walk inside to a large eat-in kitchen area. I meet Chris, a former navy sailor—with the tattoos to prove it—and others, all of whom seem remarkably

normal. These are office managers, school counselors, graphic designers. These are witches with mortgages. Former Catholics are,
again, disproportionately represented here. "Ritual junkies," they
call themselves.

We sit around for a while, sipping coffee and making small
talk—the usual stuff, someone's daughter just got married in Vegas;
someone was promoted at work—when suddenly I hear a voice announce, with a Shakespearean timbre, "Time to cast the circle."

As we walk down a narrow wooded path lined with candles,
Jamie tells me it is a good night for ritual. Drizzly. Brisk, but not
too cold.

We are about to enter the sacred circle; Wiccans are big on circles, which are said to exist "between two worlds." Once you enter
the circle you can't leave, Jamie tells me. "They need to maintain
the integrity of the border. You can't just walk out, the energy will
fall out. It's like popping a balloon."

A bell rings, then I hear that deep Shakespearean voice say:
"The temple is about to be erected. Let all who enter do so of their
own free will. Pray be silent while the temple is purified."

We enter the circle, one by one, and when it's my turn a woman,
dressed in a white robe, says "Welcome, thou art God." Whoa.
Did I hear that correctly? *I* am God? Now I definitely know this
is not a Catholic or Jewish ritual. At those services, there is only
one God and thou art not it. It may sound like blasphemy, but this
sentiment—that we are God—is not without precedent. *Tat tvam
asi*, the Vedas say. "Thou art that."

We're all standing inside this little clearing now, in a circle, when
the woman, the one who so astutely pegged me as God, speaks:
"Children of the gods, come into this circle with open heart and
open eyes, anoint your head, your heart, and your loins with these
cleansing waters." So I do. I anoint my head, my heart, splashing
water on them. I leave my loins out of it, at least for now.

Next, we bless the elements: air, water, fire, earth. Then the warder, the "keeper of the gate," says, "Do not break the circle." I can tell he means it, too. A bell rings again, then the warder draws a large sword and begins thrusting it about, with large melodramatic gestures.

They are using the sword to carve out a sacred space, Jamie whispers in my ear. They are creating a temple, with pure intentions. More than that, says Jamie, they are creating a mini universe. Everything inside the circle is sacred, special; everything outside the circle is ordinary. It is a sharp delineation—no porous borders here—and it is the warder's task to maintain the integrity of the border. There is no leaving now, not even, Jamie informs, for bathroom breaks, which strikes me as odd given how much Wiccans normally honor Mother Nature.

In the center of the circle is a large stone. The sky is dark, and it is cold. Everyone chants, in unison: "Ancient Queen of Sundown, Hecate, Hecate, the old one, come to us."

Then a woman wearing a long robe appears, as if from nowhere. Hecate, I presume. She speaks with the resonance and projection of a classical actor. "Oh my children, rise up," Hecate says, and we obey. "Look at you, just look at you. You are so beautiful. Oh, a little rough around the edges, but so beautiful. And you invite me, your patron. It is an honor for me."

The atmosphere is pure theater, with a pinch of magic. Macbeth meets Harry Potter. Something else about the ritual strikes me as surprisingly familiar—the candles, the incense, the theatrical quality. Where have I seen this before? Then it dawns on me: the Franciscans. Of course. Catholicism and paganism cross-pollinated centuries ago, even though the Catholic Church did eventually abolish paganism; they would not be the first victor to "borrow" from their vanquished. How different this ritual is, though, from the carefully scripted services of the Catholic mass, or Jewish ceremonies where, as Abraham Heschel observed, "the services are prim, the voice is dry, the temple clean and tidy, and the soul of prayer lies in agony. You know no one will scream, no one will cry, the words will be stillborn."

No stillborn words here. They are spoken with passion and, though the service is clearly scripted, it is a script that is fresh, written not thousands of years ago but six months ago. This, I think, is what Jewish, Christian, Muslim rituals must have been like at one time, before they grew stale and rigid.

Hecate continues. "I am the lady of the crossroads. I will not choose for you, I cannot, I will not advise you on which path to take, for that is your work. But I will hold you fully accountable for the consequences of that choice. Yes, the gods have indeed given you a great gift: free will. The will to dream. The will to know. The will to choose. And the will to act for yourself. There is a price for this gift that the gods and you as mortals must pay: accountability. Some see me as a harsh mistress. No, I say, you will receive from me exactly what you are willing to give. Do you keep your wits about you at all times? Do you strategize ahead for mishaps? Or do you just expect others to come and save you in a pinch? Are you aiming for your goals or are you wandering, confused, like a lamb ripe for slaughter?"

Everyone laughs, a knowing laugh. Except me—I don't know what we're laughing at. We pass some bread around. "No nuts but beware, there *are* raisins." More laughter. I am struck by the amount of frivolity manifest inside that circle. I can't remember anyone ever laughing at my childhood synagogue or any of the church services I attended. The Bible contains only four references to God laughing and in every case it is Jehovah laughing over the fate of the wicked.

A few more gods make appearances—Pan, the mischievous Greek god and companion of nymphs, is a big hit—then we all say in unison: "May the ground preserve the gods." The warder announces that "the circle is closed but never broken." Then we retire to the kitchen for brownies. I sit down with the gods, now disrobed and utterly mortal. "Hecate," who works in human resources, tells me, "The point of that ritual was for everybody to leave and remember a little bit how to play. When you were a child you looked around and everything was just wow. The point of the ritual was for everyone to stop and look at themselves and say, 'Yeah, stop being your jaded selves, stop worrying that your iPhone is too slow.'"

I'm reminded of something Alan Cooperman had told me: "Wicca is a great religion for five-year-olds." I don't think he meant that as an insult. Wicca retains a playful, whimsical quality long ago drained from most religions. It stokes wonder and awe. You get to dress up in funny outfits, run around outside, and laugh whenever you feel like it. What's not to like?

It's time to return to civilization. We have a long drive ahead of us. The roads are dark, illuminated only by the perfect half-moon dangling in the sky like a hanger in someone's wardrobe. It's cold outside, but warm inside my rented Subaru, which is equipped with seat warmers, perhaps the greatest single invention since the steam engine. Our butts warming up nicely, Jamie and I deconstruct the evening's activities. She is wearing a ski hat with little cat ears. It makes her look young, which she is, and for the first time I can see her as a wounded child, growing up with no father and many questions.

For Jamie, the takeaway was this: "Just take a moment before you make a decision and think about it. Take a look around. What are you missing when you are rushing around? Take a moment." She calls it "the cosmic two-by-four." I bet it makes a loud thwack when it hits you upside the head.

That sound probably sums up 90 percent of all religious and

spiritual practices. Saying grace before a meal. Watching our breath. Repeating the ninety-nine names of Allah. Whirling like a dervish. Prayer. They all have one objective: to get us to pause just long enough to realize that life, *your* life, is a freaking miracle. The least you can do is pay attention.

It seems so obvious now, and helps explain my melancholy. Depression makes it more difficult to concentrate, to pay attention, which makes you more depressed, which, in turn, makes it more difficult to pay attention, and on it goes. I realize that Jamie has confessed so much, and I so little. I start to tell Jamie about my troubles, but the dark roads require all the attention I can muster. Only later, safely back home, thousands of miles away, do I tell her about my depression. (I do this by e-mail, my preferred method of confessing my dark side.) And why not ask her? For starters, Jamie swears that Wicca has helped her navigate some treacherous waters. She was in an abusive relationship and wanted to get better but, as she puts it, she "didn't know what better looked like." Besides, I've tried talk therapy, various drugs and herbal remedies, countless self-help books. Spiritually, I've done—well, almost done—so much. I've almost meditated, nearly confessed, practically changed gender. Why not ask a witch—especially a logical one like Jamie? With all those gods and goddesses at her disposal, surely there is one that specializes in depression. A happiness god, perhaps. Or maybe she can invoke Paxilia, the ancient Greek goddess of mood enhancement and unpleasant side effects. I figure I have nothing to lose.

Jamie replies to my query, as she always does: epically. (Brevity, apparently, is not a pagan virtue.) It takes me several days to digest her missive. Here is the gist: Like many spiritual people, Jamie sees depression not as a pathology but as an SOS, a flare gun fired by my subconscious, signaling that "something is not right there." I'm not suffering from depression, not that only, but from a "spiritual emergency," a term I find simultaneously frightening and uplifting. Jamie is not alone in this armchair diagnosis. Viktor Frankl, a concentration camp survivor and therefore a man who knew a thing or two about suffering, puts it this way: "A man's concern, even his despair, over the worthwhileness of life is an existential distress but by no means a mental disease." I like that. Existential distress sounds so much more noble, more European, than depression or, worse, mental illness. Existential distress sounds like something that can be cured by smoking little cigars and reading Sartre.

By paragraph three, Jamie has shifted into tough-love mode. "Feeling depressed? Then fucking do something about it! Get counseling. Get meds if you need them. Move around. Eat better. Face your demons." I was afraid of this. Jamie is expressing an old Wiccan belief in personal responsibility, something I have steadfastly avoided and am loath to embrace at this stage of my life. Wiccans believe in a version of karma called the Threefold Law. Whatever you do—good or bad—comes back to you three times over. It's karma adjusted for inflation.

Pagan responsibility comes with another twist. "We hold each other accountable because we believe in change," says Jamie, "and the power of the self to cause magical transformation." Magical transformation! In other words, we do the work but then this mysterious force—call it the gods, the subconscious, whatever—kicks in and matches our efforts. It's like a divine version of a matching 401(k). Our employer—in this case God, plural—matches our efforts. Only a fool or masochist would turn down an offer like that. Which of those two categories, I wonder, do I fall into? Both, possibly, depending on the time of day.

Different gods, like different therapists, approach depression from different perspectives, Jamie explains. Aphrodite might suggest I suffer from a lack of love. Pan would suggest I need to have more fun. Celtic gods understand depression as grief, and therefore the cure is "keening and questing." (I had to look up "keening" in the dictionary; it means "to make a loud and long cry of sorrow.") Shinto gods would describe it as shame, and therefore the cure is "appropriate apologetic rituals." For a bit of much-needed levity, Jamie suggests I turn to Baubo, an ancient goddess with a penchant for sacred hilarity. ("Nothing banishes depression like laughter!") Jamie suggests I consult the gods with whom I have a good working relationship. Sound advice. One slight problem, though: I don't have a good working relationship, or any other kind of relationship, with the gods. I suspect this is a problem.

Magic. The most beguiling, and controversial, aspect of Wicca. Magic is what draws many people to this path. I admit I'm curious, especially given my own history with magic, albeit of the more mundane variety. Somewhere around age ten, I was bitten by the magic bug. I can still recall the texture and heft of the catalog from the Louis Tannen Company of New York. It wasn't so much a catalog as a book, hardcover, too, and beautifully illustrated. I'd order a trick—the sponge balls or square circle or floating zombie—and wait impatiently for its arrival. When it finally came, I greedily opened the box, read the instructions, and spent the next few days mastering the art of its deception. My repertoire grew, and eventually I was good enough to perform at neighborhood birthday parties.

I loved magic. I'm not sure why. Maybe it was the burgeoning showman in me asserting himself, or the delicious thrill of initiation into a secret society. Or maybe I figured that, if I worked hard enough, honed my skills, I could make my parents' unseemly divorce disappear, and we would be a family again. This is what I think of when I hear the word "magic" but it is not the kind of magic Wiccans practice.

Jamie suggests I meet her friend Black Cat. He is a master magician. As his name suggests, Black Cat is a shadowy figure but, Jamie assures me, a gentle spirit, "not scary at all." He'll need some convincing to meet with me, though. Jamie suggests I express a willingness to join one of his sky-clad rituals. That will show him I'm serious, not some dilettante. I tell Jamie I'll think about it.

Can I do this? Can I get naked in front of a witch named Black Cat? Yes, I can. In fact, I already have devised a plan, one that involves two pinches of Valium and one large notebook. I leave phone messages ("Hello, Black Cat, this is Eric") that make me uncomfortable and are not returned. I persist and, finally, a deep, slightly gruff voice answers.

"Black Cat?"

"Yes."

"This is Eric. Jamie Lewis suggested I call. I'd like to, um, meet with you and I want you to know that, um, I'm willing to...to...get naked."

Silence, then: "That's nice to hear, Eric. Actually, we don't work in the nude anymore. But if you want to get naked, feel free."

After he stops laughing, we agree to meet, fully clothed, at a café in Seattle.

Black Cat is in his early forties, stout and muscular, with a chiseled goatee. He is more intense than Jamie, more overtly witch-y. We order some beers as he unspools his story. Growing up in a small town in Pennsylvania, he recognized early on he was different. Unlike other children, he was never afraid of the dark. Werewolf posters adorned his room. He loved Dracula movies. Sometimes, he would just sit in the forest and feel this ineffable live-ness all around him. Most of all, he believed that if he just wished for something hard enough and long enough it would materialize, a belief that extended well beyond the usual childhood fantasies.

"You mean magic?" I ask. "What is it exactly?"

"Magic to me is bringing about change in the world through directed intention, usually in a way that seems to defy scientific measure."

Black Cat surely knows what I'm thinking: *Bewitched*. The TV show we both grew up with where Samantha crinkled her nose like a rabbit, and all sorts of crazy things happened to Darrin. Magic isn't like that, he tells me. It's more subtle, so subtle that to others it looks like coincidence. But it's not coincidence, he assures me, reading my mind, or maybe just preempting a question he probably gets all the time.

He invites me to his house to see his basement altar. It's a short walk through a leafy, normal-looking Seattle neighborhood. Black Cat, like most witches, has a day job. He works at the headquarters of a Major Coffee Corporation known for its overpriced Grande Lattes and comfy chairs and which shall remain nameless.

It's a nice house, which he shares with his daughter and Jim, his partner.

Jim pours us some wine and we all walk downstairs to the basement, and the home altar. I like the idea of a home altar. Many Hindus have them too. Having a home altar is like having a home gym; it saves time and expense and you're more likely to use it. Black Cat tells me I'm fortunate to be in his basement. Not many people are permitted here. The Wiccans have an expression: "Guard the mysteries well, reveal them often."

Black Cat's altar looks less like a holy place and more like a yard sale gone horribly awry. It is chockablock with stuff: candles, statues of various deities, a wooden snake, a large athame, or ritual sword, a whip. I ask about the whip.

"It's for scourging."

"Scourging? What's that?"

"You know, to scourge someone. It's from the Old Testament. Scourging is whipping."

I'm hearing voices again. This time from religious scholar Martin Forward: "Religion is about wild and dark and uncontrollable forces, not just about goodness, moderation and thoughtfulness." Yes, Martin, but whipping?

It's not anything extreme, Black Cat assures me. "We scourge lightly as a way of directing blood flow." How exactly does this work? I ask. It turns out that you are scourged—that is, whipped—as you circle round and round. This raises the energy, literally whips it up. "It's a purification ritual," says Black Cat.

Now, I've never been a masochist, not intentionally at least, but I have to confess this scourging thing appeals to me. Don't get me wrong: I don't want to be hurt, too much. But just as no medical procedure is entirely efficacious without the patient experiencing at least some pain, I suspect my depression will not lift until I too experience some genuine pain, as opposed to the synthetic variety I have indulged in for so many years now. I'm tempted to ask Black Cat to scourge me right then and there. He'd probably do it. I mean, he's named Black Cat, after all, and I've had just enough wine to provide a nice soft anesthetic cushion. But I chicken out, as I always do, and instead steer the conversation in another direction. I ask about all the pagan paraphernalia. What does he see in it?

They are only props, he tells me. They only possess as much power as we give them.

"But how can stuff have power?" I ask.

"Let me see your notebook," says Black Cat, and I hand over my small black Moleskine. "Is it sacred?"

"Well, I don't know about that, but it's definitely important to me."

"Is it worth the $10.99 you paid for it?"

"No, more, much more. It contains all of my notes and observations. It's been to Turkey and Las Vegas. It's worth a lot more than $10.99."

"Right. The more energy you put into it, the more important it is."

With that, the three of us toast to energy, our wineglasses clinking, the sound reverberating off the hard concrete walls.

Jim tells how he once wanted to keep someone away from him. So he performed a sort of Wiccan restraining order. He put the person's photo in a block of ice, wrapped it in tinfoil, then slid it deep into his freezer. It worked. The person stayed away.

"Why? I was changing my interaction with that person. I was not answering their text messages. I was putting out some kind of vibe that they were not supposed to contact me or be part of my life."

Okay, I wonder silently, but why was this magic? Why not just ignore the person's text messages without putting their picture in a block of ice in the freezer? Because, I think, Jim needed a physical expression of his intention. Magic may be a form of self-delusion, but it is a necessary one. It is a way of jump-starting the subconscious. We all engage in these private rituals—by getting dressed before an important tennis match in a very specific manner (shirt then shorts, left sock before right, except on Thursdays) or burning photos of someone who broke our heart. We don't call it magic, but the dynamic is the same: altering our interior climate through external actions. Witches, though, take it a step further. They believe that not only can these actions shape our thoughts, but our thoughts, our intentions, can also shape reality. They can make people stay away from us. Or money suddenly appear.

Black Cat tells me how he needed five thousand dollars so he cast a spell and, sure enough, a few days later his boss at the Major Coffee Corporation called him into his office and said he wanted him to participate in a national contest that would lead to a reward. How much was the reward worth? Yes, $5,000. Not $7,500, or $4,500 or $4,995, but $5,000.

I point out that a scientist, or any rationally inclined person, would call this a coincidence—a highly unlikely coincidence but a coincidence nonetheless.

"I love those kinds of coincidences," replies Black Cat, a wry smile forming on his lips. "I can tell you story after story like that. Did every single spell I ever cast come out that spectacularly? No. Sometimes I miss the basket, but I can tell you that most of them come out like that."

Is Black Cat deluding himself? Is he, as I suspect, paying attention only to the spells that work and calling those magic while ignoring the ones that don't pan out and calling those "magic that didn't quite work out"? But maybe there is something else going on.

Intention, more than anything else, Black Cat says, explains pagan magic. Magic is a form of visualization, or at least visualization is an important component of magic. Stand on the free-throw line, visualize making the shot, and chances are you will. It's that old Buddhist notion of faking it until you're making it. Magic works in much the same way, except there is an added element of mystery, an unseen hand helping you make that shot. It works, Black Cat assures me. This very house came about as a result of magic, as did his job. "Now, was magic the only factor? No, it was not. You still have to do the work. You want a job? Fill out a job application." It strikes me as a new witch-y twist to the old saw about God helping those who help themselves. When I suggest to Black Cat that he could drop the magic and simply work hard to make things happen, he laughs. It is a confident, though not smug laugh.

"Why are you laughing?"

"This is me. There is no me without the magic. This is my art. This is who I am. I am a magician. I always have been and I always will be." Mixing with Black Cat's voice is another. This one, with an elite, though not arrogant, Bostonian accent is talking to me through the centuries. "Truth is what works," said old William James.

Is Wicca for me? Have I found my God and is He a They? There is a lot to like. I like the way Wiccans create fresh ritual. I like the way they eschew temples and doctrine in favor of a forest and liturgy penned on the fly. I like the idea of a world infused with magic. I like the idea of a religion with no sin. Heschel believes that "indifference to the sublime wonder of living" is at the root of all sin. Wiccans are many things—wacky, rebellious, frequently kind, occasionally naked. They are not indifferent. They engage in wonder and awe on a regular basis. If that's not religion at its best, I don't know what is.

In the end, though, Wicca is not for me. For starters, there are too many choices. With all those gods and goddesses, I'm afraid I'd freeze in a futile attempt to find the perfect one for me. Another problem with polytheism is that it is, in effect, divinity by committee, and therefore suffers from the classic committee problem: Stuff can fall through the cracks. In this case, though, the "stuff" is my soul. This worries me, as it did William James. "Unless there be one all inclusive God, our guarantee of security is left imperfect." I wonder if this phenomenon explains my depression. Might I be the victim of some sort of theistic snafu? *I thought you were taking care of Eric's mental health. No, I thought* you *were. Oh shit.*

As for Wiccan magic, I tend to agree with those who find it lacking, though not for the reasons we normally think. Evelyn Underhill, in her classic *Mysticism*, writes: "Magic even at its best extends rather than escapes the boundaries of the phenomenal world. It stands, where genuine, for that form of transcendentalism which does abnormal things, but does not lead anywhere." In other words, the problem with magicians like Black Cat is not that they are too out there but, rather, that they are too "in here." They are materialists *in extremis*, manipulating reality (often for their own ends) rather than transcending it. They are so busy pulling rabbits out of hats that they never stop to look carefully at the rabbit, or the hat for that matter, and contemplate the miracle that is its existence.

The real problem, though, is that nagging, old-fashioned one of belief. I simply can't imagine any of these lowercase gods talking to me, or intervening on my behalf. The cold fact is I don't believe any of these gods or goddesses actually exist—not the way my left pinkie or my notebook exists—and I can't suspend my disbelief long enough to conjure them in my mind. Maybe that makes me more sane than Jamie and her fellow witches. Maybe it just makes me more depressed.

CWM, fed up with tricksters, looking to settle down with the right deity. Age no factor. Animal lovers welcome.

If I lived in a certain time in the past, or a certain place even today, and complained of depression, I would be dispatched not to a psychiatrist but to a shaman. Shamanism, like mythology, was an early form of psychology. Shamanism was also the world's first religion and, with apologies to prostitutes everywhere, the oldest profession. Today many religions contain trace elements of shamanism. Jewish chanting, for instance, or Shinto drumming. Wicca contains more than a trace, and is sometimes called "European shamanism." Mostly, though, shamans were, and still are, healers. Good, I think, I could use some healing. Best of all, shamans perform their healing by invoking the spirits. This appeals to me greatly. I'm tired of doing all of the work myself.

Shamanism is not exactly a religion, not as we usually think of the word. It is more a spiritual practice, a methodology, and one that has surfaced around the world, from Australia to the Arctic. The various manifestations of shamanism are remarkably similar, given that these peoples, separated by thousands of miles, had no contact with one another. As Joseph Campbell points out, we are all descendants of the shaman. For tens of thousands of years, it was the shaman who was the "guardian of the mythological lore of mankind."

But what exactly is a shaman? It's one of those words we think we know but, upon closer inspection, realize we don't. "Shaman" derives from the Siberian word *saman*, which means "one who is excited, moved, raised." I like that. The shaman is kinetic. The shaman cares. These are not cold, distant healers with no vested interest in their patients' outcome. The shaman cares about the patient and, crucially, *is* the patient. He heals and in doing so is healed. Or your money back. It is not uncommon for shamans to return their fee if the patient dies. (Our health-care system could benefit greatly from such a money-back guarantee.)

Another definition of shaman is "one who knows." Not one who *believes* but one who *knows*. There is an important distinction. Belief has no place in the shaman's world, only knowledge. What do shamans know, I wonder, and how do they know it?

Shamans' power rests in their ability to throw themselves into a trance at will and achieve an altered state of consciousness, with or without the help of psychotropics. Shamans are not gods or spirits, but they know them, talk to them. A shaman is an intermediary, a traveler, exploring William James's "unseen order," then returning to the world of ordinary consciousness. These shamanic journeys are sometimes equated with death. Indeed, the peoples of the Peruvian Amazon call *ayahuasca*, a potent hallucinogen used by some shamans, "the little death." (The French use the same phrase, *la petite mort*, to describe an orgasm. I for one hope *la grande mort* resembles its more diminutive sibling.)

Over the years, shamans have been called medicine men, witch doctors, sorcerers, wizards, magicians, seers. They have also been called crazy. After all, they experience hallucinations and delusions. Having not experienced the shaman's altered states of consciousness ourselves, we naturally label the shaman insane. But is that fair? Carl Jung, the sober Swiss psychiatrist, thinks not: "It is an almost ridiculous prejudice to assume that existence can only be physical. As a matter of fact the only form of existence we know of immediately is psychic. We might well say, on the contrary, that physical existence is merely an inference, since we know of matter only in so far as we perceive psychic images transited by the senses."

Shamans are lovers of nature, in the tradition of Saint Francis. They relate to the natural world as equals, as family. The shaman does not take pity on animals but aims to tap into their superior wisdom. Another characteristic of shamans: They work quickly. Shamanism promises a sort of spiritual shortcut, allowing people (me?) to "achieve in a few hours experiences that might otherwise take years of silent meditation," says Michael Harner, anthropologist turned shaman. This appeals to me immensely. I mean, who doesn't love a shortcut?

Not that long ago, if you wanted to explore the secret world of shamanism you had to travel to the Peruvian jungle or the Siberian tundra. I drive a few miles up I-95 to Beltsville, Maryland. It feels like cheating, since I've always equated distance traveled with wisdom accrued. But when I stumbled across an ad for a "Shamanic Workshop" in this Washington, DC, suburb, I couldn't resist. Not only is it convenient, it is also symbolic. Beltsville is where the U.S. Secret Service trains new recruits. The place practically spews mystery.

I follow the directions and find myself on a dirt road and, eventually, at the door of a geodesic dome. Inside, a dozen or so people are milling about. It's the usual pre-seminar anticipation: eyes scanning for familiar faces, hands signing in, clutching information packets. I could be attending a real-estate seminar rather than one meant to explore hidden worlds.

A high-pitched whistle pierces the morning air. "What's that?" someone asks. "Must be the coffeepot," comes a reply. "It's a shamanic coffeepot," someone else says and everyone laughs a knowing, shamanic laugh. I head to the pantry where I grab some vegan cookies and a cup of organic, shade-grown, fair-trade coffee. It is the most ethical cup of coffee I've ever had. With each sip, I sense myself becoming a better person.

I enter the main room and, along with the others, plop down on the floor. Ah, the floor, that indispensable accoutrement of spirituality, greeting me again, like the dentist I've been avoiding. I contort myself into the modified lotus position that I perfected back in Kathmandu and scan the room. It's not a particularly young crowd, but neither is it geriatric. More women than men here, I notice, and the women are laden with tribal jewelry, chunky bracelets and necklaces, heavy with significance.

One woman has brought her standard poodle with her. His name is Sasha and he looks as uncomfortable here as I do. Sasha the Poodle circles a few times before lying next to his owner. From across the room, Sasha and I lock eyes briefly and, I swear, he's thinking: "Don't look at *me*. This wasn't my idea." Good, I think, I'm already communing with the animal world, though I'm not sure where a nervous poodle fits in the shamanic universe.

In the middle of the room is an altar, of sorts. A wool blanket covered with postcards, a few stuffed bears, polar and brown, some candles, a leather wallet. I open my bag and extract the items I was told to bring: a drum, a rattle, a blindfold, and a "grapefruit-size rock." Glancing around the room, I fear I am outgunned, spiritually speaking. The competition is packing drums so large they have their own cases, and rattles the size of baseball bats, handcrafted by tribesmen living deep in the Peruvian jungle. I've brought my daughter's little plastic rattle, handcrafted by some underpaid Chinese worker, toiling deep in the capitalist jungle.

All eyes are on the workshop leader, a trim, middle-aged man wearing chinos and a purple turtleneck. He looks utterly ordinary—more executive than shaman. In fact, I'm not far off. Dana worked for twenty-five years in the classified advertising department of *The Washington Post* before retiring to teach shamanism full-time. Dana's ordinariness does not disappoint but, rather, puts me at ease. If I'm going to journey to a hidden world, I want someone in chinos to lead the way.

We settle down slowly, disruptively, like a group of giggly middle-school girls, then Dana speaks. "Welcome," he says in a reassuringly normal voice. "Over the course of this weekend, we'll be exploring non-ordinary reality." He says this matter-of-factly, like a Greek tour guide describing the day's itinerary at the Parthenon. Then he adds: "There will be surprises, and it will be good." I want to believe Dana, I really do, but in my experience surprises are rarely good.

Shamans work with spirits, says Dana, but what are spirits? Good question. "A spirit is the nonmaterial essence of anything. So we have this fine rattle here made by a Native American man in New Mexico, and the shaman would say, 'Yes, this is a physical rattle, but the rattle is also a spirit.'" Another definition of a spirit is "anything you see with your eyes closed." There is a moment of silence, with only the sound of Sasha the Poodle's panting audible, as we digest that one.

Dana holds up the rattle—a real beauty—and asks us to now close our eyes and picture it. "Don't focus on me but focus on the rattle. I will even shake the rattle as you are attempting to see it with your eyes closed. And you may see it more or less. That's great. More or less really works in shamanism."

I am in love! Not with Dana, nor with all this talk of spirit, which frankly I don't fully follow, but with the words "more or less." Finally, a religion (sort of) that acknowledges the sublime beauty of inexactitude, the divinity of "more or less." The problem with so much organized religion is not the religion bit but the organized part; it attempts to mimic science, and of course fails miserably because you can't out-science science. So many religions, oddly, have a numbers fetish. Eight days of Chanukah. Forty days of Lent. Thirty days of Ramadan. Praying five times a day, fasting for twenty-four hours; observing the Four Noble Truths, the Eightfold Path, the Threefold Law. I don't get it. I've never been a numbers person, so maybe that is why I can't seem to gain any spiritual traction, for the same reason I can't do my taxes. It's the math. These overly numeric religions could learn a thing or two from shamanism and its more-or-less approach. I would love to hear a Catholic priest request five Hail Marys, more or less. Or a rabbi declare a certain food "more or less kosher."

Shamanic imprecision more accurately reflects reality. The world is a fuzzy, imprecise place. By acknowledging that, we acknowledge our own fallibility, and without judgment. A religion that demands precision of its adherents is not only a religion without mercy, but also one that is out of touch with reality. The shaman charts a different, looser course. Yes, I may have found my God.

More or less. As the weekend progresses things grow increasingly strange. Not Raëlian strange (alas, no breasts are liberated here), but strange nonetheless. We go around the room and introduce ourselves. The first woman is an "animal communicator." Another says she is an "ontological coach." These are two professions I did not know existed. Maybe they could team up, I think, and finally speak truth to dogs. Oh no. My old smart-ass skepticism, creeping up on me like a mugger in a dark alley. I smack it down and, once again, suspend my disbelief, which is already suspended to the breaking point. Dana asks everyone to explain why they are here, and people cite all sorts of reasons. Some have had experiences they can't explain, others are suffering from illness, or have recently lost a loved one. Catholics, once again, are disproportionately represented.

In Siberia, Dana tells us, they believe that soul loss is a major cause of disease. The words "soul loss" roll off his lips so naturally, so effortlessly, as if he were speaking of hair loss. Then he reads from an old Siberian poem: "The walls of this house have tongues. Everything that is, is alive." Shamanism in a nutshell. And if everything is alive, explains Dana, we can communicate with everything. Then, as if reading my thoughts, he adds: "Now understand, if you are communicating with walls twenty-four hours a day, you might have a problem and you might be put in a special place where they will take care of you. So we are not presenting this stuff to you this weekend so that you can go nuts, okay?" I audibly exhale. I was beginning to wonder. "In fact, in my opinion we are presenting this stuff to you so that you can become more sober, more clear." Dana clearly subscribes to the belief, first espoused by French anthropologist Claude Lévi-Strauss, that shamans are more like psychoanalysts than psychopaths.

We will not be using hallucinogenic drugs, Dana announces, to subdued giggles and a few grunts of disappointment. Instead, our travel to these other worlds will be facilitated by something called "monotonous percussion." Apparently, there's something about repetitive percussion that makes us susceptible to altered states of consciousness. Dana informs us that the global standard for monotonous percussion, as established in Siberia, is 180 beats per minute, a precise figure that strikes me as a clear violation of the shaman's more-or-less philosophy.

"Okay," says Dana, "let's do some drumming." We stand and drum. Others with their formidable West African drums and Amazonian rattles, and me with my puny drum and made-in-China rattle. It feels good, though. The snap of my palm against the hard skin of the drum. Boom. Boom. Boom. The whole room is vibrating. Yes, this is good. I'm getting out of my head, at the rate of 180 beats per minute. My arm begins to ache, and that is good. My palm turns crimson and stings, and that is good, too. Everything is good.

Our eyes are supposed to be closed but I cheat and watch everyone in various stages of percussive ecstasy. Everyone, that is, except Sasha the Poodle, who is panting more heavily now.

We're really getting worked up. Boom, boom, boom. "See the world with shamanic eyes," says Dana. "Think of your favorite place in nature and be there with it as much as possible." I try but no image comes to mind, at least not anything positive. The truth is: Nature scares me. I know that shamans and environmentalists believe that nature is our friend, but that conclusion just doesn't jibe with my experience. Sure, nature is a beautiful sunset and a warm spring morning but nature is also a hurricane. Nature is an earthquake, a tsunami, a mudslide, a plague, a virus, a malaria-infested mosquito, a scorpion.

So I close my eyes and picture a gleaming steel airport terminal instead. This is my idea of paradise. Most people hate airports, viewing them as an unfortunate but necessary fact of air travel. Not me. I love airports. I look forward to spending time in them—even the bad ones—and could happily pass months ensconced in a transit lounge like that character in the Tom Hanks movie. I love the self-contained, hermetic universe that is an airport. I love the recycled unnatural air. Suspended between coming and going, I can breathe again.

The next exercise is something called "dancing the animals." We're going to find our power animal, Dana tells us. "Just let yourself go," he says, as if we were, until now, all buttoned up. "You might find that your fingers are claws; or that your arms, maybe your entire body, is covered with fur; or that your face has become a muzzle and you are now a bear; or your body is covered in scales and you're a lizard." Normally, the idea of such transfiguration would frighten me but, oddly, it doesn't. Instead, another, more petty fear squats in my mind and stubbornly resists eviction. As if reading my thoughts, Dana says, "Don't worry if you can't locate your power animal, or if you don't have one. That's okay, too." Whew.

Shamans believe they are reconnecting with an ability that all humans once had to commune with animal spirits. An animal is considered especially powerful if it can take on human form or if it can navigate in an element not ordinarily its own—a wolf that can fly, for instance. A key point: The shaman is not imitating the wolf or possessed by the wolf, he *is* the wolf.

The drum again. Boom. Boom. Boom. We circle the altar, taking care not to bump into the candle, as Dana advised. All around me, people are finding their power animals. One woman is down on all fours, crawling like a tiger, or a lion maybe. I hear people grunting, growling, trumpeting. I, though, remain fully upright, embarrassingly human. Just as I feared, my power animal has gone AWOL. I feel like the kid in class who forgot to bring something for show-and-tell. Okay, I decide, my panic mounting, if my power animal won't come to me, I'll go to it.

A bird! Yes, I am a bird. Birds are warm-blooded. They take flight. They tend to leave behind little messes. Yes, I am a bird. I extend my arms into an impressive wingspan. I bank left, then right, then left again. I lose myself, at last. Yes, this is good. Boom Boom, Boom, goes Dana's drum. "Caw, caw, caw," goes me, the birdman of Beltsville. Boom. Caw. Boom. Caw. Yes, I think, I can do this. I can fly!

Then, out of the corner of my eye, I spot something that sends me into an emotional nosedive: another bird. A woman is swooping and diving and doing it all so gracefully, so much *better* than me. I do a few more circuits around the altar, but my heart isn't in it. I've been out-birded.

Dana stops drumming and asks us to write about our experiences. But I can't think straight. I am so furious at that bird-woman for kidnapping my power animal, I want to throttle her. People are writing but I just stare at the altar candle, watching it flicker and dance. Okay, says Dana, time's up. "We were looking to have a spiritual experience in this room. Who had an experience?" Suddenly I'm back in fifth grade. Please, please, don't call on me. Thankfully, a Chinese American woman speaks up. "I became a buffalo," she says. "I was surprised. My left brain took me to that Kevin Costner movie and I felt silly." That's okay, says Dana. "What color buffalo?" he asks.

"Black," says the woman, without missing a beat. Thus began a pattern that would repeat itself throughout the seminar. As we recount each of our exercises or journeys, the descriptions are always very specific. There is no way, I think, people can be making this stuff up. Nobody can invent experiences that quickly. They must have really happened, at least on some level. Not me, though. No animals "came" to me. I *decided* I was a bird. What's wrong with me? Do I suffer from a failure of imagination? Or do these people suffer from an excess of it?

We take a break, sip some highly ethical coffee, and swap animal tales. Next, Dana informs us, we're going to take a journey. We will first be visiting the Lower World. Our mission, Dana informs us, is to "travel there and check it out." Again, he says this as if he were talking about a real place and not some imaginary destination.

Dana wants to make a few things clear. A shamanic journey is like a waking dream, and I shudder at the mention of that phrase again, flashing back to my drug-induced psychosis in India. Not everyone will have the same experience, Dana says. Some people will see it all, the works, in Technicolor on their first journey; others will not. Another thing—and on this point Dana is emphatic—we are not, repeat *not*, descending into hell. That's a Christian invention. Then Dana gives us the shamanic equivalent of driving instructions. "I will beat the drum. Then we enter the opening of our choice—don't worry, you'll fit—then immediately after that you will be in the tunnel to the underworld." He says this matter-of-factly, as if telling someone how to get to the local supermarket. "The tunnel is usually lighted," he informs us, "but if it's nighttime you can materialize a flashlight or night-vision goggles." Shamanism, an ancient practice, is apparently open to new technology.

People have questions, many questions. How exactly do we get to this Lower World?

The entry point, says Dana, might be a hole in the ground, or a storm sewer drain, or a subway entrance. I like that last suggestion. I like subway stations nearly as much as airports.

"How do we get through the tunnel?" someone asks.

"You can run, fly, or jetpack. Sometimes there's a stream you can jump in, though that doesn't happen often. Once you're there, in the Lower World, go out and experience it, touch it. It's not unusual to see landscapes, or animals. If a giraffe says, 'Hop on my back,' go ahead and do it. And don't worry. I'll let you know when it's time to come back."

With that, Dana instructs us to "assume the journey position." I lie down and tie a bandanna over my eyes. The strange thing is: I experience the same rush of anticipation I get whenever embarking on a trip, though this time the excitement is tempered by the fear that I won't go anywhere.

"Okay, have a good journey," says Dana, sounding like the ground staff of an airline bidding passengers adieu. "I'll see you upon your return." The last thing I hear before the drumming starts is Sasha the Poodle's owner saying, "Now, Sasha, don't steal other people's images."

Boom. Boom. Boom. *Okay, deep breath, Eric, you can do this.* I'm looking for the subway entrance but I can't find it. My disbelief refuses to suspend itself. I keep thinking: We're lying on the floor. How can we go anywhere? Deep breath. The room is warm, the drumming monotonous, my eyes closed. I'll just lie here until that subway entrance materializes, I think, should be any minute now. Next thing I know I hear Dana's voice, welcoming us back to ordinary reality. Oh no, I fell asleep. This is embarrassing. I just hope the drumming masked my snoring.

"Who has a story for us?" asks Dana, and I make myself as small as possible. Everyone has a story. A woman named Barbara relays how she started at the Grand Canyon then saw a highway cloverleaf and a cliff and that was it. "Sorry," says Barbara, apologizing for her relatively mundane journey.

"What kind of cars were on the highway?" Dana asks, like a curious reader of armchair travel. "Old or contemporary?"

"Contemporary," says Barbara, without hesitation.

"Congratulations. You made it to the other side."

Why didn't I make it to the other side? What's wrong with me? Usually, I'm such a determined traveler. I've made it to Iraq, Afghanistan, North Korea. You'd think I could make it to the Lower World. I wonder if my waking dream in India is to blame. It rattled my trust of ordinary reality, so how can I possibly trust the non-ordinary type?

Others share their adventures, like travelers swapping tales at a local bar. Sheri ended up in a place that looked like something out of *The Sound of Music*, with fairies and talking flowers. She got lost but, thankfully, the fairies escorted her back to the Middle World. "Sounds like a highly supportive place," says Dana.

The stories grow increasingly fantastical, culminating with that of a Polish woman. She emerged from the tunnel and was instantly grabbed by pterodactyl chicks but she didn't panic because she knew that, even though the birds were digesting her, they meant her no harm. Then they spit her out and she became a butterfly then a fish, and finally she washed back to the Middle World in the seed of a coconut. Whoa, I think, no wonder we're not using hallucinogens. No need with this group. I sit there, tempted to shout, "But we didn't go anywhere! We're just sitting on the floor blindfolded, listening to monotonous percussion and a panting poodle." Of course I don't say that. Besides, we're wrapping up. Tomorrow is another day. Maybe I'll have a breakthrough then.

The next morning I arrive back at the geodesic dome. Everyone is friendly, intimate even. The stranger the experience, the quicker the bonding process. Everyone seems happy to be here. Everyone except Sasha the Poodle, who looks like he'd rather be at the vet being neutered. The Pole has baked a vegan key lime pie, which tastes *exactly* the way I imagined a vegan key lime pie would taste. She also hands out "Amazonian smudge sticks." Good for cleaning our auras, she says.

Dana shushes everyone. It's time to get back to work. "There's a lot of talent here," he says, as if we were a college basketball team with a deep bench. But I don't feel talented. I feel like a fraud. Okay, it's time to do some animal work, announces Dana. We circle the altar, which today includes a small stuffed wolf. There's more howling and grunting. The bird competition today is fierce—a lot of talent here—so I decide to invoke my favorite animal: the groundhog. I love groundhogs. All that cozy burrowing, long periods of time to yourself and then the burst of celebrity on February 2. Then back to your hole and more cozy burrowing. If there is such a thing as reincarnation, I wouldn't mind coming back as a groundhog. Hands tucked under my chin, like little groundhog paws, lips pulled tight, baring my groundhog teeth, I circle the altar. Boom. Boom. Boom. It feels good. Then the drumming stops.

A new assignment. We'll be traveling to the Upper World. Once again, we will need an entry point. We can fly to the Upper World on our power animal (do groundhogs fly?) or take the space shuttle or have a volcano shoot us upward or, says Dana, take an elevator. I like this last option. It sounds the safest, the most plausible. Then, continues Dana, we'll be passing through a membrane, maybe a thick layer of smoke or perhaps a rubbery substance. If it's rubber, Dana suggests we materialize a knife or a blowtorch. "Let's just enjoy the journey," says Dana. "I'll see you upon your return."

We lie down. The lights grow dim. The drumming starts, slowly at first—boom. Boom. Then increasingly rapid: boom, boom, boom. I try to relax, to suspend my disbelief, to be more "tenderminded," as William James put it, and I do much better this time.

"Okay," says Dana, shouting to be heard over the drumming, "now materialize your power animal."

I conjure a groundhog, only for some reason this is no ordinary groundhog. This is an intellectual groundhog. He's holding a coffee mug in one paw, a clipboard in the other. Tucked behind his little groundhog ear is a ballpoint pen, perched on his little groundhog nose a pair of glasses, quite stylish frames too, I think. The groundhog and I are riding the elevator to the Upper World. We don't say much on the way up, just stare at the door, watching the numbers go up, up, up. Suddenly, the elevator stops. I look up and see a wall of dirt. Oh no. We're stuck. "Don't worry," says the groundhog, "I can handle this," and he burrows through the dirt effortlessly until we pop out into clear blue sky. It's cold and, as I look around, I see why. We're in the Arctic. Ice and snow everywhere. The vista is desolate, but beautiful. Then, inexplicably, we are on a ship. I stop at an island and decide to climb an ice formation—again the terrain is Arctic tundra—and somehow manage to get stuck on the pointy end of the ice. I'm stranded. The pace of the drumming has picked up, signaling that soon we'll need to return to ordinary reality. What to do? "No worries," says the groundhog, who really is good under pressure. "Get on."

"Get on what?"

"My back."

So I do. I hop on the groundhog's back, violating a few more laws of physics, and then, it turns out, the groundhog *can* fly and we soar off this Arctic island to the elevator entrance. I push the down button. Nothing. I press it again. Still nothing. The drumming, meanwhile, has quickened further. Boomboomboom. Finally, the elevator arrives and we go down—swoosh!—arriving in the Middle World just in the nick of time.

"Okay," says Dana as we remove our blindfolds, "how many people made it to the Upper World?" Many hands go up, including mine. "Excellent," says Dana, and I smile, like a kid who finally got one right. I did it. I had a shamanic journey, although it was not a typical one, given my companion, a flying, brainy ground-hog, and I'm not sure if I experienced the journey or conjured it. It doesn't matter. The point is: I did it.

My elation lasts for about twenty seconds. Others recount their journeys to the Upper World, and they were considerably more fantastical than mine. Someone encountered glowing crystals. Someone else met a dragon. Dana listens to this account carefully before asking, very earnestly, "Do you think there's a potential for a relationship with this dragon?"

"Oh yes," says the woman, "he was very friendly." I feel like I'm trapped in a Gabriel García Márquez novel. As usual, the Pole out-does everyone. She landed in a field of unicorns and was told by the chief unicorn that she had to braid all of the hair of the other unicorns. Then things got fuzzy. Something about her tears becom-ing a galaxy, and an angel riding a hermaphrodite.

Dana announces that, for our final exercise, we'll be doing a "power-animal retrieval," followed by a "power-animal insertion." I don't really have a problem with the retrieval part but definitely *do not* like the sound of an animal insertion. While I am prone to vacillation, on this issue I have remained remarkably consistent: No animal insertions.

I'm relieved to discover I'm not the only one a bit nervous about this whole insertion thing. People have questions. We will be working with a partner, Dana explains. Our partner will go into a trance and find a power animal for us. They need to see the animal four times before it counts as the proper power animal. They are to clasp one of these animals to their chest—"in that reality as well as this one"—and Dana demonstrates by pressing his arms to his chest. Next, the shaman—the one doing the inserting—is to lean over and blow twice into the solar plexus of the patient, the insertee, who is lying prone. "Now," he says, "and this may sound a little strange, but there are some things we don't want to blow into people: insects, spiders, fish. You could hurt someone." Finally, just to set the record straight, Dana adds: "Remember: This is for real."

My partner is JoAnne, the ontological coach. First, she'll need to identify the power animal she'll be inserting into me. I'm praying, *praying*, for something small. A chipmunk, perhaps. But no, as my luck would have it, she returns from her trance informing me that the power animal she's retrieved is a water buffalo. God have mercy on me.

"Okay," says Dana. "Time to insert the power animal into your partner." A murmur of nervous excitement flitters through the room. The drumming begins again. Sasha the Poodle is having some sort of canine panic attack and is escorted outside. I wish nothing more than to join him. Then the power-animal insertion happens. I will spare you the details, but had you walked into that room you would have seen a sixty-something ontological coach with a beehive hairdo bending over me, hands cupped, as if holding a coffee mug, and blowing forcefully into my solar plexus. And then it's over. Under the circumstances, it was much less painful than I imagined. We do a few more exercises—some reading of rocks and greeting of the sun—but nothing eclipses the power-animal insertion.

The workshop is drawing to a close. Everyone is collecting their drums and rattles and blindfolds when Dana interjects with an important announcement. "Remember," he says, "and this is important: It's non-ordinary reality here but it's ordinary reality out there, with cars whizzing by at seventy miles an hour." He suggests we eat a cookie, get grounded, before getting behind the wheel. It's good advice, perhaps the best I've heard all weekend.

I drive home vigilantly, fending off distracting thoughts of birds and wolves and cerebral groundhogs. Eventually those visions fade, but one I can't shake, no matter how much I try. I picture a large white poodle, panting heavily, eyes darting nervously, clearly wondering what in the world these humans can possibly be doing, and why. I wish I had an answer, Sasha, but, alas, my friend, I do not.

CWM, tired of strangers who don't get me. Looking to come home but not sure where that is. Are you the One? Foodies a plus.

Judaism, at last. I've been dreading this moment. It was inevitable, I suppose, given my nominal Jewishness, but that does little to ease my apprehension. Or guilt. My crimes are self-evident. I have lusted in my heart, flirted with a bevy of exotic gods, dabbled in witchcraft. I feel like the wayward spouse, reeking of sweet perfume and cheap booze, sheepishly knocking on the front door after a lengthy and unexplained absence. Will Hashem have me? And, the more nettlesome question, Do I want to be had?

The truth is: I don't know Him. How could I? Jews don't talk about God. I've always found this oversight strange, given that love of the Almighty is central to our faith and that Jews will happily talk nonstop about basically anything. Why the sudden reticence? As for me, you could say I'm a self-hating Jew but that's not quite accurate. In order to hate something you need to know it, at least to some extent, and I don't know enough about Judaism to hate it.

I can't be the only one who feels so alienated from my own faith. So I ask my friend Michael, a gastronomical Jew like myself, how he would sum up Judaism in a single word. Michael thinks for only a brief moment before answering. "Rules," he says. "Judaism is about rules." I nod. A sad commentary but, as far as I can tell, an accurate one. Eat this, not that. Do this, not that. Put on your right shoe before the left but tie your left laces before the right. (Really.) Rules upon rules upon rules. A never-ending litany of dos and, more often, don'ts. Judaism is the perfect religion for the obsessives and compulsives of the world.

Over the years, though, I had caught wind of another Judaism, a Judaism of the head *and* the heart. A Judaism that actually talks about God, that encourages us to talk *to* God, and without blushing, a Judaism that facilitates a direct experience of the divine. It's called Kabbalah, and it is perhaps the only spiritual path shrouded in both mystery and celebrity. Whenever I ask people what they know about Kabbalah (Jews and non-Jews alike), I always receive a one-word reply: Madonna. That's it. Surely, I thought, there must be more to Kabbalah than an aging pop star who refuses to age. And surely the heart of this ancient tradition, its *axis mundi*, must reside somewhere beyond the rolling hills and neon boulevards of Hollywood.

I board the flight for Tel Aviv with more than a little trepidation. I haven't been to the so-called Holy Land since my days as a correspondent for National Public Radio. You'd think a few years in the Jewish homeland would strengthen my Jewish identity, extend it beyond the gastronomical realms to the spiritual. You'd think, but you would be wrong. If anything, I felt *less* Jewish living in Israel than I did in, say, India. Political conflict, twinned with naked tribalism, discouraged me from exploring Judaism. As a journalist, I was too busy remaining impartial to dip my toe into those waters. So I kept my head down, my heart closed, and did my job.

Yet here I am again, though this time on a very different mission. I'm waiting for a bus in an ultra-orthodox suburb of Tel

Aviv called Bnei Brak. All around me is black. A wall of black, relieved only by the occasional glint of white. The only primary color within a five-mile radius is my berry-blue shirt, which, in this colorless environment, might as well be hot pink. Standing under the bus shelter, I feel eyes scanning me, judging. The bus finally arrives and it's packed with the religious. Women, their heads covered with drab scarves; men, wearing bushy fur hats in the spring heat. And then there's me, with my hot blue shirt and naked head. I feel invisible and exposed at the same time. Like a *gaijin* (literally "outside person") in Japan. Or a *dalit*, an untouchable, in India. Then I am touched, bumped, by a woman. *Sleecha.* Excuse me, she says, as if she had just stepped in something untoward.

The bus wends through downtown Bnei Brak. Peering out the window, I see stores selling identical black suits and black dresses. We pass a nursery and I am startled by the lonely splash of green, of life. I spot a store called "Discreet" and that, I realize, sums up this place. Nothing is revealed. I have no idea what takes place underneath the fur and the black, no inkling of people's inner lives. All I know is the exterior, and that strikes me as terribly dark and unhappy. Of course appearances can lie. Sometimes, as I learned in Kathmandu, what you see is not.

I reach into my pocket and finger my *kippa*, the Jewish skullcap. Good, it's still there. I feel relieved, assured, the way a plainclothes cop feels, I imagine, once confirming the presence of his sidearm. I don't like all *kippas* but I like this one. I like its heft and its not-blackness. (It is a modest gray but gray is a color too, a beautiful one that, as Chesterton extolled, reminds us of "the indefinite hope that is in doubt itself.") When my in-law Avi handed it to me, he told me to wear it in people's homes, and of course in synagogues. His urgent tone of voice, though, suggested that this was not only the proper thing to do but the prudent one as well, that this small skullcap doubled as a kind of talisman, protection against unseen malevolence.

As the bus trundles north, the Tel Aviv suburbs yield to open fields. I extract a few books from my bag and read about my destination. Tzfat (also spelled Safed), perched high in the hills above the Sea of Galilee, is one of those small cities that punches above its weight. Over the centuries, it has seesawed between the sacred and the profane. Tzfat has, at various times, been a hill-station retreat for Tel Avivians seeking to escape the summer heat, a magnet for gamblers and prostitutes, an artists' colony, a sleepy Arab village, a battlefield. Its golden era, though, was the sixteenth century, when it was a hotbed of Kabbalistic thought and experimentation.

When the Jews were evicted from Spain in 1492, some settled in North Africa. Others in Italy. And some in Tzfat. Among them were scholars and mystics who had studied Kabbalah in Spain and France. They brought with them their passion for the subject, and soon several schools of Kabbalah took root. Theirs was not the parched Judaism that I grew up with but a fierce and experiential faith. These men were "mighty God seekers" and "daring stormers of heaven," as historian Lawrence Fine puts it. They were refugees, like Rumi and Einstein, and possessed the same reckless creativity. They had the untethered disposition of the mendicant. They also engaged in some unusual, and controversial, practices: fasting for extended periods, spreading themselves across the graves of great rabbis, communing with animals, à la Saint Francis.

Sixteenth-century Tzfat was one of those rare places, like early-twentieth-century Paris or fifteenth-century Florence, where circumstances combined and, through a kind of alchemy, produced an extraordinarily creative atmosphere. Only in Tzfat's case, the output wasn't artistic or scientific but spiritual. "Tzfat," writes scholar and translator Daniel Matt, "seems to verge on heaven."

When the Egged bus finally pulls into Tzfat's Central Bus Station, I am excited. I am a creature of place, and I sense this place could be where I finally make a spiritual breakthrough, where I find my God, or some reasonable facsimile. I am greeted by Eyal, head of an institute for Kabbalah and my guide to the mysteries of this path. Eyal is a large man and promptly gives me a large hug. "Welcome to Tzfat," he says with seemingly practiced enthusiasm. Eyal is dressed in Hasidic black and, for a moment, I feel as if I have traveled nowhere. I follow him through the city's cobblestone streets, a miniature version of Jerusalem's old city. We pass shops with names like Kabbalah Jewelry and cafés that consist of no more than a table or two, serving impossibly fresh salads and juice. Soon we arrive at his office, located on the second floor of an old building, and stuffed with books. Not that long ago, such a sight would set my heart aflutter, but not now. Have I finally escaped my head?

Eyal is an intense man of indeterminate age with a biblical beard and eyes that frequently bug out of his head. He came here eighteen years ago. Not long before that, he was a DJ, completely secular, living in Tel Aviv, Israel's sin city. Then one day he decided to keep the Sabbath. Just like that. And from there it was a straight line to the world of ultra-orthodox Judaism.

Eyal clearly loves Tzfat. He speaks effusively of the "transformative power of this place." Every person is affected by this city, he tells me. "When I say 'Welcome to Tzfat,' their eyes open, and their souls too." I have experienced no such transformation yet, but it is still early.

Eyal promptly plants me in front of a video, a sort of beginner's guide to Kabbalah. A voice-of-God narrator intones: "Studying Kabbalah increases and develops self-awareness. People who study Kabbalah learn to use their spiritual power for personal development and their realization of their purpose in life. The Kabbalah brings joy and inner meaning to every aspect of life." Sounds good, I think. Sign me up.

Then things get complicated. In a rapid-fire presentation, I am told of the ten *sefirot*, or "divine emanations"; about the tree of life; about how for centuries Kabbalah was studied secretly by an elite group (the word "cabal" comes from Kabbalah). Kabbalah, this deep, authoritative voice tells me, explains quantum physics, string theory, and the Big Bang. Wow. My head is whirling in ways it hasn't since Istanbul. It sounds good but...complicated.

Back in Eyal's office, he tells me that over the course of the next few weeks I will not study *about* Kabbalah. I will study Kabbalah. That's an important distinction, he assures me, though he doesn't explain exactly why.

We hop into Eyal's car, a beat-up mini van with a broken door handle, and drive through Tzfat's cobblestone streets. We're heading down, down, down, the spiritually incorrect direction, I know, but a necessary prelude to growth. As Karen Armstrong puts it: "There is no ascent to heaven without a prior descent into darkness." So down we go.

I roll down my window. Tzfat is known for its air. That's what everyone told me. The air in Tzfat is special. It does feel soft, what cotton would feel like, I imagine, if converted into gas.

Within seconds, I'm not sure how this happens (maybe it's the air), we're engaged in a heavy metaphysical discussion. God is not a spiritual entity, Eyal tells me. He's above spiritual. There is simply no definition of God. *Ein sof*, as the Kabbalists say, literally "without limits." Yet God is involved in every aspect of life. "There's a specific divine providence over every matter, every molecule, every atom."

"So God is a micromanager?" I say.

"Yes," says Eyal, ignoring my sarcasm, "except freedom of choice is still granted. Just like nothing can obligate God to do this or that. The same thing applies to us; nothing obligates us to do good."

"So life is not pre-ordained? We are not puppets of fate?"

"No, it's not pre-ordained; it's foreseen. Foreseen means God knows but that doesn't obligate us in any way. You can screw up and He knows about it. What is unknown? The future is unknown, but He is above all that." God, explains Eyal, is like a father teaching a child. He sees that you're about to do something incredibly stupid but He lets you do it anyway, because we have freedom of choice and we might learn a lesson, provided, of course, this incredibly stupid thing we do doesn't kill us.

Interesting, but frankly I'm not sure how deep Eyal's faith runs. There's something about his cartoonish hand gestures and bulging eyes that makes me wonder whether he means all this or is merely going through the motions, reading from a Jewish playbook. I say this realizing fully that it is folly to gauge the mettle of another man's faith.

Eyal and I arrange to meet the next morning at ten. When I had suggested 9:00 a.m., he balked. Tzfat is not an early-rising town, an exception to the early-bird-gets-the-God rule. In fact, there is a tradition of studying Kabbalah at midnight, when the mind is quiet and the sky smeared with stars.

I spend the afternoon exploring Tzfat on my own. The only way to know, really know, a city is through solitary explorations. Nothing else will suffice. So that's what I do, walking its cobblestone streets and alleyways, eating its falafels and *shakshukas*, dipping into its bookstores, sipping its *café-hafuch*, literally "upside-down coffee."

I find a café where they make an especially good cup and tolerate my toddler Hebrew. I grab a table outside and watch the world go by. In some ways, it looks similar to the drab world of Bnei Brak, the same head coverings and muted colors. But there's a difference. People here smile. They make eye contact. I see a woman dressed in the convention of an orthodox Jew—ankle-length dress, scarf-covered head. Only when she turns the corner do I notice the yoga mat slung over her shoulder. A few days later, walking through the old city, I see a Hasidic Jew, dressed in the traditional long black coat and hat, riding a unicycle, like the kind you might see clowns atop at a circus. I can't believe my eyes. I've never seen such a display of overt whimsy and joy from a member of the ultra-orthodox.

The denizens of Tzfat are children of a less uptight God. Sure, they follow the rules, most of them anyway, but they're not afraid to bend a few, to honor the spirit if not the letter. Tzfat attracts Jewish misfits, those who don't feel at home in the straitjacket world of orthodox Jerusalem, nor in the anything-goes world of secular Tel Aviv.

What makes a place spiritual? Is there really something in the air? Is it that fuzzy-headed New Age catchall, energy? Or is it the cumulative intentionality that lends a place specialness? Does a place become holy because holy people choose to live there, or do holy people choose to live there because the place is holy? I'm not sure, and suspect these are unanswerable questions, but any place with a reputation for being "magical" and "transformative" bears a heavy burden. Holy places, like holy people, always contain the potential to disappoint. Tzfat does not disappoint. It may not be Heaven, not exactly, but the soft air and unhurried atmosphere lend a lightness to a heavy land, straining under the weight of all that history, and God. It's one of those places people visit for a few days, on a lark, and next thing they know a lifetime has passed.

Tzfat is spiritual but it is still Israeli, so a base level of rudeness is maintained at all times. It's the law. People elbow me without any apparent regret. I pay for goods and services without receiving even a simple "Thank you." For Israelis, this rudeness is a strange source of pride. They don't see themselves as rude but, rather, pleasantly informal and refreshingly honest. *Look, we're surrounded by enemies and living in a desert. Our national dish is ground chickpeas. You want polite? Go to Japan.* Or they fall back on the old saw about the sabra fruit. We Israelis are like the sabra, the smiling tourist official will tell you: hard on the outside, soft on the inside. I once asked an Israeli woman whether this was true. She pondered it briefly, *very* briefly, before answering, "No, I'm pretty much a bitch on the inside too." I had to respect her honesty.

The sun setting over the hills, I buy a bottle of kosher wine (the only kind available) and return to my hotel room. I sit on the balcony, sipping the not-bad wine, smoking little existential cigars, and studying Kabbalah—or, rather, *about* Kabbalah. Still, I learn many things. I learn that the Hebrew word *Kabbalah* means "receiving" or "that which has been received." I learn that for centuries these received teachings were considered dangerous. That's why they were restricted to married men over forty years old. Got that covered, I think smugly. I read on. "Other requirements included high moral standards, prior rabbinic learning... and mental and emotional stability." Enough of this ancient history. I turn the page.

I learn that Kabbalah, as Daniel Matt puts it, "represents the revenge of myth.... The Kabbalists appreciate the profundity of myth and its tenacious appeal." (Jamie the Witch would approve.) I learn that Kabbalists believe none of our acts are inconsequential. They reverberate, are amplified, in the divine realm. Likewise, disposition matters. Isaac Luria, the greatest Kabbalist of sixteenth-century Tzfat, took a dim view of sadness, considering it an impediment to mystical insight. This does not bode well for me. My depression has lifted slightly, owing to Tzfat's soft air perhaps, but it remains an unwanted presence, the guest from hell.

I learn that Kabbalists share the traditionally Jewish thirst for knowledge, but it is a different kind of knowledge. It is knowledge that is not acquired but absorbed or, as one of the earliest Kabbalists, a great visionary named Isaac the Blind, put it: "The inner, subtle essence can be contemplated only by sucking, not by knowing."

I put down my wineglass and take a deep breath. That is not the kind of passionate, somatic language I associate with Judaism. In my childhood synagogue, there was never any talk of sucking. I would have remembered that. I read on and learn that Kabbalists, like Christians, believe the one who strays and returns is better than the one who never strays at all, just as a fractured bone, once healed, is stronger than before the break. As someone who has both fractured a bone and strayed from my faith, I find great comfort in this. I pour myself another glass of Yarden wine, and soon I am asleep.

"You're starting to have that look," says Eyal when I meet him at his office the next morning, and as if to underscore his point his eyes bulge to the size of silver dollars.

"Really, I am?"

"Oh yes."

I briefly worry that I might be displaying early signs of Tzfat Syndrome. A variation of Jerusalem Syndrome, Tzfat Syndrome is when people who come to this city become delusional, convinced they are some biblical prophet, or maybe the Messiah Himself. Or does Eyal say that to everyone he meets? It's possible. We are susceptible to such spiritual flattery. We all want to be special, even if that specialness entails a hint of mental illness. Better crazy than ordinary.

Eyal is sitting behind his desk, gesticulating wildly, occasionally pivoting to check his e-mail. I'm eager to share with him what I've learned. I mention something I had read about how Kabbalah teaches that not only does man need God but God needs man. I find this fascinating. God needs *us*? I had never thought of it that way. If true, it catapults my search out of the realm of narcissism—what can I get out of this?—and into something else, something more noble. God *needs* me.

"Not that He needs us but that He *wants* us," says Eyal, deflating me.

I mention another Kabbalistic concept: that God conceals Himself from us. (The Hebrew word for "world," *olam*, shares a root with the word for "to conceal.") It is a familiar idea, echoed in the other religions I've explored. Why, I wonder, does God insist on playing hard to get? I mean, if You want to be known, then please send us a sign. It is Your universe, after all. Surely You know our number.

Eyal senses my confusion and does what Jews often do when confronted with a particularly vexing question of great importance: He asks more questions. "Why did God create then conceal? What's going on? Where is God?" Eyal scans the room. I find myself looking too, as if God might be under Eyal's desk, or maybe behind the door. Eyal, though, also possesses the Jewish habit of asking questions without answering them. And so we never do find God. Not that day at least.

Then Eyal gives me advice that could have easily come from the lips of the Tibetan lama I met in Kathmandu. In essence, he says, I need to familiarize myself with my own mind. "It all starts here," he says, jabbing his temple with such force I worry he might burst a blood vessel. "Learn your psyche. Know what is going on inside of you. Know your soul, know your godly soul. Know the animal soul inside you also. Know the higher soul, not the lower soul."

I follow Eyal but only so far. Not seven-eighths. More like three-eighths, maybe. I need another teacher. Eyal understands and is not insulted. He is a busy man. He has eight children, and is constantly in motion. He suggests I get in touch with one Yedidah Cohen, an emigrant from Britain who is among the most popular teachers of Kabbalah. I call Yedidah, and find her British accent refreshingly polite and reassuring. We arrange to meet the next morning.

Of all the religions I've explored, Judaism is by far the oldest. Jews were praying to their one God for thousands of years before the Sufis were whirling or the Buddhists meditating or the Raëlians cross-dressing. Is that a good thing or not? I wonder. We like our technology new and shiny but our religion old and musty. Well worn. Longevity, of course, does not necessarily equal truth. People believed the earth was flat for a very long time. That didn't make it true. But religion, I think, is true in a different way from the way, say, arithmetic is true. Religion is true the way a good poem or novel is true. We still read Shakespeare not only because his writing was good but because it was *true*. So, yes, in matters of faith, endurance counts. I silently add a few points in the Jewish score box.

Not only does Judaism have a past, but I have a past with Judaism, a history I do not share with, say, Buddhism or Wicca. This is good, and not. On one hand, I have a foundation on which to build. But that foundation is shaky, suspect.

Judaism never stuck with me, but it did with my younger brother, who, in his early twenties, underwent a dramatic transformation, from indifferent to religious Jew. I don't know exactly how this transpired. The fact is we don't talk about Judaism, and if anything his orthodoxy has driven us further apart, not closer. When my family visits his for the Jewish holidays, a vague but undeniable tension fills the air. I resort to my default strategy— humor—which only serves to heighten that tension. He once accused me of poking fun at his faith, an accusation that I initially bristled at but, upon reflection, couldn't deny. I joke about his Judaism, though, not out of malice but because of my own troubled relationship—or, more accurately, nonrelationship—with it. If he had become, say, a Hare Krishna, I would no doubt find it fascinating and would pepper him with thoughtful and respectful questions about his chosen path. Instead, his embrace of the faith I abandoned triggers in me a response that is as predictable as it is lamentable: guilt.

My own faith is alien to me, but not alien enough. My knowledge, such as it is, keeps getting in the way. I encountered no such obstacle with, say, Taoism or Sufism. With Judaism, I know just enough to trip me up. Hebrew words, words like *nefesh* and *mitzvot*, trigger some long-dormant synapses in my brain, but these synapses, tired and rusty, misfire. The fact is I don't *really* know what the words mean and never did. I've been too busy running away from a faith I considered at best irrelevant, and at worst something of an embarrassment, like the uncle at family gatherings who balances wineglasses on his forehead. Yet, Joseph Campbell tells me, evasion is futile. We never fully escape our indigenous mythology, he says, nor should we. "It's a good thing to hang on to the myth that was put in when you were a child, because it is there whether you want it there or not. What you have to do is translate that myth into eloquence.... You have to learn to hear its song."

I never thought of it that way. Reluctantly, I realize that is my challenge. To translate Judaism into not only a language I can understand but one I can sing. This won't be easy. I have many wonderful attributes, or so my wife tells me. A musical ear is not one of them.

After some linguistic confusion, I manage to call a taxi. The taxi drivers are all Moroccans, happy men who live more and ruminate less than the angst-ridden European Jews, like me. My driver knows Yedidah's house; she is a "vip" he tells me in broken English. The taxi climbs a long, winding road, up into the hills above Tzfat, before stopping in front of a small house. And there is Yedidah, waiting for me at the front gate. On the phone, she sounded so British but in person she looks very Israeli. Weathered skin. Unruly hair. No smooth edges, and what looks like a permanent tear lodged in the crease of her left eye. She reminds me of a character from *The Hobbit*.

"It's a magic gate," she says, pointing to the orange metal contraption before me. "Press down and see what happens." I press down and it swings open without any further effort on my part. Like magic. It's not the sort of magic that would likely impress Black Cat or Jamie the Witch—too rudimentary—but I enjoy it nonetheless.

She shows me to her study, which is floor-to-ceiling bookshelves. I scan for titles and my eyes land on *Sacred Geometry* and *Tips for Longevity*. The centerpiece, though, is the complete Zohar, all twenty-one volumes. The Zohar is the mysterious, virtually impenetrable canonical work of Kabbalah. "Every word is a gold mine," Yedidah says, pouring two cups of mint tea—always tea, not coffee, a vestige from her British upbringing.

She tells me her story. She was born into a religious family but never connected to the rituals. "There was this feeling that we do this because we do it," she says, and I nod knowingly. She was, though, an emotive Jew in a land that frowned upon such displays. She was thirsty to know more of her faith, to burrow deep. She taught herself Hebrew riding London's Northern Line. Trained as an anesthesiologist, sensitive to the pain of others, she came to Israel in 1981 during the First Lebanon War. She worked in the emergency room at Hadassah hospital. "I felt, here's my place." She also felt something was missing from her spiritual life but didn't know what it was. Then, at the suggestion of her husband, Mark, she went to Findhorn, the eclectic spiritual retreat in Scotland, despite her father's vociferous protests. He saw it as a betrayal of her faith. She saw it as an affirmation of that same faith. "I wanted to make peace. I didn't want to put my spirituality in one box and my Judaism in another. I wanted it in a whole way." In Findhorn, she found what she was looking for, and soon returned to Israel, this time for good.

"Why Tzfat?" I ask.

"It came to me in a dream. It sounds crazy, I know, but I got this picture of golden sunlight around the name of Tzfat."

"But how did you fall into Kabbalah?" I ask, reaching for a cookie.

That, she says, is a story for another time. She will teach me Kabbalah. We agree to meet at her house, just past the magic gate, every morning at ten. But not tomorrow. Tomorrow is the Sabbath, and that special day possesses, as I would soon discover, a magic all its own.

In one of the many ironies that is Judaism, the hours before the day of rest are marked by frantic activity, the storm before the calm. Downtown Tzfat is a buzz of escalating energy. It's like Washington, DC, before a snowstorm. Everyone is stocking up, feeling the press of a rapidly approaching deadline. Tzfat is in motion but it is not random motion. Everyone is heading to the same place—or, rather, to the same time. The Sabbath exists in time, not space. I too am in motion. I buy a falafel and a bottle of Yarden wine just before the stores close. I like the way the shopkeepers, strangers, say *Shabbat shalom*, good Sabbath. A softness in this hard land.

Eyal calls. He sounds harried. We're going synagogue shopping, he says.

"How should I dress?" I ask.

"It doesn't matter," he says. "What matters are the garments of the soul."

I'm tempted to fire off some quip about my soul garments being at the dry cleaners, or no longer fitting, or something smart-ass like that, but I refrain, recalling that smart-assness is an impediment to spiritual growth.

At 5:20 p.m. a quiet swaddles Tzfat. The cars have vanished, as if swooped up by the Elohim's spaceships. I could safely lie down in the middle of the city's busiest street.

At 5:45 p.m. my hotel goes into Sabbath lockdown. The elevator stops running. The staff disappear. The TV in the room next door, normally blaring, falls silent. I use my Swiss Army Knife to open the bottle of Yarden, my last act of labor before the Sabbath officially begins. I pour a glass, step onto the balcony—and listen. I hear birds chirping, a flag fluttering and, off in the distance, a goat bleating. Otherwise, nothing but silence—not an eerie silence but a ripe, plump silence that feels like a benign presence. On the question of silence, the Kabbalists have much to say. "Speech is worth a penny, silence is worth two," advises the Zohar. The Jews, the people of the mouth, also have a rich tradition of silence. Who knew?

At 6:37 p.m. a siren sounds. The Sabbath has officially begun. For once in my life, I am going to observe the Sabbath, and step foot into what Abraham Heschel calls "a sanctuary in time."

Time. We don't know what to do with it. We can find time, waste time, make time, spend time, do time or, if we're feeling especially vindictive, kill time. On the Sabbath, we do none of this. On the Sabbath, we dwell *in* time. We ease into this dwelling as we ease into a warm bath after a hard day's work. On the Sabbath, we are up to our neck in time, and nothing else.

At least that is the idea. On some level, I, like most people I think, fear time. Not the existence of time but, rather, its finiteness. I equate time with death. (Indeed, if time were infinite, if we literally had all the time in the world, I wonder if religion would exist at all.) I agree with Heschel when he says, "We suffer from a deeply rooted dread of time and stand aghast when compelled to look into its face." The Sabbath forces just such a confrontation with time, one that I typically lose in grand Chicago Cubs fashion.

Here, though, my odds are better. Here it is not only me against time. I have thousands of allies, and that makes all the difference. Back home, whenever I entertained the idea of observing the Sabbath, I was always overwhelmed by the fear of what I'd be missing: soccer games, tennis matches, shopping sprees, the latest movie, countless opportunities for leisure and self-improvement. I was overwhelmed by the opportunity costs, the price of things not done. In Israel (or at least in religious Israel), the Sabbath comes with no opportunity cost. I'm not missing anything. I can turn off my cellphone, knowing full well no one is trying to reach me. I can turn off my laptop, safe in the knowledge that my inbox will remain unmolested.

Heschel says our reaction to the Sabbath defines us. "What *we are* depends on what *the Sabbath is* to us," he writes. What am I? Is my ability to observe the Sabbath some sort of test, an exam devised to gauge my talent for doing nothing? Ah, the old ego at work. It can transform anything, even the most spiritual of impulses, into an opportunity for self-aggrandizement, or self-loathing. No, I vow to resist that impulse. I am tired of testing myself. Even if I pass those tests, it still comes at a cost. The Sabbath is beyond performance, beyond good and bad, beyond success and failure, even beyond doing and nondoing. It is pure being. That is the idea at least.

At 6:47 p.m. I walk down the stairs, enjoying the mild exertion, and meet Eyal in the lobby, as we had planned. He is dressed in all black—black hat, black trench coat—and has a vaguely mischievous grin, as if he knows something that I don't, which may very well be true. I follow him through the alleyways of the old city. "*Shabbat* is not about what you don't do," Eyal says as we walk along the deserted streets. "It's about what you do."

"What do we do?"

"We disengage from the world so that we can engage with God."

We enter a tiny synagogue, a simple square building with black plastic chairs arranged in neat rows and a low wooden partition separating the genders. (Men in front, women in the rear, where they are heard, not seen.) It reminds me of a synagogue I once visited in New Delhi during a very brief and unexplained bout of Judaism. It too was a small cement-block structure. There must have been seventy of us packed into that hut of a building, no larger than a kindergarten classroom. There was no air-conditioning, only a couple of squeaky ceiling fans swirling impotently through the hot Delhi air. About half of the congregants were Indian Jews, the remainder diplomats, Israeli backpackers, and sundry expats like myself. Outside those concrete walls stood a crowd of others: some 600 million Hindus, 130 million Muslims, a few million Christians, Sikhs, Buddhists, Jains, Parsis. Something stirred in me, something unfamiliar and not entirely unpleasant. Maybe it was an embryonic spirituality blossoming, as it sometimes does when we find ourselves suddenly out of our element. Or maybe it was simply a primal surge of belonging, an ancient tribalism that resides deep in our reptilian brains and derives binary pleasure from the us-against-them equation. I don't know, but I am sure of one thing: Never before or since have I felt more Jewish than I did that warm Delhi evening.

Eyal and I push our way through a sea of black and fur and take our seats. Language is a barrier. I don't understand a word of what is said. Eyal finds me a *siddur* in English and points to the page in the prayer book from which the rabbi is reading. It's the usual stuff about how Hashem is King of Kings, Lord of Lords, a force to be obeyed and feared. It's the kind of overwrought biblical language that has always turned me off. It's also long. I'm bored. I'm starting to devise an exit strategy when I feel a hand on my shoulder. Suddenly, inexplicably, I'm in a circle of sweaty men, chanting, *aye, aye, aye*. And then just as suddenly and inexplicably I am chanting too. Well, sort of. I feel like a fraud, a spiritual poseur. I fear that at any moment someone in the crowd will shout: "Hey, he's not a real Jew! He's mumbling the words! He doesn't know what he's doing!"

That doesn't happen, though. Instead, a sense of joy permeates the small synagogue, though what sort of joy, tribal or spiritual, I couldn't say. We chant some more and then the men start davening. Bending at the knees, they rock back and forth, rapidly, feverishly, as if they suffered from some sort of nervous condition. I feel compelled to join them, partly out of a need to *be here now* and partly to relieve the unbearable pressure to conform. I'm swaying back and forth, terribly self-conscious, and am reminded of that syndrome where orphans who are deprived of physical affection develop this habit of rocking back and forth. Self-soothing behavior, psychologists call it. I wonder if davening—indeed all spiritual exercises—is really a sort of self-soothing behavior for adults. And if so: Is that so bad?

I'm back in my plastic chair. We sit. We stand. We sit again. This goes on for what seems like a very long time. "That was only a prelude," Eyal whispers to me. "Now the real prayer begins."

Oh no. I'm not going to make it. I pass the time by surveying the sundry headgear on display here. There are plain knitted *kippas*, bold rainbow *kippas*, large black ones that cover the entire crown of the head, elegant fedoras and giant fur hats. I see a girl, maybe two years old, cradled in her father's arms, playing with his beard and pointing to a man wearing one of these giant fur hats. She smiles, and no wonder. It must look like the man has a large animal squatting on his head. At that moment, I know, without a doubt, that she is the most joyous one here.

We walk back to Eyal's house. Downhill. Chesterton lodges in my head again: "A man going down and down until at some mysterious point he begins to go up and up." How much further down must I go, I wonder, before I reverse trajectory?

Eyal's house is nice, simple. His wife, Natalie, introduces herself. I am careful not to extend my hand. I have a strict policy when traveling in religious circles. I never offer my hand to a woman until she offers hers first. Natalie does not offer hers.

Natalie is a *bal tschuva*, someone who has returned to her faith. Born in Venezuela, she was raised in a completely secular household, like Eyal. Then, on her way to college in Boston, she stopped over briefly in New York. A cousin suggested she join her to see Rabbi Schneerson, leader of the Lubavitch sect. For his followers, he was, and is, a modern messiah. Natalie had never heard of Schneerson, had no interest in meeting him, but she reluctantly agreed, just to humor her cousin. They waited for hours to see him and then there he was. He looked her in the eye and wished her good luck at the religious school. What was he talking about? Religious school? She was on her way to Boston to study architecture. But those eyes, those luminous eyes, had an inexplicable effect on her and, sure enough, she found herself enrolling in the religious school, much to her mother's horror. That was years ago. Now she has eight kids, wears a wig, and sits behind a partition at synagogue.

We sit down to a fulsome meal of fresh salads, tuna fish, hummus, and other dishes, which we wash down with Fanta served from large plastic bottles. (I don't know what it is about orthodox Jews and Fanta but I've detected a definite connection.) I notice that the table is segregated, boys on one side, girls on the other. Also here is a young man named Asaf. He has an impressive beard, long *payot*, curlicues of hair that dangle below his ears, and steady brown eyes that say: "I know things."

Natalie brings more food. I thought that the salads and the

hummus and the fish were the main course, and had devoured them as such, but apparently those were only the appetizers. "Just like the prayers at the synagogue," says Eyal drily. We make small talk. Natalie tells me how much she likes living in Tzfat, but worries when her teenage kids go to the beach. "It's not safe," she says. "There might be Arabs there." She says this in the same way one might say, "There might be sharks in the water." Her comment rattles me, and reminds me that underneath Tzfat's undeniably spiritual surface lurks the old bugaboo: tribalism. I feel anger welling up inside of me, but I don't want to insult my hosts, not directly at least. So I resort to my favorite strategy under these circumstances: passive-aggressiveness. I tell them about my flirtations with various *goyim* Gods: Buddhism, Taoism, Catholicism, and, the kicker, Islam. I go into great detail, knowing full well that my explorations constitute a form of heresy. An uncomfortable silence fills the room.

Finally, it is Asaf who speaks up. He wants to tell me a joke. Good, I could use some levity.

There was this Jew. Let's call him Moshe. Moshe decided one day he wanted to become Catholic, so he walks to the local church and says, "Father, I'd like to be Catholic."

"No problem," says the priest. He sprinkles water over Moshe and says, three times, "You're not Jewish, you're Catholic." He then sends Moshe on his way but with a warning: "We Catholics only eat fish on Fridays. Okay?"

Moshe assures him that is no problem. Except a few days later, on a Wednesday evening, Moshe develops a huge craving for fish. He can't resist so he slips off to a local restaurant. There, the priest happens to see him tucking into a huge fillet of halibut.

"Moshe! What are you doing? I told you to only eat fish on Friday."

Moshe, without missing a beat, says, "This isn't a fish. It's a carrot."

"What are you talking about, Moshe? I can plainly see it's a fish."

"No, it isn't. I sprinkled water on it and said, 'You're not a fish, you're a carrot, you're not a fish, you're a carrot...'"

Everyone at the table laughs. Except me. What am I to make of the joke? Am I a fish and always will be? Or am I a carrot with fish tendencies? Or some sort of carrot-fish hybrid? The obvious moral of the story: Go forth and meditate with the Buddhists, do yoga with the Hindus, pray with the Muslims, if you must, but you'll be back. You have a *nefesh*, a Jewish soul, and nothing you do will ever change that.

Walking back to town, Asaf and I talk. He tells me how not that long ago, I would not have recognized him. He had dreadlocks down to his butt and a wild side. He had done everything, *everything*, in this world, and his tone of voice makes it clear that any further inquiries about exactly what that everything entailed are ill advised; my "suburban American mind" might explode.

When it comes to Judaism, he says, he was like me. He used to think that Torah was about a bunch of silly rules—a kind of prison—but then he realized that no, *this life* was the prison. The answers to all of life's riddles can be found in the Torah, he tells me, and then looks at me with the most steady unblinking eyes I've ever seen and says: "Everything is good."

The next morning. The Sabbath day. There is nothing to do, nowhere to go. Exertion is futile. So I lie in bed, reading about Kabbalah and listening to the sounds of Hebrew prayers, wafting into my room like a cool breeze on an August evening. I enjoy a day of blessed nothingness. The next morning, I shower and prepare to see Yedidah for my first official lesson into the mysteries of Kabbalah.

I'm not sure what to expect. I like Yedidah. She seems adequately sane and sufficiently skeptical (a physician after all) yet with a big, Sufi-ish heart and a sense of humor, albeit a quirky British one further warped by several decades in Israel.

My taxi chugs up, up, up then drops me at her house. I press down on the magic gate and enter the garden.

Yedidah is waiting for me. She seems awfully chipper, suspiciously so. She has a routine, she says by way of explanation. She wakes at 5:00 a.m., makes herself a pot of mint tea, sits in her rocking chair, and says the Shema, the most important Jewish prayer, savoring the silence before her children stir and chaos follows. She doesn't meditate. She prays.

She packs her two daughters off to school. Her grown sons, Suffy and Iggy, are in the Israeli army. Suffy is in tanks. That's how she puts it—"he's in tanks"—as if he lived in a tank, which may not be far from the truth. Iggy does something else, which I don't understand, though I'm fairly sure it does not involve tanks.

Four years ago, Yedidah's routine was dramatically and irrevocably altered. One evening, after the children were put to bed, she noticed that the house was unusually silent. Where was her husband, Mark? After a brief search, she found him on the toilet, dead of an apparent heart attack. A life together suddenly erased. Just like that. For a long time, she blamed herself, a physician after all, for not noticing that something was wrong, that his listlessness that evening was more than the flu or jet lag.

All of this I learn before we crack a book or even mention the word "Kabbalah." We're sitting in her study. A large wool blanket covers her desk. She puts on the kettle and makes a pot of mint tea. She offers me a cookie. I accept, and the world outside recedes.

I feel honored that Yedidah is teaching me. She is particular about her students. She doesn't teach people who are interested in "magical Kabbalah." She doesn't teach impatient people looking for an "insta-God." She *does* teach people in crisis, and people who "don't know why they are Jewish." Confused fish, lost carrots. People like me.

Pouring more tea, she warns the work will not be easy. "We're not just making nice here," she says. "We're not making mutzy-putzy." She says that a lot. Mutzy-putzy. I'm not sure if it is some Hebrew term, or a British-ism, or a Yedidah-ism. In any case, I quite like it.

"It's important to keep breathing during the lessons," she says, sounding more like Yedidah the Anesthesiologist than Yedidah the Kabbalist, and then we hit the books. I read aloud while she listens intently, correcting even my smallest mispronunciation. The words are difficult to follow. There's much talk of vessels and light and "the will to receive." That last one I find especially baffling. Personally, I've never had trouble with my willingness to receive. It's the giving part that trips me up.

It's not that simple, she says. There are different ways of receiving. You can receive begrudgingly, contemptuously, and even aggressively. Or, says Yedidah, you can receive with love. Most religions focus on the giving, but Kabbalists consider receiving the more important, and less easily mastered, art.

In Kabbalah, words matter. They are slippery, though. Often, what you hear is not. Yedidah reinterprets Hebrew words that have always befuddled me, put me off, in more meaningful ways. *Melach*, for instance, literally means "king" but actually refers to "the channel of goodness," she says.

"But I always pictured a man with a long beard and a jeweled crown."

"That's because you don't know the code." The Zohar, like most Kabbalistic texts, was written in code. Nothing means what you think it means.

"So it would be like me trying to read Chinese?"

Worse, explains Yedidah. The words are intelligible but their meanings scrambled. The texts are *intentionally deceptive*. This strikes me as odd, and possibly cruel. But Kabbalists had their reasons. These teachings were so powerful, the rabbis believed, they posed a real danger to those not ready to receive them. By encrypting their work, the rabbis reached the "right" people while everyone else dismissed their tales as nothing more than nice stories about kings and their crowns. So the modern Kabbalist is, first and foremost, an expert code breaker.

Yedidah loves it, though, not despite these obstacles but because of them. She is not a masochist, she assures me. She simply knows what most of us have always suspected: Insights unearned don't stick. It's our sweat and blood that provide the glue, preventing these wisps of clarity from floating off into space. It might take her a full day to "get" one sentence, but then she owns that sentence, forever.

More tea is poured and cookies consumed. We tackle the basics, but even these prove tricky. What is Kabbalah? It is not a body of knowledge, Yedidah explains, but a way of being. It's not what you do but how you do it. Specifically, says Yedidah, how you "put yourself in the state of consciousness to be inspired."

"Inspired by what?"

"Never mind the what. Focus on the how."

Okay, I can play that game. "*How* did you fall into Kabbalah? You promised me a story."

Yedidah sips her tea, then unfurls a tale worthy of a *magus*.

It was her father's *yahrzeit*, the one-year death anniversary that Jews observe. She wasn't on good terms with him when he died. He never forgave her for her time at Findhorn, the spiritual retreat. As so often happens, Yedidah had unfinished business with the dead. She visited a rabbi in town and said she wanted to do something to mark her father's death. He suggested lighting a candle or donating money to charity. Neither idea spoke to her. So he said, "Okay, meet me at the cave tomorrow."

Yedidah knew the place, inside a synagogue dedicated to Rabbi Luria, the lion of Tzfat. But why should she go? That she didn't know. She went anyway. Inside the cave, the rabbi handed her a book and told her to read. She did. The words were alien, and familiar. "Know that before the creatures were created, there was one light filling all reality. And there was no empty space, everything was filled with the same, simple light of the infinite, and it didn't have a beginning and it didn't have an end. Everyone and everything was one simple light."

The words hit her "like an atom bomb." For the next three days she couldn't function. She was in a state of complete chaos. She couldn't sleep. She couldn't eat. She couldn't care for her children.

"What's happening?" she asked the rabbi when they met again. "I can't function."

"Oh, this is good," he said. "This is very good."

"What is possibly good about this?"

The rabbi explained that when you climb a ladder you must let go of one rung before you can grasp the next and there is a brief moment—so brief we don't usually notice it—when you are no longer grasping the old rung but have not yet taken hold of the new one. This moment, this chaos, is a kind of birth pang. And those words in the cave? They were from the Zohar. Yedidah knew she had found her way.

"Wow," I say lamely. "You were that certain?"

"I knew totally that I was born to learn this material, that I had waited incarnations for this material."

"Wow," I say again, even more lamely, reduced, apparently, to monosyllables. Maybe that's where I am, between rungs, adrift. Where, though, is that next rung? And how do I know I'll successfully grab hold of it and not plummet to a terrible death?

Every religion has its creation story, and the Kabbalists are no exception. Theirs is as colorful and fantastical as any I've encountered. Basically, it says, God dropped the universe. He was creating it when—oops!—the pieces shattered. We are now living among these shards, and it is our duty to repair the world, to put Humpty Dumpty back together again.

Thus a key concept in Kabbalah (and Judaism in general) is *tikkun*, or "repair." Kabbalists believe we each have a unique task, an assignment, to help repair the world by repairing ourselves, our consciousness. There is a multiplier effect, the Kabbalists teach. Every *mitzvah*, or good deed, performed in the physical realm reverberates in the divine realm.

Now, I am not an especially neat person—more of a mess freak than a neat one—so the idea of all these broken shards lying around doesn't particularly bother me, and *tikkun haolam*, repairing the world, sounds like a lot of work, a bit too much. The Buddhists say: Just be. The Taoists say: It just is. The Raëlians say: Just do it. And what do the Kabbalists say? Just get to work already. Kabbalah views the world as one giant renovation project. Like all such projects, this one will no doubt run behind schedule and over budget. Jews have no desire to escape the physical world. They embrace it, *all* of it, even the bad parts. As the poet Allen Afterman says: "The Jewish way is to know the world, to deny nothing—holding the Holocaust, holding the anger and the bitterness—and sing." *In spite of*, he might have added.

Before circling back to Judaism, Yedidah had dabbled in eastern faiths. She tried watching her breath and contemplating nothingness, but it did nothing for her. Kabbalah does share some similarities with eastern faiths like Buddhism. Both are methods as much as theologies. Buddhism is a method for stilling our monkey mind and squelching desire. Kabbalah is a method for receiving God's light. Both believe in nonduality—that our separateness is only an illusion. Both Kabbalah and Buddhism (Tantric Buddhism, at least) see every one of our actions, no matter how seemingly "unholy," as fuel for enlightenment.

But there is at least one key difference. Kabbalah doesn't ask that we extinguish our ego. As Yedidah says: "It tells me that I have an ego and it is good to have an ego. Wow! What a relief. And it is okay to be me. Why would we nullify it? It is God's precious vessel of inspiration and light." Another difference: The aim of Buddhism is to transcend the physical world, to become nothing. No-thing. That doesn't sit well with Yedidah, who is very much an everything. "I can't become nothing and I need to be honest and I want to say to God, 'You created me with all the problems I've got. It's Your fault. I want to know why You did that. If You didn't want me to get mad or angry, then why did You create me like this? It's Your problem. And I want You to know that.'"

Instead of abolishing the ego, Kabbalah calls on us to transform it from an entity capable of receiving only for itself to one that serves as a conduit for God's love. The aim of Kabbalah is not to check out of the physical world but to transform it, to sanctify even the crudest of physical acts. Unlike Buddhism, Judaism does not believe desire is the root of all suffering. Desire can be good.

I tell Yedidah about my pet depression. She is sympathetic and recommends I talk to myself in the third person, something I do already and have always found to be something of an embarrassment. *Oh, there goes Eric again, talking about himself in the third person.* I've always considered it a sign of pending madness, but Yedidah says no, it's the opposite. "When I do that one-step back, I've got room to breathe and I don't feel guilty. We have to understand ourselves."

That's when she mentions the mystical falafel. I am a big fan of falafel; it is, as far as I'm concerned, the best possible use of mashed chickpeas ever devised by Man. But mystical?

"Absolutely," says Yedidah, as if there were any doubt. This ought to be interesting.

"We have to acknowledge our part in something much bigger than ourselves. We are part of the unfolding of the universe. Let's say you go to a falafel place. You don't know why you went to this particular falafel place, but you did, and in walks Mr. X and you have no idea that Mr. X will be so important in your life. You meet Mr. X and you and he become fast friends. That friendship is part of the universe unfolding."

"Some would say it is simply coincidence."

"But it isn't."

My skepticism bubbles to the surface. Is Yedidah suggesting that God is a puppet master and we are the puppets?

"No, that's not what He's interested in. In fact, in Kabbalah we believe God is hidden. Otherwise, if the light of God were always present we'd be in total bliss all the time."

"And this is a problem because?"

"I used to think the same thing. I asked my teacher about this and he said, 'No, you wouldn't want that.' And I said, 'Yes I would.' And he said, 'Well you think that, but'—and this is a very profound Kabbalistic question—'Why did God create, then go to all this trouble to hide Himself? Why?' The answer is so that we can come to God through our own work and our own free will. Otherwise it is like getting something for nothing, and nobody appreciates that much. The truth of the matter is that deep down we are tough mutts and we want to do this ourselves."

"So the fact that God is hidden is a good thing?"

"It's a fabulous thing."

Two hours have flown by. I sip my last sip of tea, press down on the magic gate and, as I climb into the taxi, wonder: Have I found Judaism's lost heart?

I head to my favorite café, order an upside-down coffee, and attempt to digest my hours with Yedidah. I like her even more now. I'm not sure, though, if she is teaching me Kabbalah or *about* Kabbalah—or, more likely, about Yedidah. Sometimes, it's difficult to separate the teacher from the teachings. Sometimes, there is no difference.

Later, I have some free time, so I dip into Eliezer's House of Books, the only bookstore in town with a selection in English. An odd selection it is, though. There's an inordinate number of books concerned with the issue of interfaith marriage: the no-nonsense *How to Stop an Inter-Faith Marriage*, for instance, and the cheekier *Dear Rabbi, Why Can't I Marry Her?* I knew assimilation was a concern for some Jews; I didn't realize it was also a genre. I keep scanning the shelves and spot a copy of Aryeh Kaplan's *Jewish Meditation*. This is a classic. It's the book that many of the people I've met in Tzfat tell me drew them to Kabbalah in the first place.

When I first heard of the book, I didn't know what to think. Jewish meditation? I pictured a group of middle-aged men and women sitting in the lotus position, silently worrying that their children won't amount to anything. Thankfully, I was wrong. There is a genuine tradition of meditation that, Kaplan informs me, dates back to the days of Moses. These meditative practices, varied and rigorous, have dwelled in the nooks and crannies of Jewish teaching, keeping a low profile so as not to raise suspicion.

This being Jewish meditation, many of the exercises have a verbal component: repeating certain mantras, or concentrating on certain, supposedly powerful, letter combinations, such as *YHWH*, the tetragrammaton for God. I flip through the pages and find one exercise that seems simple enough. I am to repeat these words: *Ribbono shel Olam*, Lord of the Universe, over and over, for thirty minutes. That's it. Normally, this is exactly the kind of feudal language that turns me off (Who made *you* Lord of the Universe?), but I set aside those concerns, putting them in the same lockbox where I put my inhibitions about cultivating my *chi* and protesting at abortion clinics and dressing like a woman. It's a large box.

I try to get comfortable in my hotel room. How should I sit? My modified lotus position doesn't seem right (too Buddhist), and neither does lying on the floor (too Raëlian), so I opt for simply sitting on a chair. I take a few deep breaths then begin: *Ribbono shel Olam, Ribbono shel Olam, Ribbono shel Olam.* The thing about these repetitive exercises is that they are very...repetitive. My mind protests: *This is stupid. Why are you saying these words over and over? You don't even know what they mean. You're an idiot; I knew you wouldn't amount to anything.* Then at some point—around minute seventeen—something happens: My mind gives up. It surrenders to the sheer monotony of the mantra (Okay, fine, You *are* Lord of the Universe), and this act of surrender yields an alien and not entirely unpleasant sensation that some people call "relaxation."

Not quite that alien, actually. I felt something similar after the Sufi *dhikr*, or remembrance, *La ilaha illallah.* "There is no God but God." One mantra is from the Jewish Torah, the other from the Muslim Hadith, yet they produce remarkably similar results. Clearly, there is something about the repetition of a simple phrase that triggers a relaxation response, or something akin to that, in the human brain. I wonder, though: Does the content matter, or is it the sounds themselves that do the trick? As I've discovered, certain languages, like ancient Sanskrit or modern Arabic, are vibrational. The sound of the words themselves elicits a physiological response. All sorts of words vibrate, though. Yabba-dabba doo, for instance. What if I repeated that for thirty minutes? Would I also feel relaxed, transcendent? There's only one way to find out.

I sit in the modified lotus position and repeat yabba-dabba doo for thirty minutes. It goes well. Nobody calls the meditation police.

I feel better afterward, more relaxed, more present. Better, but not *as* better as with the Jewish or Muslim meditations. The reason, I think, is that when uttering those religious mantras my mind's eye conjured up vague images of majesty and awe. I raised myself. When saying yabba-dabba doo, my mind conjured up very specific images of Fred Flintstone. I lowered myself. Words operate on a number of levels. The somatic level of vibration and sound, the cerebral level of meaning and context. It's the interplay of these two levels that converts mere utterances into mantras and prayers.

Words matter. Kabbalah takes words familiar to me—words like *mitzvah* and *Shabbat*—and turns them upside down, like the *café-hafuch* that I so love. As Jewish mystics say, "The world is wrong names." And what are we to do with these wrong names? Who can set the record straight? It is not the scientist's job, nor the theologian's nor even the linguist's. This is the poet's work. Kabbalah *is* poetry. Good poetry. Like all good poetry, it speaks to us through image and sound, bypassing our critical mind, surprising us with what we already know, and leaving us sated and thirsty for more. Always more. *Ein sof.*

One day, sitting in Eyal's office, I notice a painting hanging on the wall. I've never seen anything quite like it. It's a brightly colored wheel, like a mandala, only with Jewish instead of Buddhist iconography. It's a gift, explains Eyal, from one of Tzfat's best-known artists, an American immigrant named David Friedman. I need to meet him, I tell Eyal.

We walk a short distance to the Kabbalah Art Gallery. There we find David, baseball cap and neatly trimmed beard, giving a lecture to a group of tourists from Brazil. He's pointing to a painting and explaining how you can read it forward or backward. A few minutes later, the tourists gobble up paintings like so many chocolate brownies. David's wife, Miriam, can barely keep up, counting dollars and shekels, swiping credit cards. David's art favors bold colors and sharp geometry, often using letters in the Hebrew alphabet as subjects. Some paintings look like molecular models. Others are overtly psychedelic. One, where Hebrew letters form a circle, mandala-style, is called *The Big Bang*. The Brazilians are effusive with their praise, and I notice how David accepts the compliments graciously—not overly proud but not too humble either. Clearly, this is a man well practiced in the art of receiving.

Once the Brazilians have left, David and I sit and talk over coffee and homemade pickles. He tells me how years ago, when he was still an ultra-orthodox Jew, he visited a doctor in Jerusalem, an oncologist. The doctor plopped his CT scan on the desk and offered David a cigarette.

"No thanks," said David. "I don't smoke."

"Maybe you should start," the doctor said. That was his way of telling David he had cancer, at age twenty-eight, and the prognosis was not good. David's illness, and the questions it raised, accelerated his departure from the cloistered world of the ultra-orthodox. Ultimately, though, it was a jar of mayonnaise that tipped the balance. Well, not exactly a jar of mayonnaise but a billboard depicting one. Some of his Hasidic friends were arrested for spray-painting over billboards that showed scantily clad women or other forbidden images. One of his friends had spray-painted over a picture of a jar of mayonnaise.

"Why would you spray-paint mayonnaise?" David asked him. "It's not forbidden."

"But I couldn't look at the billboard in case it was a picture of a woman, so I just spray-painted it. I didn't know it was mayonnaise until afterward," explained his friend. That is when David knew he had to find a new path.

Today, still religious, but on his own terms, David describes himself as an "ultra-paradox Jew." Like Yedidah, he rarely attends synagogue, choosing to begin the Sabbath with a walking meditation in the woods. He owns a variety of headgear—baseball caps, Bukharan hats, and others that he wears rather than a traditional *kippa*. He doesn't want people to put him in a box.

David's approach to Kabbalah, though, is very different from Yedidah's. He leads with his head, not his heart. This approach, he believes, renders the teachings more accessible, more transferable, than ones that rely on a teacher's—even a brilliant teacher's—mystical insight.

The Kabbalists of sixteenth-century Tzfat didn't just make this stuff up, says David, they discovered it, they *saw* it. David sees "an incredible, logical consistency that goes into amazing detail." It is a grammar of God and, like all grammars, there are plenty of exceptions and irregular verbs but at its core lies a discernible, *learnable* pattern. This clearly appeals to David, who has the mind of a scientist and the spatial bias of an artist.

"It's like looking at a beautiful jigsaw puzzle. It's all interconnected," he says. That is one word he is fond of and where Kabbalah, again, shares common ground with eastern faiths—the belief that nothing, and no one, exists independently. Everything is connected.

David reminds me of Wayne of Staten Island. Patient. Comfortable in his own skin. Both were born Jewish. One drifted and found a home in Buddhism. The other drifted and circled back to his own faith, albeit a do-it-yourself version of that faith. William James would say that both men underwent a conversion. James defined conversion as "the process, gradual or sudden, by which a self hitherto divided or consciously wrong, inferior, and unhappy becomes unified and consciously right, superior and happy." In that sense, David is a convert to his own faith. Such a thing is possible. Conversion, after all, means "to turn," and we can turn away from something or toward it or, as the Sufis taught me, we can turn in a circle, returning to where we started, the same yet not.

The way David explains it, God created this messed-up world, shattering the vessels *on purpose*, in order to provide a teachable moment, the ultimate teachable moment, an opportunity for all of us to do God's work. I am still intrigued by this concept that God *needs* us. Does He? Not exactly, says David. He needs us the way a teacher needs students. If my daughter's kindergarten teacher gives her an assignment, say, to draw a cow, she doesn't "need" Sonya's help. The teacher could do it on her own. But then my daughter wouldn't learn how to draw a cow.

Family, says David, is how most of us practice *tikkun*, repair, and I'm reminded of what Brother Crispin told me: Your family is your apostolate. I am guilty, I realize, of looking for my spiritual nourishment elsewhere. I put family in one box and spirituality in another. Not so, these two souls say. Same box.

I tell David my Tokyo story, about how I awoke in a state of utter joy, saying over and over, "I didn't know, I didn't know." David listens patiently, revealing nothing, then walks over to a bookshelf and extracts a hefty-looking tome. He turns immediately to a page, and reads: "And Jacob woke from his sleep and said, God is in this place, and I did not know it."

The passage is from the Bible (Genesis 28:16). Jacob later changed his name to "Israel," which means "one who wrestles with God."

"Interesting," says David, tilting his head upward slightly and arching his eyebrows.

"Freaky," I say, again at a loss for words. Tzfat is managing to accomplish in a few short days what others have failed to do over a lifetime: render me mute.

David agrees to teach me Kabbalah. I feel a bit like I'm cheating on Yedidah, which is silly, I know, but there you have it. The sessions are very different. David uses terms like "the science of Kabbalah," which I can't imagine Yedidah ever uttering. He draws diagrams of the *sefirot*, the ten emanations of God, that remind me of something from high school chemistry and produce an identical throbbing in my head. Then there is the code, which is even more complex than Yedidah let on. Kabbalists believe that every sentence, letter, word, and even accent mark in the Hebrew Bible contains hidden meaning, and that this meaning can be deciphered by assigning a numeric value to each word. Words with similar numeric values are thought to be related in some way.

My lessons with David are fascinating, and I always leave his studio intellectually sated, but half an hour later I'm confused again. He'll be talking about a particular *sefirot* and how it relates to the *ein sof* and I get it, I really do, for about ten minutes then— poof!—it's gone forever. Nothing sticks. The pickles, though, are quite filling.

My days in Tzfat fall into a routine. I forage for coffee in the morning, then take a taxi to see Yedidah. Afterward, I break for lunch, eating a mystical falafel, sipping an upside-down coffee, and attempting to digest what I've learned. Then, sometime in the afternoon, I drop by David's studio for homemade pickles and metaphysics. David feeds my head, Yedidah my heart.

My favorite time of day is late afternoon. That is when the Tzfat air is at its softest and the Tzfat light its most brilliant. Closest to Heaven. I sit on my hotel balcony, smoking my little existential cigars and reading the writings of the great Kabbalists, who, only a few hundred years ago, walked these very streets and asked the very questions I ask: Where did we come from? What happens when we die? Why can't you get a decent cup of coffee in this town before 8:00 a.m.?

Kabbalah makes all of the other faiths I've dabbled in so far seem like child's play. "Maddeningly abstruse" is how the poet Rodger Kamenetz describes Kabbalah. (When poets accuse you of fuzziness, you know you're in trouble.) If Kabbalah were part of any other faith, I'm sure Jews would dismiss it as nothing but a bunch of mumbo-jumbo. Yet they don't. As one orthodox rabbi put it: "Kabbalah is nonsense, but it is Jewish nonsense and therefore worthy of consideration."

Here I've finally found a path that honors my love of books, and yet I'm still lost. More lost than ever. It's one thing to fail at Buddhism or Taoism and another thing altogether to fail at my own faith, especially now that I'm giving it an honest try. It's this blasted code! Aramaic translated into Hebrew translated into English and, from the outset, intentionally deceptive. It's like some warped game of telephone, which would be fine if I could just write off the person on the other end as a lunatic, but I can't. Sure, it's all interesting—in the way that, say, nuclear fusion is interesting—but where is it getting me? How does it help salve this dull ache in my heart? I put my book down and stare blankly at the horizon: a few wispy clouds, an Israeli army watchtower, a road slicing through brown hills that look like the backs of sleeping animals. That's when I spot the hawk.

It's riding the air currents, so effortlessly, propelled not by exertion—its wings remain perfectly still—but by its intuitive understanding of the laws of thermal dynamics. It is an example of pure *wu-wei*, effortless action. My mind drifts to Lao-tzu and Chuang-tzu and the gentle wisdom of the Way. No. That was another experience, another place. I am here in Tzfat. *Be here now, Eric, place your mind in your body*, as Wayne of Staten Island would say. No, that was Kathmandu and Buddhism. Wrong religion, again. *Listen to your heart, Eric*. No, no, that's Sufism.

My head is spinning—clockwise, I believe, in the Buddhist direction, though I'm not sure. I'm not sure of anything. Might I be suffering from what psychiatrist and author M. Scott Peck calls "spiritual confusion"? Is the sum of all these religions I've sampled less than their parts? Am I overdosing on God? The not-still voice in my head is prodding me, taunting me. Just pick up the book, the one right there, called *Kabbalah and Consciousness*. Read that and all will become clear, the voice says. Yes, that's what I ought to do.

Someone, I don't remember who, said that in the spiritual realm there is no compulsion. As soon as we think *I ought to do this*, whatever "this" is, however noble and therapeutic, it's game over. *Ought* has ambushed more spiritual journeys than all of the charlatan gurus, New Age pap, and fuzzy-mindedness combined. So I put the book down and watch the hawk. I do this for a long time. I'm not sure exactly how long but when I finally decide it's time to go inside, it is still up there, swooping and diving, like a child playing in the surf.

I meet Baruch, a musician, who, like others I've met here, seems happy, happier than any Jew has a right to be. We sit and chat in his living room, a cave-like house with arched ceilings and pictures of dead rabbis on the wall. It's a good talk. I'm about to leave when he invites me to join him at the *mikva*, a Jewish ritual bath. I've never been before. Why would I? Water makes me uncomfortable—my swimming style is best described as a controlled flail—and so does Judaism. Not surprisingly, the combination of these two activities has never held much appeal.

"You've never been to a *mikva*?" says Baruch, incredulous, the way my friends back home might respond if I had told them I had never eaten sushi or had a hot-stone massage. "You're missing something magical," he continues, a glint in his eye. "I'll be reading a certain passage, won't be getting it, simply can't get it, then I'll dip into the *mikva* and suddenly it becomes clear." After a dip in the *mikva*, he says, the sun shines brighter.

He had me at magical. Adding to the mystical quality of what I'm about to experience is the fact, as Baruch informs me, that the word *mikva* has the same numeric value as "womb." So, in the Kabbalistic interpretation, I am about to return to the womb, which is something I've been meaning to do for a long time now. Another interpretation, Baruch tells me: I am going to be reborn, not on the physical level but on the level of consciousness. This seems an awful lot to ask from a tub of water, but I know by now that such skepticism won't get me anywhere. We don't see what we are convinced does not exist.

We walk down a narrow path to a small simple structure. We pay the *mikva*-keeper a few shekels and go inside. There are towels laid out drying and, a few feet away, a small pool the size of a hot tub, the *mikva*. Outside, I hear birds chirping, the wind.

I watch as Baruch bends down, naked, touching his forehead to the chipped blue stone floor. He looks at me, his eyes saying, "Okay, it's your turn."

I confess to Baruch that I don't know what to say. "Just be honest," he says. "Prayer is a craft, and all craft requires a high degree of honesty." I never thought of it that way. I always thought of prayer as a kind of test, not a test of God's abilities but of mine. I kneel on my right knee, naked, and silently say the only word that comes to mind, one that William James believed was the source of all religious impulses: "Help!"

The water is bracing. I close my eyes before submerging. If this is the womb, it's nothing like I remember. Not nearly as warm and enveloping. Within a few minutes, we've toweled off and are walking back up the hill, the Tzfat air soft, the sun still high in the sky, perhaps a bit brighter than I recall, or maybe that's just my imagination.

Viewed from outer space, by aliens (the Elohim, perhaps?), the scene I just described would look like this: A middle-aged human, bald, with a slight paunch but a fairly good specimen nonetheless given his age and genetic background, takes off his clothes, touches his head against a tiled floor, and then submerges himself in an element that is two parts hydrogen, one part oxygen, which earthlings call "water." That is a perfectly accurate description of what transpired. It is incomplete, though, for it fails to take into account one important factor: *kavanah*, intention. *Kavanah* bridges crude physical action and larger meaning. *Kavanah* explains why some gifts we receive feel like gifts and others feel like an obligation, a quid pro quo. Our legal system explicitly recognizes *kavanah*. Someone accused of murdering a person with intention faces a harsher sentence than someone who committed the same act but without such intent. *Kavanah*, the Kabbalists believe, is what is too often missing from contemporary Judaism. Some even believe that to perform a *mitzvah*, or commandment, without proper intention is worse than not doing it at all.

Another morning, another session with Yedidah. She had warned me that we would be engaging in "circular learning," and oh was she right. Our lessons are like jellyfish: squishy, with no discernible structure, but managing to maintain a forward trajectory nonetheless. We read from the Zohar, or one of the rabbinical interpretations of it, then break for tea and cookies, then trade anecdotes about our travels or our families, then read another passage, then make more tea, and before I know it two hours have passed.

I don't know how to classify our time together. Officially, she is teaching me Kabbalah, but she also acts as therapist, tea maker, taxi dispatcher, friend. All the while, she says things that are incredibly wise or blindingly obvious—or both, wisdom being nothing more than common sense in drag. "You cannot dance on one foot," Yedidah says one morning. "Start where you are," she says another. She says some things that, at the time, make no sense—"The opposite of sadness is not happiness but clarity"—but later, over an upside-down coffee, ring true. She says things that make me smile, like when she suggested I spend time "resting in God" and I immediately pictured the Almighty as a goose-down comforter. And she says things that hint at a benevolent and mysterious force. "Your needs will get met, but differently, in un-expected ways, in ways you never thought about."

On this particular day, I have a question I've been meaning to ask but have yet to screw up my courage. It's a question I've posed to others—Raëlians, Wiccans, and the like—without any hesita-tion but here, among my own faith, I balk. Oh, what the heck. I take a stiff sip of tea.

"Yedidah, forgive me, but can I ask a question that might sound, a bit, well, blasphemous?"

"Oh, those are usually the goodies," she says, inching forward on her chair, like a teenage girl eager to hear the latest school gos-sip.

"Well, what if it is all, you know, just rubbish? What if you've been misled? What if *all* Kabbalists have been misled and the Zohar is just, you know, the fantastical invention of some rabbi smoking dope out in the desert?" I brace myself for an earful that never comes.

"It's a very good question," she says with complete sincerity. "I tell my students to ask themselves this: After studying Kabbalah, are you more patient with your husband, with your children? Are you less angry? For me, the answer is yes." A different accent, a different God, but once again the same sentiment that William James uttered a century ago: *Truth is what works.*

This is all well and good for Yedidah, who has a close working relationship with God, but I don't. "We're not on speaking terms, God and I," I say.

"I don't believe that."

She's right. He did talk to me once, that night in Tokyo, but He doesn't call anymore. "Look," I say. "He's just not that into me."

"Well, hold on just one second. When you picture God, what comes to mind?"

I explain how it's either one of two very different images: God as the Cosmic Male Parent, long white beard and all, or else God as the Infinite Whatever, a milky nebula, formless but vaguely benevolent. That's it. One of those two.

"But there is a third image, and that is this: Your inner essence and the essence of God are one."

"Are you saying I am God?"

"There is a part of you, yes, which is God, and it's called soul. One of the most helpful things about Kabbalah is it says specifically we do not know what God is. It says we cannot know what God is, even the highest angels do not know what God is. But God manifests in His actions, okay? For some people, God manifests Himself through creativity. For others, it is through their families, or through voluntary work. For you I think I would say God speaks to you very much through the arrangement of people you meet."

"I do meet interesting people."

"You really do. It is very amazing. And you seem to have some inner guidance system, an inner GPS that somehow steers you in the right direction, which to me is very phenomenal. I think God is actually speaking to you. It's just that you don't call it God."

"So we are on speaking terms?"

"Yes, in fact I think God loves you very much. I don't know why. But He does."

"And my sadness?"

"That is a *kippa*, a shell."

During one of our last sessions, Yedidah teaches me how to

pray. Normally, this is not something that I thought needed to be taught, any more than breathing or masturbation needs to be taught. Either you know how to do these things or you are in a world of trouble. No, Yedidah assures me, prayer is learned.

First of all, she says, synagogues are nice but hardly necessary. She doesn't go very often. Her study is her synagogue, her rocking chair the altar. "Prayer is mobile," she says, and of course she's right. We live in a world that worships mobility, as all those BlackBerrys attest, yet we largely persist in the belief that God is confined to certain buildings. Surely, the Almighty has gone wireless.

As she had mentioned, she begins her day with the Shema, the mother of all Jewish prayers. It's blissfully short, but extremely powerful. *Hear, Israel, the Lord is our God, the Lord is One.* She likes those words but likes those that follow even more: *And you shall love.*

"Okay, shall we say it?"

Predictably, performance anxiety kicks in. Talking to God makes me nervous, especially when I think He might actually be listening. "Well, how should I say it? With feeling?"

"With intention. *Kavanah.* It is the key to everything."

She's right, again. When we are caught up in feeling, we are a passenger. It might be a bumpy ride or a pleasant one but we are still a passenger, passive. When we do something, anything, with intention, we are the driver—*and* the passenger.

I try, but stumble horribly. When I speak Hebrew, I am thirteen years old again, gangly and pimple-faced, wearing a polyester suit at my Bar Mitzvah. I don't want to be thirteen again. Once was enough.

"Okay, listen to me." The way she says it is with such passion— *Shema Yisrael*—her voice strong and resonant. Yet the words are also infused with an undeniable sadness. The prayer, like all prayers, is both celebration and lamentation, a dirge for "life's sad incompleteness," as Immanuel Kant puts it.

"Try it again, with all of the *chazak* you've got."

I have no idea what *chazak* means, but I give it all I've got. This time it feels better, more real.

"Very good," she says, like a first-grade teacher praising the slow student. "Now I'll teach you a real bit of Kabbalah." She says the prayer again, this time her voice alternating between a full-throated bellow and a whisper. The whisper, though, is no less intense; in fact, it is *more* intense, the same amount of energy squeezed into a smaller container.

We pray again, over and over, our voices rising and falling together, until our session is over and, once again, I slip through the magic gate and take a taxi down, down, down to Tzfat and the café where a mystical falafel and an upside-down coffee await me.

During one of my last lessons with David, I notice a coffee mug in his kitchen that I hadn't seen before. It reads "Kabbalah blah blah blah." His friend Daniel, a potter, made a few of them, but only a few, and they tend to keep them hidden away, lest outsiders suspect that all of this "Jewish nonsense" is just that. The existence of the mugs, though, belies a pleasing whiff of self-deprecation among the Kabbalists. They pass the Chesterton test: They can laugh at themselves.

David, it turns out, is quite fond of religious humor. One of his favorite jokes is about the rabbi and the fingernails. Students at a *yeshiva*, a Jewish seminary, noticed that the chief rabbi always cut his fingernails after he bathed in the *mikva*—never before. This confounded the students, who were certain the rabbi's habit contained some important truth.

"Why, Rabbi," they finally asked, "do you only cut your fingernails after bathing in the *mikva*, never before?"

"Because," said the rabbi, pausing for dramatic effect, "they are softer then."

Of all the trip wires lining the spiritual path, the most treacherous is overreaching, reading great significance into events or people that contain no such significance. We are so busy looking for the big signs, the revelations, that we miss the smaller ones, the glimpses of the divine that, collectively, might add up to something very big indeed. And despite David's intellectual approach to these teachings, Kabbalah, like all mystical traditions, remains intensely personal, wholly subjective. As Gershom Scholem, the great scholar of Kabbalah, put it, "There is no such thing as mysticism in the abstract." That is what makes the mystical path so beguiling—and frustrating. Questions about the insights attained by others are inevitably met with these words: *You had to be there.* Fine, I think, but what if I wasn't?

On my last Sabbath in Tzfat, David invites me to join him on his walking meditation.

"Walking meditation? Sounds awfully Buddhist," I say.

"It is," says David, "but it's also Jewish." Back in the sixteenth century, Rabbi Luria, a man many consider a mystical genius, would walk with his followers, hundreds of them, to the fields outside the city and welcome the Sabbath like subjects welcoming their queen.

David and I walk to the head of a trail, where we meet his friend Daniel, the potter. The sun is slipping beneath the horizon. The Sabbath siren has already sounded. The day of rest has officially begun. We walk normally for a bit, making small talk. Tzfat small talk, that is, which in this case is a lengthy discourse on the etymology of the modern Hebrew word for "electricity." Not for the first time, I wonder: Are these people capable of having an inconsequential thought? All of this profundity must grow tiresome. (I was later pleased to learn that David has a soft spot for donuts and college football. There may be hope for him yet.)

"Okay," says David, pausing at a bend. "We begin here." Our task is simple. We are to walk slowly, very slowly. Simply be aware. We are to take one breath for each step. One breath, one step.

We begin. Breath, step. Breath, step. I pull into the lead, which I briefly find exhilarating until I realize that, no, this is not a good thing, not now. We're engaged in a kind of inverted race, with victory going to the slowest. Only this is not about victory, of course. It is about awareness. On this score, the Buddhists and the Kabbalists concur. The Kabbalists, though, take it a step further. More than awareness, they say, it is about sanctification. It is about taking an everyday activity—in this case walking—and raising it, elevating it from the physical realm to the divine. It is about making Heaven manifest on earth. It is about doing God's work, one step at a time.

Which is not easy, of course. At first, I exert a huge amount of mental energy as I attempt to recalibrate my walking speed from its usual frantic pace to something more human. It's like trying to stop a huge cruise ship; it takes time for all of that forward momentum to dissipate. It is physically painful; I am aware of each muscle in my calves expanding and contracting. Soon, though, I get the hang of it and, lo and behold, actually *enjoy* it. I am consciously aware of how I walk not only with my legs but also with my shoulders, with my entire body. I'm aware of the variety of terrain. What before I saw as only a dirt path I now experience as much more complex and varied topography: stubborn rock, crunchy gravel, a soft carpet of pine needles.

I become intensely aware of the auburn light, infusing everything around me with a plush glow. And the sounds. My God, the sounds! I hear everything: a lone car swooshing by on a distant highway, a bird chirping, a man praying. Where were these sounds before? It's as if I had been wearing a pair of those noise-canceling headphones popular with frequent fliers. These headphones work by producing a converse sound to that which needs blocking; they block noise with noise. Our minds work much the same way. We miss so many sounds not because we fail to listen but because we're too busy talking—to ourselves. Our chattering minds produce a steady stream of countervailing noise; other sounds don't stand a chance. Now, though, I have removed the headphones, and I can hear again.

Breath, step. Breath, step. Then I experience the strangest sensation. I am no longer walking on the ground. The ground and I are walking together. The walking is—how to describe it?—interactive. The earth is an active participant. The path is pushing back, meeting me, pressing against me. I'm in control but not totally. There is another willful entity here. It's like riding a horse. Or perhaps another activity that involves a kinetic interplay. A well-known Sufi master, Pir Zia, once told me that whenever he walks he imagines himself "making love to the earth." Now I know what he means.

I'm now in last place, behind David and Daniel. Good. Never before have I derived so much joy from lagging, and I make a silent commitment to lag more often. David's final words before we began were: "Just let go." Watching the two of them walking in this ethereal, almost ghostly, manner, I am intensely aware of their inevitable death, and mine too. They are walking a few steps ahead of me. That makes sense. They are a few years older, but I am not far behind. I imagine the three of us walking to our death *right now*, part of an unbroken chain of human beings who have come before and who will come after. The inevitability of death dawns on me in a way it hasn't before. That and its naturalness. *As it was, is now, and will be forever.* For once, the thought of death, the *knowledge* of it, does not terrify me.

We are back where we began. Our walking meditation is over.

I look at my watch; twenty-five minutes have passed. It seems like only five or ten. We stretch and say *Shabbat shalom*, good Sabbath, to one another. I feel a lightness descend upon me like pixie dust. That, and a faint but undeniable urge to smoke a cigarette.

Later, I join Daniel and his family for the Sabbath dinner. It's the nicest I've ever had. There is none of the unacknowledged stiffness that I've encountered at other Sabbath dinners. The four of us—me, Daniel, his wife, and his grown son—are crammed into his eat-in kitchen. We are eating by candlelight. Daniel blesses the bread and the wine, and then he blesses his son, placing both hands on his head and saying these words: "May God bless you and watch over you. May God shine His face toward you and show you favor." I know without a doubt that I am not witnessing a man fulfilling some tribal obligation, or parroting empty words because some rabbi said he must. No, I am witnessing a man expressing love for his child, a love so strong and precious that he calls upon something bigger than himself—call it God, Hashem, Yahweh, the Way, the Infinite Whatever—to collaborate in this love, to amplify it. It is an act of great self-assertion and great humility at the same time and, if the Kabbalists are right (and I hope they are), it is an act that rippled across this world, and others too, in ways we cannot begin to fathom.

At that moment, I vow that when I return home, I will bless my daughter in the same manner, with the same intention. What I am witnessing, and partaking of, this Sabbath is so different from the OCD Judaism I had encountered all of my life, and I say as much to Daniel. He thinks about this for a moment then pronounces: "Judaism is like driving." I'm not sure where he's going with this.

"If you learn to drive, you need rules. You need to know what a red light means and what a yield sign means. You need to obey the speed limits. But it would be silly to view driving as only a collection of rules and nothing else. You drive in order to get to a destination, someplace special perhaps. You drive for the sheer pleasure of driving. The rules are only part of the story of driving."

He had me, but I wasn't ready to surrender yet. What about the overtly silly rules of Judaism, like putting on your right shoe before your left? Surely, those serve no purpose.

"The right represents kindness, the left rigor. We start our day with kindness and only then do we add rigor. It's just a reminder."

I cry uncle, and recall what James Hopkins had said about Buddhist rituals being "Post-it notes for the brain." Maybe all religions are simply a collection of these Post-it notes. They come in different sizes and languages, but that's what they are: fluorescent reminders that "hey, you're not the only one on the planet" or, "Yo! How would you like to be treated the way you treat others?" These reminders are almost always brief and to the point, small enough to fit on a Post-it note, big enough to stick.

My last session with Yedidah. After our lesson, we decamp to her kitchen for tea. I now feel comfortable enough with her to be brutally honest, so I point out that her kitchen is a complete mess—a collage of dirty dishes, pita-bread fragments, and various unidentified substances.

"I know," she says. "But my kitchen is a metaphor for the process of creation."

It's nonsense, of course, but it is Yedidah nonsense and therefore worthy of consideration.

She has an errand to run at the post office, so we walk down the hill together. It's a perfect, cloudless day, and for the first time I can see the Sea of Galilee below us, close enough to touch, it seems. The sun feels warm on my face. We reach the post office, and find it's closed, even though, according to the sign, it is open. Yedidah is confused. Another woman arrives, and is equally confused. There is much harrumphing, Israeli-style. "*Ma Kara? Ze lo tov.*" (What happened? This is not good.) Yedidah is upset too, but then she lets it go. It's God's will, she says, the universe at work. Maybe the guy who works there, a nice guy, is sick or has some other good reason for closing early. She will go do some grocery shopping instead. It is a generous explanation of the situation. It is also a Kabbalistic one, though I couldn't tell you exactly why.

It's time to say goodbye. I want to hug Yedidah but am not sure if that's appropriate. She is both British and a religious Jew, not exactly a hug-friendly demographic. So I am pleasantly surprised when she opens her arms and briefly envelops me.

I decide to walk into town rather than call a taxi. It's a gorgeous day and, besides, I'm experiencing pangs of happiness and don't want my good mood, which I've worked so hard to achieve, ruined by some happy Moroccan taxi driver who achieves his contentment with no apparent effort. I walk, not exactly in a meditative way, but it feels good nonetheless. As I round a bend, I pass a police station then a building that, according to the sign, houses the Ethiopian Absorption Ministry. I smile at that. New immigrants to Israel aren't merely welcomed or integrated or even assimilated. They are absorbed. When something is absorbed by a larger entity it is transformed, but not fully. Something of its indigenous self remains. When it is the nation-state doing the absorbing, we attain citizenship. When it is God doing the absorbing, we attain—what? Enlightenment? Heaven? I take a deep breath and, as Yedidah advised, address myself in the third person. *Take it easy, Eric, it's only a sign. Not all signs are signs. Sounds like you're coming down with a touch of Tzfat Syndrome there, big guy.*

It's important to know when to travel to a holy city. It's just as important to know when to leave such a place. It is time for me to leave Tzfat. The next morning, I board the Egged bus, heading south for Jerusalem, a city that, over the centuries, has also attracted its share of carrots and fish, trying to find their way.

I know there is one person I must meet there. During my time as an NPR correspondent, I knew Yossi Klein Halevi mainly as an astute analyst of Israeli politics. He is much more than that, though, a religious man in the best sense of the word, a spiritual iconoclast, and now that I've dropped my journalistic armor of objectivity, I am eager to see him again.

I meet Yossi at a sushi restaurant in a trendy neighborhood in Jerusalem. To look at him, one could easily conclude he is a typical orthodox Jew: knitted *kippa*, unruly beard, plain white shirt. But if I've learned anything in my travels it is that appearances can lie. *What you see is not.* Yes, he has his rabbis but he is "totally freelance." Over the decades, he has fashioned his own Judaism, incorporating what works, dropping what doesn't. Like Yedidah and David, he rarely attends synagogue, and observes the Sabbath in his own way. For a while, he was not using electricity at all, but he found that made him more, not less, stressed, defeating the purpose of the Sabbath, so he turned the lights back on. Yossi's practice is Jewish, his reading eclectic. He is especially fond of the great Hindu sages.

The waitress brings us menus, chunky tablets that would make Moses proud. Then it dawns on me: God is to religion as food is to a menu. Both the menu and the religion suggest a variety of options, and while the waiter can make recommendations, ultimately the choice is ours. To say you know God because you are religious is like saying you have dined well because you read the menu. One act *may* lead to another but not necessarily. Both the menu and religion entice us with promises they don't always fulfill, and overly elaborate descriptions of the delights that await are to be treated with suspicion, as anyone who has ever ordered the artisanal farm-fed beef carpaccio can attest. Good religions, like good menus, tell us u pfront what price we must pay, and that price, while high, is always one we can bear.

Our food arrives. I know better by now than to just dig in. I wait for the blessing.

"We say this blessing because—"

"Wait," I interrupt, eager to show off my knowledge. "To raise our consciousness."

"Yes," says Yossi, "but also to raise the consciousness of the food."

This is a new one. I'm not sure how we can raise the consciousness of a small slab of dead tuna. Yossi explains: "The Kabbalists believe everything is alive, so as they eat, they think of the sacrifice that their food made. Your food is the sacrifice and you are the altar. Kabbalah, at its best, fills the practitioner with a constant sense of responsibility, awe, and love."

We say the blessing together. Yossi leading with the Hebrew and me repeating, with *kavanah*, and fresh appreciation for my *tekka maki*.

I tell Yossi about my brush with gas, about the nurse and The Question—Have you found your God yet?—that demanded an answer. I tell him about how I meditated like a Buddhist, whirled like a Sufi, prayed like a Christian. I leave out a few bits, like shaving my legs in Vegas, but am otherwise comprehensive in my recounting. I tell him how I came to Israel in hopes of checking off the Judaism box and moving on but then came the fish-and-carrot story, and my time in Tzfat, which actually revised my dismal view of Judaism, a view that hasn't seen an uptick since I was eight days old and that *mohel* lunged at my privates with a knife.

"So, Yossi, am I a fish or a carrot?"

"You are a fish but you have definite carrot tendencies, and you need to honor those as well. If you searched for five years and came back and told me you found that your heart is Buddhist, I would say 'Be blessed' and mean it. The way of the soul is mysterious and I can't judge a Jewish soul that feels it needs to be fulfilled in this incarnation through Buddhism. But if people like you turn away from Judaism, Judaism will die. It will be smothered by the rote-ists."

I had never thought of it that way. Maybe God doesn't need me but the Jews do. My search so far has been a bit—what's the word?—selfish. I've been looking for God, in His many guises, in order to dampen *my* fear, scratch *my* spiritual itch, fill *my* God-shaped hole. It never occurred to me that others might have a dog in my hunt. Yossi has appealed to something very real, and very Jewish.

"Are you guilting me, Yossi?"

"I prefer to think of it as appealing to your sense of responsibility."

I was afraid of that. My sense of responsibility is stunted—not absent, mind you; that would be better. Then I could behave selfishly and sleep at night. No, I have just enough of a sense of responsibility to stoke my guilt but not enough to do anything about it.

I was so convinced of my carrot-ness, I never stopped to question it. I am a seeker, a man of the world's religions. Judaism is for the parochial among us. It is for the Fanta drinkers and the observers of petty rules. I am much more *interesting* than that. Yet as we eat and talk, Yossi's words continue to chip away at my carrot identity, and I begin to eye the tuna dangling on my chopsticks as, perhaps, family. Every religion, he says, is a language, "a language of intimacy with God," and once you have mastered one it's easier to learn others. The implication is that I set off on my search not knowing any language, yet expecting to acquire others. It doesn't work that way. It's one thing to be a skeptical universalist and another to be a spiritual dilettante. The universalist stands on solid ground and explores; the dilettante stands nowhere and gropes.

We talk for hours, covering a lot of territory. We talk about belief ("an irrelevant term") and about Jerusalem ("If this city can be holy then any city can be holy") and about the concept of the soul ("Who knows what a soul is? We are talking about matters we know nothing about"). When we eventually say goodbye, though, it is not Yossi's words careening through my mind but, oddly, those of the ancient Greek mathematician Archimedes: *Give me a place to stand and I shall move the world.* Yossi clearly has a place to stand. Do I? It's a question that, until now, I had not considered the least bit relevant. Stand? Who had time to stand? I was a man in motion.

It's a warm day, and I have nowhere I have to be, so I decide to walk back to my hotel. I walk slowly, attentively, aware of the ground beneath my feet, solid and well trodden.

EPILOGUE

God: Some Assembly Required

The French writer Guy de Maupassant despised the Eiffel Tower. He found it hideous. Every day, though, he would dine at the tower's restaurant. It was the only place in Paris, explained Maupassant, where he didn't have to look at the Eiffel Tower. Maupassant never said whether he continued to loathe the tower after lunching in it for so many years. I suspect he did not. Familiarity does not, as we're told, breed contempt but, thankfully, affection. From a distance, I found Judaism about as appealing as Maupassant's Eiffel Tower. Up close, my perspective shifted. Or to put it another way: I could only see Judaism clearly once I could no longer see it.

Jews pride themselves on being not only the people of the book but the people of the question, and there is no bigger question than the one the nurse asked me in that cold and sterile hospital room: Have you found your God yet? Those six words propelled me around the world and way, way out of my comfort zone. Alas, I now realize it is the wrong question. God is not a set of missing car keys or an exit on the New Jersey Turnpike. He is not a destination. He's as close as our jugular, as the Muslims say. In that sense, all spiritual searches are round-trip journeys. We travel in order to discover that there is nowhere to go. We turn, like a dervish, returning to the same spot where we started. The spot is the same but we are not. The point of turning—as well as praying, meditating, fasting, genuflecting, and every other spiritual technique out there—is to elicit a slight shift in our orientation. Rilke was right: God *is* a direction. We're like satellite dishes, swiveling, scanning the heavens for a signal, swiveling a bit more, scanning again. A few degrees in this direction or that can mean the difference between a strong signal and dead silence. Usually, it's the latter. We swivel and swivel, and nothing. The atheist says that's because there is no signal to receive. The devout and confused keep swiveling, searching. *In spite of.*

There's a great line from Fellini's *La Dolce Vita*: "He who looks for God, finds Him where he wants." If true, then I consider my search a success, for I have learned much. I learned about the importance of breathing and the primacy of the human heart and the beauty of slowness and the creative impulse that lies at the heart of all religions. I learned that I am fishier than I thought. I learned that shaving one's legs is a task not to be undertaken lightly, and that it is much easier to liberate breasts than minds. I learned all these things, and more, not from a book but from "the voice of a stranger," as Thomas Merton, the Trappist monk, puts it. My strangers—Sandie and Jamie and Yedidah and Wayne and the rest—changed the way I think of God. He is not the Cosmic Male Parent, not that only. God is also loving and generous, and silly. Mostly, though, He is elusive. "Something like the wind, not much more," as Rabbi Adin Steinsaltz puts it.

I learned (or, rather, confirmed) that there is a lot of bad religion out there. It's about time, I think, that we distinguished between bad religion and good religion, just as we distinguish between bad science and good science, bad food and good food. Bad religion diminishes us. Good religion elevates us, makes us better people than we thought we were, than we thought possible. Good religion is a kind of applied philosophy, and with all philosophy, asking the right questions is at least half the game. What do you believe? That is a common question, but not a particularly helpful one. With all due respect, I don't care what you believe. What do you *experience*? What do you *do*? That's what William James wanted to know, and it's what I want to know too.

Eight might seem like a lot of gods, but I barely scratched the surface. I could continue flirting with these deities for a lifetime— or lifetimes, as my Buddhist friends would say. Yet a still, small voice inside me, a voice with a distinctly nasal Staten Island timbre, warns against such spiritual promiscuity. Sporadic flirtation makes life interesting. Persistent flirtation suggests we're afraid of something. Flirtation, it's been said, is "the art of keeping intimacy at a safe distance." That is not what I want. No, my flirting days are over.

At the start of my journey, in California, I met a Sufi named Wali Ali, who told me, "You can't be any wiser than you are." At the time, I thought it was just another New-Age-ism uttered by a deep-fried hippie with a funny name. I was wrong. What Wali Ali meant was that we start our journey in a certain place, and as much as we'd like that place to be, say, Paris or Bali, it's usually Cleveland or Baltimore. We must recognize that, accept it. We never fully escape our past, nor need we. We sip from these wisdom traditions, imbibe of their truths, yet they will always remain the "other." The best we can hope for is that bits and pieces of this wisdom seep into our marrow. This happens more often than I thought possible, and not despite our basic fuckedupness but *because* of it.

Indeed, that is the goal of all religion, all *good* religion: to transform the most repulsive parts of ourselves into something worthy not only of acceptance, but of love. "To make our darkness conscious," as Jung puts it. Toward this aim, spiritual calisthenics like prayer and meditation help, but ultimately this transformation, this alchemy, remains a mysterious process, one that Christians call grace and Buddhists suchness, and Taoists don't even bother to name. It is always a gift, never an entitlement, and it only appears once we stop looking. Madam H. was right. We don't choose a religion. It chooses us. What is required of us is a kind of passive action. We need to do our part—pray, meditate, read—and then wait. As they say, the waiting is the hardest part.

I still have many doubts. Indeed, I am a tower of doubts, and that is okay for, as the renegade economist E. F. Schumacher says: "matters that are beyond doubt are, in a sense, dead; they constitute no challenge to the living." Doubts are not an end but a means; they are desirable. William James once said that "the word 'or' names a genuine reality." It took me awhile to wrap my mind around that one but now I think I know what he meant. We always live on the cusp, caught between two robust jet streams blowing in opposite directions, and that is okay. That is the way things are. The way things *should* be.

So, instead of looking for my God, I must invent Him. Not exactly invent. Construct. Assemble. His foundation is Jewish, but His support beams Buddhist. He has the heart of Sufism, the simplicity of Taoism, the generosity of the Franciscans, the hedonistic streak of the Raëlians. For a long time, I didn't think such a composite God was possible. The New Agers I met in California had cobbled together a God, of sorts, except they forgot the glue. There's nothing holding their God together, so they're constantly chasing after the little bits and pieces. Yes, glue is important. Another difference: The New Agers never know, *really* know, the components that make up their composite God. So the entire enterprise is shaky.

Not that mine is so solid. I observe the start of the Sabbath, though not as often as I should. I meditate, though not very well or for very long. I say grace before meals, though sometimes I forget. I do some *qi gong*, more or less. Together, though, these parts add up to *something*. Is it true? Yes. No. *Truth is what works*. And this composite God works for me. I now look forward to the Jewish holidays at my brother's house. When my daughter, now almost seven years old, speaks of God, I no longer wince. I am grounding her in her own faith, but will not despair should she choose another, or none at all.

As for my Tokyo story, there has yet to be a sequel. I've stopped expecting one, expectations being the great enemy of experience. Yet I continue to wait and, every now and then, swivel a few degrees this way or that.

In spite of.

ACKNOWLEDGMENTS

Writing a book about God, I discovered, is a tremendous act of faith. Fortunately, I was not alone in this endeavor. I had much help, of the human variety. Those who appear in these pages, without exception, welcomed me with open arms, and hearts, not questioning what a middle-aged Confusionist was doing on their little plot of earth. I thank each one of them, and hope they glimpse at least some of their collective wisdom in these pages.

Many more people, working behind the scenes, made this book possible. My assigning editor, Jon Karp, believed in the project from the outset and, thankfully, kept me on course. His successor, Cary Goldstein, took the baton and ran with it. His steady hand and razor-sharp pencil made this a better book. I am indebted, again, to my faithful agent, Sloan Harris. No potted plant he, Sloan offered valuable suggestions and, as always, encouragement. I am also grateful to Colin Shepherd at Twelve Books, as well as the imprint's publicity wizard, Brian McLendon.

I owe a huge debt to my research assistant, Alyson Wright, who possesses the patience, and persistence, of a saint. No one on the planet is better at finding an elusive witch or tracking down a whirling dervish than Alyson. I am also grateful to American University for providing that most divine of gifts: a library card.

Dan Charles and Bobbie Roessner read early drafts of the manuscript and offered valuable suggestions. So did Steve LeVine, who also provided plenty of encouragement and single malt. Laura Blumenfeld has listened to me prattle on about this quixotic project for longer than any person should be expected to endure. Her editorial advice and emotional succor sustained me throughout. Barbara Brotman and Chuck Berman rose to the occasion, and then some. They met my impossible demands with their trademark humor and grace, and have earned my eternal admiration—which, actually, they already had.

During every step of the way, I relied on what my friend Laurey Masterton calls "the Golden Thread." One person recommends another person who might know this third person, and before long I have found, miraculously, just the right person in just the right place. Keepers of the Thread include Ellen Bork, Ilene Prusher, Jay Michaelson, Rosyla Kalden, Rob Gifford, Jane Feldman, Manjushree Thapa, Daniel Lak, Chelan Weiler, Susan Weiss, and many others whom I'm sure I'm forgetting. In the earlier stages of my research, Llewellyn Vaughan-Lee and Don Lattin sat down with me, separately, for extended conversations, patiently fielding my often-ignorant questions. So did several bighearted Sufis: Jennifer Alia Wittman, Jo Ann Ross, and Fatima Durrani Khan. Fellow wanderers Maarten Troost and Sarah Ferguson offered empathy and sound advice. Aliza Marcus and Emma Camatoy helped on the home front. Stephanie Genkin expertly organized that disaster zone otherwise known as my office. Seth and Elaine Akst helped in many ways, big and small.

On the road, many people graciously opened their homes to me: Steve Herman in Delhi, Carla and Christian Geerdes in Berlin, Barbara Demick in Beijing. In Israel, Avi and Chava Moshavi treated me like royalty, providing hospitality, delicious food, and invaluable contacts in the Kabbalah community. Likewise, Eyal Riess and the staff of the International Center for Tzfat Kabbalah made my visit there productive and happy. "Cool Jew" Lisa Klug was also helpful, and funny. In India, Shugan Jain gave selflessly of his time and wisdom, as did Shivani and Sanjeev Bothra. In China, Daniel Crevier served as my interpreter, in more ways than one. When it came time to put words on the page, several people generously offered a place to write: Lisa Collins, Bob and Bobbi Pincus, Bud Meyer and Anne Robertson. I decamped from these idyllic homes reluctantly.

My family, as usual, came through for me. My parents, and brother, Paul, tolerated my absences and general grumpiness like, well, like family. My daughter, Sonya, continues to amaze me with her wisdom and love. God has no greater ambassador than her. Finally, I want to thank my wife, Sharon. Patient and loving beyond all mortal bounds, she kept me going through the darkest nights, never losing faith in me, or this project, and for that I am grateful beyond words. Her innumerable contributions include: editor, parent, sounding board, amateur therapist. Goddess. I could not have written this book without her. This I do not believe. This I *know*.

SELECT BIBLIOGRAPHY

Adler, Margot. *Drawing Down the Moon: Witches, Druids, Goddess-Worshippers, and Other Pagans in America Today.* Viking, 1979.

Afterman, Allen. *Kabbalah and Consciousness and the Poetry of Allen Afterman.* Sheep Meadow Press, 2005.

Anonymous. *The Cloud of Unknowing.* Translated by Mishtooni Bose. Wordsworth Editions, 2005.

———. *The Way of a Pilgrim.* Translated by R. M. French. Quality Paperback Book Club, 1998.

Armstrong, Karen. *A Short History of Myth.* Canongate, 2005.

———. *The Great Transformation: The Beginning of Our Religious Traditions.* Anchor, 2007.

———. *Buddha.* Viking Penguin, 2001.

Bancroft, Anne. *The Spiritual Journey.* Element, 1991.

Batson, C. Daniel, et al. *Religion and the Individual: A Social-Psychological Perspective.* Oxford University Press, 1993.

Blofeld, John. *Taoism: The Road to Immortality.* Shambhala, 2002.

Campbell, Joseph. *Pathways to Bliss: Mythology and Personal Transformation*. New World Library, 2005.

Campbell, Joseph, ed. *The Portable Jung*. Penguin, 1971.

Chesterton, G. K. *Saint Francis of Assisi*. Sam Torode Book Arts, 1924.

Chittick, William C. *Sufism*. Oneworld, 2000.

Chuang-tzu. *Basic Writings*. Translated by Burton Watson. Columbia University Press, 1996.

———. *The Book of Chuang Tzu*. Translated by Martin Palmer. Penguin, 1996.

Cohen, Yedidah, ed. *A Tapestry for the Soul: The Introduction to the Zohar*. Nehora Press, 2010.

Cunningham, Scott. *Wicca: A Guide for the Solitary Practitioner*. Llewellyn Publications, 2004.

Fadiman, James, and Robert Frager, eds. *Essential Sufism*. HarperCollins, 1999.

Felder, Hilarin. *The Ideals of St. Francis of Assisi*. Franciscan Herald Press, 1982.

Fine, Lawrence, and Louis Jacobs. *Safed Spirituality: Rules of Mystical Piety, the Beginning of Wisdom*. Paulist Press, 1984.

Fontana, David. *Psychology, Religion, and Spirituality*. Blackwell, 2003.

Forward, Martin. *Religion: A Beginner's Guide*. Oneworld, 2001.

Frankl, Viktor E. *Man's Search for Meaning*. Beacon Press, 1959.

Gandhi, Mohandas K. *Prayer*. Edited by John Strohmeier. Berkeley Hill Books, 2000.

Gardner, Martin. *The Whys of a Philosophical Scrivener*. St. Martin's Griffin, 1999.

Green, Arthur. *A Guide to the Zohar*. Stanford University Press, 2003.

Harner, Michael. *The Way of the Shaman*. HarperCollins, 1980.

Harvey, Andrew. *Teachings of Rumi*. Shambhala, 1999.

Helminski, Kabir. *The Knowing Heart: A Sufi Path of Transformation*. Shambhala, 2000.

Heschel, Abraham Joshua. *God in Search of Man*. Farrar, Straus and Giroux, 1955.

———. *Man Is Not Alone*. Farrar, Straus and Giroux, 1951.

———. *The Sabbath*. Farrar, Straus and Giroux, 1951.

Hopkins, Jeffrey. *The Tantric Distinction: A Buddhist's Reflections on Compassion and Emptiness*. Wisdom Publications, 1984.

Huang, Chungliang Al. *Embrace Tiger, Return to Mountain: The Essence of Tai Ji*. Celestial Arts, 1973.

Huxley, Aldous. *The Perennial Philosophy: An Interpretation of the Great Mystics, East and West*. HarperCollins, 1944.

James, William. *The Heart of William James*. Edited by Robert Richardson. Harvard University Press, 2010.

———. *The Varieties of Religious Experience: A Study in Human Nature*. Barnes and Noble, 1902.

Kaplan, Aryeh. *Jewish Meditation: A Practical Guide*. Schocken, 1985.

Lao-tzu. *Tao te Ching*. Translated by Red Pine. Copper Canyon Press, 2009.

———. *Tao te Ching*. Translated by Brian Browne Walker. St. Martin's, 1995.

Lattin, Don, and Richard Cimino. *Shopping for Faith*. Jossey-Bass, 1998.

Lewis, James R., ed. *The Gods Have Landed: New Religions from Other Worlds*. State University of New York Press, 1995.

Martin, Nancy M., and Joseph Runzo, eds. *The Meaning of Life in the World Religions*. Oneworld, 2000.

Matt, Daniel C. *The Essential Kabbalah: The Heart of Jewish Mysticism*. HarperCollins, 1995.

Merton, Thomas. *New Seeds of Contemplation*. Harper San Francisco, 1961.

Narby, Jeremy, and Francis Huxley, eds. *Shamans Through Time: 500 Years on the Path to Knowledge*. Penguin, 2004.

Nasr, Seyyed Hossein. *The Garden of Truth: The Vision and Promise of Sufism, Islam's Mystical Tradition*. HarperCollins, 2008.

Needleman, Jacob. *The New Religions*. Doubleday, 1970.

Newberg, Andrew, and Mark Robert Waldman. *Why We Believe What We Believe: Uncovering Our Biological Need for Meaning, Spirituality, and Truth*. Free Press, 2006.

Occhiogrosso, Peter. *The Joy of Sects: A Spirited Guide to the World's Religious Traditions*. Doubleday, 1994.

Palmer, Susan J. *Aliens Adored: Raël's UFO Religion*. Rutgers University Press, 2004.

Raël. *Intelligent Design: Message from the Designers*. The Raëlian Foundation, 2005.

Rambo, Lewis. *Understanding Religious Conversion*. Yale University Press, 1995.

Rinpoche, Sogyal. *The Tibetan Book of Living and Dying*. HarperCollins, 1992.

Rohr, Richard. *Simplicity: The Freedom of Letting Go*. Crossroad, 1991.

Roof, Wade Clark. *Spiritual Marketplace: Baby Boomers and the Remaking of American Religion*. Princeton University Press, 1999.

Rumi, Jalaluddin. *The Essential Rumi*. Translated by Coleman Barks. Castle Books, 1995.

Schumacher, E. F. *A Guide for the Perplexed*. Abacus, 1977.

Schwartz, Stephen. *The Other Islam: Sufism and the Road to Global Harmony*. Doubleday, 2008.

Shah, Idries. *The Sufis*. Anchor, 1964.

Shantideva. *A Guide to the Bodhisattva's Way of Life*. Translated by Stephen Batchelor. Library of Tibetan Works & Archives, 1979.

Sharma, Arvind, ed. *Our Religions: The Seven World Religions Introduced by Preeminent Scholars from Each Tradition*. Harper San Francisco, 1993.

Shermer, Michael. *How We Believe: The Search for God in an Age of Science*. W. H. Freeman, 1999.

Simon, Linda. *Genuine Reality: A Life of William James*. University of Chicago Press, 1999.

Smith, Huston. *Why Religion Matters: The Fate of the Human Spirit in an Age of Disbelief*. Harper San Francisco, 2001.

———. *The World's Religions*. HarperCollins, 1991.

Starr, Mirabai, ed. *Saint Francis of Assisi*. Sounds True, 2007.

Straub, Gerard Thomas. *The Sun and Moon Over Assisi: A Personal Encounter with Francis and Clare*. St. Anthony Messenger Press, 2000.

Tolstoy, Leo. *A Confession*. Penguin, 1882.

Trungpa, Chögyam. *The Path Is the Goal: A Basic Handbook of Buddhist Meditation*. Shambhala, 1995.

Vaughan-Lee, Llewellyn. *The Face Before I Was Born: A Spiritual Autobiography*. Golden Sufi Center, 1997.

Walsh, Roger. *The World of Shamanism: New Views of an Ancient Tradition*. Llewellyn Publications, 2007.

Watts, Alan. *The Philosophies of Asia*. Tuttle, 1995.

———. *Buddhism: The Religion of No-Religion*. Tuttle, 1995.

———. *Tao: The Watercourse Way*. Pantheon, 1975.

Weil, Simone. *Waiting for God*. HarperCollins, 1951.

Welch, Holmes. *Taoism: The Parting of the Way*. Beacon Press, 1957.

Wines, Leslie. *Rumi: A Spiritual Biography*. Crossroad, 2000.

Yeshe, Lama. *Introduction to Tantra: The Transformation of Desire*. Wisdom Publications, 1987.

———. *Ego, Attachment and Liberation: Overcoming Your Mental Bureaucracy*. Lama Yeshe Wisdom Archive, 2006.

ABOUT THE AUTHOR

Eric Weiner is author of the *New York Times* bestseller *The Geography of Bliss*, which has been translated into eighteen languages. A former correspondent for NPR and *The New York Times*, Weiner has reported from more than three dozen countries. His work has appeared in the *New Republic, Slate, Los Angeles Times, The Washington Post, Foreign Policy, The New York Times Magazine,* and the anthology *Best American Travel Writing.* He divides his time between Starbucks and Caribou. For more information, you can visit www.EricWeinerBooks.com.

ABOUT TWELVE

TWELVE

TWELVE was established in August 2005 with the objective of publishing no more than one book per month. We strive to publish the singular book, by authors who have a unique perspective and compelling authority. Works that explain our culture; that illuminate, inspire, provoke, and entertain. We seek to establish communities of conversation surrounding our books. Talented authors deserve attention not only from publishers, but from readers as well. To sell the book is only the beginning of our mission. To build avid audiences of readers who are enriched by these works—that is our ultimate purpose.

For more information about forthcoming TWELVE books, please go to www.twelvebooks.com.